Passion under the desert moon...

Arabian Nights

AN ARABIAN COURTSHIP
by
Lynne Graham

DESERT MISTRESS
by
Helen Bianchin

DESERT HOSTAGE
by
Sara Wood

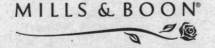

MILLS & BOON®

*MILLS & BOON and MILLS & BOON with the Rose Device
are registered trademarks of the publisher.
Harlequin Mills & Boon Limited,
Eton House, 18-24 Paradise Road, Richmond, Surrey, TW9 1SR*

ARABIAN NIGHTS
© by Harlequin Enterprises II B.V., 2000

*An Arabian Courtship, Desert Mistress and Desert Hostage were first
published in Great Britain by Harlequin Mills & Boon Limited in
separate, single volumes.*

An Arabian Courtship © Lynne Graham 1989
Desert Mistress © Helen Bianchin 1996
Desert Hostage © Sara Wood 1990

ISBN 0 263 82418 7

05-0008

*Printed and bound in Spain
by Litografia Rosés S.A., Barcelona*

Lynne Graham was born in Northern Ireland and has been a keen Mills & Boon® reader since her teens. She is very happily married with an understanding husband, who has learned to cook since she started to write! Her five children keep her on her toes. She has a very large Old English sheepdog, which knocks everything over, and two cats. When time allows, Lynne is a keen gardener.

AN ARABIAN COURTSHIP

by

LYNNE GRAHAM

CHAPTER ONE

POLLY'S throat constricted when she saw the long limousine turning through the gates of her home. She linked her hands together to stop them trembling. Prince Raschid ibn Saud al Azarin was about to arrive. She turned away from the view.

'Why are you standing over there?' her fifteen-year-old sister demanded. 'You won't be able to see him.'

'I think I can wait for that pleasure,' Polly muttered tightly.

Maggie was swiftly joined by twelve-year-old Joan and four-year-old Elaine, who had not a clue what the excitement was about but was determined not to be left out of it. The window-seat was a tight squeeze for the three of them, each craning their necks for a better view. In an effort to to calm her nerves, Polly breathed in slowly. What her sisters were finding so fascinating was sheer purgatory for her. Could this be real? she asked herself tautly. This was England in the eighties, an era of female liberation. How could she possibly be on the brink of an arranged marriage to a complete stranger? But she was.

'The car's stopping...it's got a little flag on the bonnet. Those must be the colours of the Dhareini royal family.' It was Maggie cheerfully keeping up the running commentary. 'The chauffeur's getting out...oh, he's very dark, he does look foreign...he's opening the rear door...I can see a trouser leg...'

'Oh, for pity's sake, stop it!' The plea broke from Polly on the back of a stifled sob, shocking everybody into silence.

Guiltily biting her lower lip, Maggie watched her sister sink down into one of the shabby nursery armchairs, covering her face briefly with her spread hands.

'He's not wearing robes,' complained Joan.

'Shut up!' Maggie gave her a pointed nudge. 'Polly's not feeling well.'

Joan stared at her eldest sister with unconcealed horror. 'You can't be ill now! Daddy will blow a gasket and Mummy's nearly in orbit as it is!'

'Polly!' cried Maggie suddenly. 'Raschid is gorgeous— I'm not kidding!'

'Prince Raschid,' Joan corrected loftily. 'You can't be too familiar.'

'For heaven's sake, he's going to be our brother-in-law!' Maggie shot back witheringly.

Polly flinched visibly. Her temples were pounding with the nagging beat of a tension that no amount of painkillers would put to flight. The morning had crawled past. Hardly anybody had talked over the lunch table. Polly hadn't eaten. Her father hadn't eaten either. As if he couldn't stand the look in Polly's helplessly accusing eyes any longer, he had taken himself off to the library even before dessert arrived.

Maggie placed an awkward hand on Polly's taut shoulder. 'He really is scrumptious-looking, honestly he is.'

'Then why can't he buy a wife at home?' Polly spluttered tearfully into her tissue, her nerves taking her over again.

'Scram!' Maggie glowered at Joan and Elaine. 'And don't you dare tell Mother that Polly's crying!'

Irritated by these histrionics, the ever practical and status-conscious Joan frowned. 'What's she got to cry about? She's going to be a princess. I wouldn't cry, I'd be over the moon.'

'Well, isn't it a shame you weren't the eldest?' Maggie threw the door wide.

The door slammed. Ashamed of her over-emotional behaviour, Polly pushed an unsteady hand through the silvery blonde curls falling untidily over her brow and wiped at her wet eyes. 'I still can't believe this is really happening,' she confided stiffly. 'I thought he mightn't turn up.'

'Dad said there was no question that he wouldn't, it being a matter of honour and all that.' Maggie sounded distinctly vague. 'Isn't it strange that we all used to laugh when Dad bored on about the time he saved King Reija's life by stopping a bullet? I mean, if we've heard that story a hundred times, we've heard it a thousand,' she exaggerated. 'And I used to pull your leg something awful about you becoming Wife Number Two…it was a family joke!'

Well, it certainly wasn't a joke now, Polly conceded miserably. Thirty-odd years ago Ernest Barrington had been a youthful diplomat attached to an embassy in one of the Gulf States. During his years in the Middle East he had spent his leave exploring neighbouring countries. On one such trip he had ventured into the wilds of Dharein in Southern Arabia, a country still torn by the fierce feuds of warring tribes and relatively little more civilised than it had been a century earlier. Her father had been taken ill on that particular journey and had sought assistance from a nomadic encampment presided over by Prince Achmed, brother of Dharein's feudal ruler, King Reija.

Fearing for the young Englishman's health, Achmed had taken him to the palace outside Jumani where he had received proper medical attention. There he had recovered his strength, and shortly before his departure he had been honoured by an invitation to join a royal hunting party.

Out in the desert an assassination attempt had been made on his royal host. The details of that shocking episode were somewhat blurred. Polly's father tended to embellish the story year by year, pepping it up to keep it fresh. Shorn of extras, the most basic version ran that, seeing a rifle glinting in the sunlight, Ernest had thrown himself in front of the

King and dragged him to the ground, suffering a minor head wound in the process. Overcome by gratitude and a sense of masculine fellowship, King Reija had stated there and then that his firstborn son would marry Ernest Barrington's firstborn daughter.

'Let me tell you, I was pretty taken aback,' Ernest was wont to chuckle at that point in the story. 'I wasn't even married then! But it was obviously the highest honour the King could think to offer. I should add that, since he's highly suspicious of Westerners, it was an even bigger mark of esteem.'

Thus the tale had been told to entertain dinner guests— a rather lighthearted anecdote of exotic climes and a bygone age. Ernest had not met King Reija again. He had retired from the Diplomatic Service as soon as his bachelor uncle died, leaving him a country estate several miles outside Worcester. However, twelve years ago he had chortled when he learnt of Raschid's marriage to Prince Achmed's daughter, Berah. The news had come by way of an elderly diplomat dining with them. Since then the family had often teased Polly about Raschid, reminding her that the Koran permitted a follower of Islam four wives. But never had anybody seen the idea of Polly marrying an Arab prince as anything other than hilariously funny.

Only when their father found himself in serious financial difficulties a month ago had he thought of renewing his acquaintance with King Reija. As Raschid's father was coming to London on a diplomatic visit, Ernest had requested an appointment with him. 'I shall ask him for a loan. I should think he'd be delighted to help,' he had contended confidently. 'I can't understand why I didn't think of this sooner.'

He had duly gone off to keep his appointment at the Dhareini Embassy. Even before he left home the grey anxiety and strain which had marked him for days had been

banished by a very characteristic surge of optimism. Since
Ernest had long since forgotten his Arabic, King Reija had
talked courteously to him through the offices of an interpreter. Family updates had naturally been exchanged. Ernest had cheerfully produced a photograph of the four
daughters and infant son he was so proud of possessing. In
return his host had informed him that Raschid had been a
widower for four years. Berah had died tragically after trip-
ping and falling down a steep staircase. She had been only
twenty-six.

'Naturally I offered my condolences…it could never
have occurred to me that the old boy could be leading up
to making a thirty-five-year-old promise good. But once I
was on the spot, as it were, it wasn't that easy to work up
to mentioning the loan,' Ernest had confessed. 'You could
have knocked me down with a feather when he announced
that his conscience had long been troubled by his failure to
honour that promise. I lost no time in assuring him that no
offence had been caused, but he seemed annoyed at that,
so I dropped the subject. Even when he began asking questions about Polly, I still hadn't an idea of what was on his
mind.'

Polly had listened, as aghast as her mother initially was,
while the older man lumbered at ever slower pace to the
climax. 'He told me that it was his dearest wish to see
Raschid married again, and then he shook hands with me
and the interpreter said, "It is agreed" and I said, "What's
agreed?"

'"My son will take your daughter as his bride," came
the reply. I was struck dumb!' her father had bleated, mop-
ping at his perspiring brow. 'Then he started talking about
the bride price and things just got out of my hands altogether…if they'd ever been in them, for he's a wily old
buzzard. Hard to think, though, where there could be any

advantage to him in the arrangement. The chap really does take this honour business very, very seriously.'

Surfacing from these unwelcome memories, Polly emitted a choked laugh. 'I was sold! Why did I ever believe that white slavery was a thing of the past? It's a wonder Dad didn't ask for my weight in gold!'

Maggie's eyes were reproachful. 'Polly, that sounds so awful!'

It is awful, Polly reflected bitterly. Why couldn't the King have offered her father a loan? Why had there had to be conditions attached? Even as she thought that, her saner self intervened to point out that her father was in no position to repay a loan.

'Dad said there was no pressure on you and that it was a decision that only you could make. I know—I was listening outside the library door,' Maggie admitted grudgingly. 'He didn't say you had to marry Raschid.'

That he had ever entertained the crazy concept at all, however, had been effective proof of his desperation. Maggie was still at the age where she saw no flaws in her parents. The sad truth was that Ernest Barrington was much too fond of the good things in life and had always lived above his income. Ladybright had been a small and prosperous estate when he inherited it, but the income from the land had never been up to the demands of a large family and a busy social calendar. When the bank had announced their intention to foreclose and force the sale of Ladybright to settle a backlog of mortgage repayments and an enormous overdraft, the accumulated debts of years of extravagance had finally been catching up on their father.

King Reija had stunned her desperate parent with the offer of a huge cash settlement, equal to meeting his debts and securing the family fortunes into the next generation. A drowning man thrown a rope does not hesitate. Polly doubted that her father had objected to the terms once the money was mentioned; he had been dazzled by the miraculous solution to all his problems. Within an hour of his return home, his attitude of apology and bluster had changed into one of determined good cheer.

'I'm not surprised I've taken your breath away, Polly,' he had been saying by then. 'A prince—what's more, a prince who will eventually become a king.'

Her mother had already had the stirrings of dreamy abstraction on her face. Ten minutes later she had whispered reverently, 'My Polly, a princess!'

Anthea Barrington had been in an awed state of ecstasy ever since. Indeed, both of Polly's parents had a remarkable talent for glossing over unpleasant realities. The jaws of the steel trap had closed round Polly slowly but surely. How could she personally sentence her family to poverty? Her mother was no more capable of coping without money than her father was. And what about her sisters and little Timothy, presently building up his bricks at her feet? Could she deny them the secure and comfortable upbringing which she herself had enjoyed when it was within her power to do otherwise?

And for what good reason could she deny her family her help? It was not as though she was sacrificing the chance of a loving marriage at some time in the future. Why shouldn't she marry Raschid and make everyone happy? The man she loved did not love her…at least, not in the right way. Chris Jeffries was very fond of her, but he treated her like a sister.

His parents were neighbours and close family friends. Polly had known Chris since childhood. And that, she had grasped dully, was the problem. Chris thought of himself as the big brother she had never had.

Polly's teenage years had not been painless. She had often turned to Chris for comfort when the going got rough in her own home. A late bloomer, she had been a podgy ugly duckling in her slim and beautiful mother's eyes. She had been further cursed by shyness in a family where only extroverts were admired. Anthea had never been able to hide the fact that quiet, studious Polly was a distinct disappointment as a daughter. A boy-crazy, clothes-mad teenager always on the trot to parties would have delighted her; one who worked hard at school and went off to university intending to train as a librarian had not. Chris, two years her senior and already enrolled in medical school, had been the only person to understand and support Polly's academic aspirations.

Loving Chris had been so easy. If she had a problem he was always ready to listen. From adolescence Polly had innocently assumed that she would eventually marry Chris. When her puppy fat had melted away and she miraculously blossomed into a slender young woman with a cloud of pale hair and flawless features, she had shyly awaited the awakening of Chris's interest in her as a girlfriend. It had never happened, she reflected painfully.

A year ago at her nineteenth birthday party she had been forced to accept that her dreams were that—just dreams. Chris had lightly introduced her to his current girlfriend as 'Polly, my honorary kid sister,' affection and warmth in his manner and no hint of any other form of feeling. She had stopped living in her imagination.

Returning to university, she had sensibly thrown herself into the dating scene that she had scrupulously avoided during her first two terms. But the dates she had since ventured out on had without exception turned into disastrous grappling sessions concluded by resentful and bitter accusations that she was frigid and abnormal. Her efforts to forget Chris had got her nowhere. She still loved him; she was convinced that she would always love him.

Since she would never marry Chris, did it really matter who she married? Reasoning on that coldly practical basis, she had agreed to marry Raschid and solve her family's problems. And once she had agreed, everybody had forgotten the financial bribe and had begun to behave as if she was being singled out for some great honour.

Unfortunately a decision forged in the valiant heat of the moment was tougher to sustain in the hard face of reality. Reality was the arrival of that car outside and the awareness that downstairs was a stranger who was to become her husband, no matter what he was like and no matter how he behaved. She had given her word and she could not go back on it now. Why would she anyway? A spinster in the family would break her mother's heart. It was ironic that for the very first time she was shining like a bright star on her mother's ambitious horizon.

'You're not dressed yet!' Anthea's harassed lament from the door shattered her reverie. 'You can't possibly let Raschid see you looking...'

'The way I usually do?' Polly slotted in drily. 'Well, he might as well see what he's getting, and I'm no fashion-plate.'

'Don't be difficult, darling,' Anthea pleaded, elegantly timeless in her silk suit and pearls. 'You simply must get changed!'

'Where is he?'

'In the library with your father. We discussed the wedding arrangements. St Augustine's of course, but apparently there'll have to be a second ceremony after you fly out to Dharein. We had a very interesting chat before I left them,' she confided with an almost girlish giggle. 'Do you realise that Raschid didn't see his first wife's face until after the wedding? Evidently that's how they do it over there.'

Polly shuddered. She hadn't even met Raschid and already the wedding was fixed! In addition her mother was managing to behave as if this peculiar occasion was quite commonplace. 'It's barbaric!' she protested.

'Now, darling!' Anthea reproved. 'At least he's broken with tradition to come and meet you properly. What may seem strange to us is perfectly normal to him.'

'You think it's normal for a male of thirty-two to let his father pick a foreign bride sight unseen?' Polly exclaimed helplessly. 'You think he's doing me a favour in even coming here?'

'He is a prince, Polly.'

'I don't care!'

'Parents often do know what's best for their children,' Anthea was beginning to sound shrill. 'Remember what your father said—the divorce rate on arranged marriages is very low.'

In receipt of that grim reassurance, Polly was hurried down to her bedroom where the dreaded dress hung on the wardrobe door—powder-pink georgette. She would look like a little girl in a frilly party dress. What flattered Anthea at five foot nine did considerably less for a daughter of five foot one. Outright panic suddenly seethed up inside her. 'I can't go through with this…I can't!' she burst out.

'Of course you're nervous—that's only natural,' Anthea soothed. 'Raschid's bound to be staying for a few days, and you'll get over that silliness. You really don't seem to appreciate how lucky you are.'

'L-lucky?' gasped Polly.

'Any normal girl would be thrilled to be in your position,' Anthea trilled irritably. 'At eighteen I was married and at nineteen I was a mother. Believe me, I was a lot more happy and fulfilled than you've ever been swotting over boring books. When you have your first baby you'll understand exactly what I'm talking about.'

The threat of future offspring turned Polly as white as a sheet. 'A baby?'

'You love children and he doesn't have any. Poor Berah must have been barren,' Anthea remarked cheerfully. 'Raschid's father will be very anxious to see a male grandchild born to ensure the succession. Only think of how proud you'll feel then!'

Her mother was on another plane altogether. Children... intimacy... Polly was feeling physically sick. The prospect of being used to create a baby boom in Dharein did not appeal to her. No wonder King Reija had decided she was suitable! She was one of five children.

'He's wonderfully self-assured for his age, so charming and quite fabulously handsome. One can tell simply by looking at him that he's a prince. He has an air,' Anthea divulged excitedly. 'His manners are exquisite—I was very impressed. When one considers that he wasn't educated over here like his brother Asif, his English is excellent. Not quite colloquial, but...'

The rolling tide of her mother's boundless enthusiasm was suffocating.

'I'll put your hair up—you'll look taller.' Hairpins were thrust in with painful thoroughness. 'He has the most gorgeous blue eyes. Can you believe that?' Anthea gushed. 'I was dying to ask where he got those, but I didn't like to.'

What the heck did Polly care about blue eyes? Her mother had fallen in love with her future son-in-law's status. He could do no wrong. If he'd been a frog, Anthea would have found something generous to say about him. After all, he was a prince, wasn't he?

'I'm so happy for you, so proud.' With swimming eyes Anthea beamed down at her. 'And it's so romantic! Even Princess Diana was an earl's daughter.'

In appalled fascination Polly stared while Anthea dabbed delicately at her eyes with a lace hanky.

'Polly!' Her father's booming call, polished on the hunting field, thundered up the stairs. 'Where the devil are you?'

She could practically hear the tumbril pacing out her

steps to the execution block. But when she froze at the top of the stairs, only her father's impatient face greeted her stricken scrutiny.

'Come on…come on!' He was all of a fluster, eager to get the introduction over with. That achieved, he could sit back and pretend it was a completely ordinary courtship. Clasping her hand, he spread wide the library door. He was in one of his irrepressible, jovial host moods. 'Polly,' he announced expansively.

Ironically the very first thing Polly noticed about the tall, black-haired male, poised with inhuman calm by the fireplace, was his extraordinary eyes—a clear brilliant blue as glacier-cool as an arctic skyline and as piercing as arrows set ruthlessly on target.

Ernest coughed and bowed out. He nudged her pitilessly over the threshold so that he could close the door behind her. Once she was inside the room, Polly's legs behaved as if they were wedged in solid concrete. She awaited the charm she had been promised, the smooth breaking of the horrible silence. Unable to sustain that hard, penetrating appraisal, she fixed her attention on a vase of flowers slightly to the left of him.

'You cannot be so shy.' The accented drawl was velvet on silk and yet she picked up an edge within it. 'Come here.'

Tensely she edged round a couch. He didn't move forward a helpful inch. What was more, the nearer she got, the bigger he seemed to get. He had to be well over six feet, unusually tall for one of his race.

'Now take your hair down.'

Her lashes fluttered in bemusement. 'M-my h-hair?'

'If it is your desire to become my wife, you must learn that I do not expect my instructions to be questioned,' he drawled. 'When I command, my wife obeys.'

Polly was transfixed to the spot. That cool of absolute

conviction carried greater weight than mere arrogance. She flinched when he moved without warning. Long fingers darted down into her hair, and in disbelief she shut her eyes. He was a lunatic, and you didn't argue with lunatics. He was so close she could smell a trace of expensive aftershave overlying the scent of clean, husky male. In other words, he was ten times closer than she wanted him to be. Her bright hair tumbled down to her shoulders, the pins carelessly cast aside.

'You are amazingly obedient.' Abrasion roughened the low-pitched comment.

Reluctantly, fearfully, she looked up. Some treacherously feminine part of her was seized by an almost voyeuristic fascination. He was superbly built, dramatically good-looking. Even Polly would have sneaked a second glance had she seen him somewhere on the street. High cheekbones intensified the aristocratic cast of his features. Sapphire-blue eyes were set beneath flaring dark brows, his pale golden skin stretched over a savagely handsome bone structure. Up close he was simply breathtaking. But in spite of his gravity and the sleek trappings of a sophisticated image, Polly sensed a contradictory dark and compelling animal vibrancy. He had the unstudied allure of a glossy hunting cheetah, naturally beautiful, naturally deadly. He also had a quality of utter stillness which unnerved her. Overpowered, she instinctively retreated a step, steadily tracked by fathomless blue eyes.

His cool, sensual mouth firmed. 'In the circumstances, your timidity seems rather excessive. I value honesty above all other virtues. It would be wiser if you were to behave normally.'

Silence fell.

'You are still very young,' he continued. 'Can you really have reflected upon the kind of life you will lead as my wife?'

Anybody with the brain power of a dormouse would have run a mile the moment they paused to reflect, Polly decided ferociously. Why did she have to stay put? Because, as Maggie had innocently reminded her, this had been her decision. Her lips moved tremulously into a firmer line. 'Of course I've thought it over.'

'You are probably aware that as I handle my country's investment funds, I frequently travel abroad, but as my wife, you will remain in Dharein. You will not accompany me,' he emphasised. 'There you will mix only with your own sex. You will not be able to drive a car. Nor will you be allowed to leave the palace either alone or unveiled. From the hour that I take you as my bride, no other man may look upon you if that is my wish. Within our household we will even eat separately. Perhaps you have heard that certain members of my family are less strict in their observances of these traditions. I am not. I would not wish you to be in ignorance of this fact.'

Ignorance suddenly seemed like bliss. He described an existence beyond the reach of Polly's imagination. Purdah—the segregation of the sexes that resulted in the practice of keeping women in strict seclusion. Sufficiently challenged by the thought of marrying him, all she could produce was a wooden nod.

Audibly he released his breath. 'You cannot have been accustomed to many restrictions. I understand that your parents regularly entertain here.'

'I don't put in much of a presence.' Polly was thinking of her mother's wrath when she had hidden in a landing cupboard at the age of eleven sooner than recite poetry to family friends.

A winged jet brow ascended. 'When I entertain, you will have no choice.'

Her forehead indented. 'But you can't entertain women on their own?'

His brows pleated.

'You just said that I'd never see another man again. I wouldn't be much use as a hostess,' she pointed out flatly.

A disconcerting quirk briefly shifted his unsmiling mouth. 'It is possible that I have been guilty of some exaggeration on that count,' he conceded. 'But you must understand my surprise that a young woman, raised in so free a society, should be willing to enter an arranged marriage. I was concerned that you might have erroneously assumed that your position as my wife would grant you an exciting and glamorous existence.'

'I expect it to be dull.' The impulsive admission just leapt off Polly's tongue. She shrank from the incredulous glitter irradiating his narrowed stare. 'I mean, not dull precisely, but—well, an Arab wife, who has servants and doesn't get out either…well,' she was faltering badly, 'she can't have very much to do with herself.'

'An Arab wife concerns herself with the comfort of her husband,' he intoned coldly.

He was most erratic in his arguments. 'But you said you wouldn't be around much.'

Even white teeth showed in an almost feral slash against his bronzed skin. 'By that I wished to warn you that I will not dance attendance on you.'

But you expect me to dance attendance on you! she thought. He was a male chauvinist pig, an award-winning specimen. He put chauvinism in line with a capital offence. Stonily she studied the carpet. 'Yes.'

'Our alliance will be one of extreme practicality,' he delivered in hard addition. 'I am not of a romantic disposition. I tell you this…'

'You didn't need to. You wouldn't be here if you were romantic,' Polly interrupted thinly. 'I suppose Mother said something which made you worry that I might be suffering from similar delusions. I'm not.'

For a male receiving a reassurance he had surely sought, Raschid looked unrelentingly grim. 'This becomes clear. Then we are of one mind. I will not receive complaints of neglect when I am involved in the business concerns which take up most of my time.'

By the sound of it, if she ran into him once a week she would be doing well. She smiled. 'No, I won't complain.'

'Had I sacked Dharein from border to border, it appears that I could not have found a more conformist and submissive bride,' he declared very softly. 'But I warn you of this now—should we prove incompatible, I will divorce you.'

That was a piece of good news Polly had not even hoped for. How could they be compatible in any field? He intimidated her. A close encounter with an alien would have been less terrifying. The unashamed threat of domestic tyranny echoed in all his stated requirements.

'You have nothing to say to this either?' he prompted in a husky growl. 'You are composed and content with this future?'

'Are you?' Glancing up unwarily, Polly encountered a hypnotically intense stare which burned flags of pink into her fair skin. A curious tightening sensation clenched her somewhere down deep inside. It made her feel very uncomfortable.

A chilling smile slanted his well-shaped mouth. 'Could I be impervious to the allure of such beauty as you possess?'

No doubt this was an example of the charm her mother had mentioned, and it was absolutely meaningless. When Raschid had first seen her in the doorway, neither admiration nor warmth had coloured his impassive appraisal.

'Although I should confess that I am not in accord with the meeting of East and West in marriage,' he added smoothly. 'I will treat you with consideration and respect, but I will not alter my way of life. The adaptation required will, necessarily, be yours alone. I can only accept your word that you feel yourself equal to this challenge.'

Out of the blue the strangest suspicion came to her, infiltrating her self-preoccupation. Could he possibly want her to refuse him? Surely he could not have come here to invite a rejection which would be an intolerable insult to one of his race and status? Polly cast aside that highly unlikely interpretation. A purist might have respected his refusal to offer empty reassurances about their future together. But all he achieved was a deepening of each and every one of Polly's nervous terrors at the picture of herself, marooned in a strange environment, forced to follow foreign customs while at the mercy of a husband who planned to make no allowances for her.

'I'll do my best,' she mumbled, hating him with every fibre of her being for redoubling her fear of the unknown. He defined an existence which chilled her to the marrow.

He studied her downbent head. 'I can ask no more of you. One must hope that the sacrifices entailed are not more than you find the elevation worthy of. Since I have established to my own satisfaction that you fully comprehend the nature of our future relationship, there can be no necessity for a further meeting between us.'

Laser-bright eyes met her startled upward glance in cool challenge.

'But you'll be staying now…for a while?' she queried.

'Unfortunately that will not be possible. Late this evening I am leaving for New York,' he revealed. 'Nor will it suit my schedule to return here again before the wedding.'

Nonchalantly untouched by her dismay that he cherished no plans to stay on as her parents expected, he bent down to enclose lean fingers to her wrist and raise her firmly upright. Her knees were cottonwool supports. Dazedly she watched him clamp a heavy bracelet to her wrist.

'Your betrothal gift,' he explained, answering her blank stare.

Of beaten gold and studded with precious stones, it was decorated with some primitive form of hieroglyphics. Polly was put grotesquely in mind of a slave manacle. Valiantly she tried to express gratitude.

A cool hand pressed up her chin, enforcing contact with black-lashed eyes of lapis lazuli which were dauntingly enigmatic. Raschid ran the forefinger of his other hand very lightly along the smooth curve of her jawbone, silently studying her, and somehow, while he maintained that magnetic reconnaissance, she could not move. A peculiar disorientation swept her with light-headedness. He dropped his hand almost amusedly. 'I think you will be very responsive in my bed, Polly. I also suspect that you may find your training as a librarian of small advantage to you there. But I await enlightenment with immense impatience...'

Had the door not opened, framing her parents' anxious faces, Polly would have fled there and then. A deep crimson had banished her pallor. Raschid turned to them with a brilliant smile. 'Your daughter is all that I was promised—a pearl beyond price,' he murmured smoothly. 'Truly I am blessed that I may claim so perfect a bride.'

CHAPTER TWO

THE ORGAN played Purcell as Polly came down the aisle, parchment-pale, her screened gaze avoiding the tall, exquisitely dressed male watching her with untraditional cool from the altar. Throughout the past fortnight of hectic preparations she had existed in a dream state, her brain protectively hung in an emotional vacuum. That was the only way she had coped.

Her mind shifted inexorably back to her parents' dismay when they had realised that Raschid was not remaining with them as a house guest. She had hoped...what had she hoped for? Dismay had swiftly become acceptance. In awe of him, her parents had put up no objections. They were not even attending the second ceremony in Dharein. From the moment Polly left the church she would be on her own.

At the altar she received a wide smile from the smaller, younger man to Raschid's right—presumably his brother Asif. Reddening, she dropped her head and the vicar's voice droned on in her ears. Beside her lounged a primitive male, who regarded her solely as a piece of sexual merchandise he had bought off a shelf. Involuntarily she shivered. Raschid had made it brutally clear that she would have no place in his life beyond the bedroom door. Her blood had run cold under the intensely sexual slide of those assessing eyes, the appraisal of a natural-born predator.

They were on the church steps when she saw Chris. As he waved, her shuttered face came alive. It was three months since their last meeting. Raw and seething bitterness surged up inside her. It should have been Chris beside her posing for the camera...it should have been Chris inside

23

the church. The ceremony she had just undergone was a mockery. Without hesitation she hurried down the steps towards the slim, fair-haired man smiling at her.

'Aunt Janice said you mightn't be able to come,' she murmured tightly.

Chris laughed. 'Wild horses wouldn't have kept me from your wedding! You look stunning.' Grasping both her hands, he looked her over and grinned. 'What happened to your ambition to be a career woman?'

'You tell me.' Responding to his easy smile took all her concentration as she fought back stinging tears. She was embarrassed by her adolescently eager dash to his side, but the familiar sight of him had drawn her instantly.

'Hey,' he scolded, and the underlying seriousness of his gaze deepened, 'the bride's not supposed to cry! Whirlwind romance or not, I hope he's the right man for you. You deserve the best.'

Polly's throat closed over. The truth of what lay behind her sudden marriage would have appalled him, yet pride kept her silent. What more proof did she require of his indifference to her as a woman? He would dance at her wedding with a light heart. He had never realised how she felt about him, and now he never would. 'I wouldn't have settled for less.' Her over-bright smile stretched to include Asif as he approached them.

'Sorry, I have to kidnap the bride. The photographer's fuming,' he explained in a clipped Oxbridge accent.

'Oh, lord, I forgot about him!' Polly gasped.

He steered her away, lustrous dark eyes skimming her guilty face, his appreciative grin widening. 'Is there anything else that you forgot? Like a new husband? If you'll forgive me for saying so, it's not terribly tactful to go surging at ex-boyfriends with Raschid around—unless you have a death wish, of course. But I'll grant you one point. You staggered him—a rare sight to be savoured.'

Reluctantly Polly met Raschid's veiled gaze a moment later. 'I'm sorry,' she lied.

He cast her a grim glance. 'You don't appear to know how to behave in public,' he drawled in an icy undertone that flicked down her spine like the gypsy's warning. 'But you will be taught, of that I assure you.'

In angry disbelief, still trembling from the force of her disturbed emotions, she flared, 'Who the blazes do you…?'

His jawline clenched. 'I will not tolerate disrespect from you!'

Gritting her teeth, Polly spun to walk away again. The long-suffering photographer had finished. Raschid's hand closed round hers, denying escape, but she broke her fingers violently free, muttering bitterly, 'Tell me, what do you do when you're not bullying women half your size? Beat them? I'd sooner know now!'

The blaze of fury that silvered his gaze shook her rigid. Had they not been surrounded by people she had the certain knowledge that she would have discovered exactly what Raschid did for an encore. Guiltily conscious that hating him for not being Chris was irrational and inexcusable, she retreated hastily.

'Lordy, what sparked that off?' Maggie whispered.

'An unholy temper that I never suspected he had.' Polly stole a driven glance over her shoulder to check that she hadn't been followed. A choking sense of trapped misery enfolded her.

She should have apologised on the drive back to the reception at Ladybright, but she didn't. Like an over-shaken bottle of Coke, she was afraid to uncap her sealed lips lest she explode. Her nerves were jangling a dangerous discordancy. Seeing Chris, so near yet so far, had agonised her, and her self-discipline was threatening to crumble.

Over the meal she did her utmost to ignore Raschid. The tension zapped in the air like static electricity. Unable to

face food, she knocked back the champagne. She didn't
even notice how much she was drinking. When everybody
began circulating, Polly, who was normally retiring in company, was suddenly to be seen speaking personally to every
guest present. Absently marvelling that she no longer felt
like throwing herself under a bus, she laughed at another
one of Chris's medical jokes, frowning when Maggie pulled
at her sleeve.

'You have to get changed.' Maggie hustled her determinedly out of the room. 'What on earth are you playing
at? You're sozzled! Mother hasn't even realised—she's
busy telling everybody what wonderful confidence a
woman gains from getting married.'

Polly gripped the banister and pronounced with dignity,
'I have never taken alcohol to ex—excesh in my life.'

'That's why it's gone straight to your head. How could
you be so stupid?' wailed Maggie. 'Even I can see that
Raschid doesn't like it. Didn't you notice that he hasn't
touched a drop? He's not knocking it back like his brother.
This just isn't like you!'

'But I'm a confident married woman now.' Polly pirou-
etted and nearly tripped over her train, remaining dizzily
still long enough for Maggie to detach her veil. 'I shall
stand up for myself. I won't be bullied!'

'How about strangled?' her sister groaned, struggling to
unzip her. 'Sometimes you are a klutz, Polly. When Raschid saw you in the church he couldn't take his eyes off
you—and no wonder, you looked ravishing! But now he
looks...well, if I were you, I'd eat humble pie.'

'Rubbish—start as you mean to go on,' Polly overruled
as if her craven evasiveness had been the first step in a
deliberate offensive.

'And as for the way Chris kept on following you
about...'

'Any reason why he shouldn't have?' snapped Polly,

turning her head away. When would she ever see Chris again? If she had made the best of a last opportunity to be with him, who could blame her?

Maggie frowned uncomfortably. 'He couldn't take his eyes off you either. I've never seen Chris act like that with you before.'

Polly hadn't noticed anything. An insane thought occurred to her. Wouldn't it be simply hysterical if Chris had finally appreciated that she was a woman and not a sister the day she married someone else? Macabre and unlikely, she decided bitterly.

Attired in her elegant going-away outfit, she was propelled out on to the landing to throw her bouquet. She peered down at all the upturned faces and swayed, dropping the bouquet in their general direction. Negotiating the stairs rivalled coming down an escalator the wrong way. On the bottom step she lurched, and strong arms came out of nowhere and caught her.

'Whoops!' she giggled, clashing accidentally with sapphire eyes that emanated all the warmth of an icebox. 'Go on the wagon,' she mumbled as if she was making a New Year resolution, the remainder of her alcohol-induced euphoria draining away. 'Promish.'

The hiccups started on the way to the airport. Clapping a hand to her mouth in horror, she tried to hold them in. It was about then that she began to notice the silence. By the time she was steered into the opulent cabin of the private jet, she was sending Raschid's hard-edged profile unwittingly pleading glances. The derisive charge of the look she received nearly pushed her over the edge into tears. She fumbled for the right words of apology for her outburst on the church steps. After take-off, she voiced them hesitantly.

Raschid leant forward without warning and snapped hard fingers round her narrow wrists to yank her up to face him. 'You are drunk!' he raked down at her in disgust.

'T-tiddly,' Polly corrected unsteadily, moisture shimmering in her unhappy eyes.

His contempt unconcealed, he released her to sink back white and shaken into her seat. She mumbled another apology, shrinking from the shamed awareness that he was right. But just for a while, under the influence of Dutch courage, her fear of him had vanished. Now it was returning in full force, stronger than ever before.

'Silence!' he cut across her stumbling apology. 'Was it not shame enough that I must accept a bride who sells herself for money like a vendor sells his wares in the street? But that you should dare to turn up at that church and then make an exhibition of yourself as my wife is intolerable!'

'I'm sorry!' she sobbed again.

'I told you to keep quiet,' he lashed icily down at her. 'I may have been deceived, but it is you who will suffer for it. After the brazen behaviour I witnessed today, you will find yourself confined to the palace!'

'I wasn't going to get out anyway!' Polly wept all the harder while he towered over her like a hanging judge pronouncing sentence.

'I will not acknowledge you publicly as my wife until you learn how to conduct yourself like a lady, and I have never seen anything less ladylike than your display this afternoon!'

The harsh condemnation genuinely shattered her. Without warning all the dammed-up tensions and resentments she had been forced by family indifference to suppress exploded from her. Her head flew back. 'I...hate...you!' she launched. 'Don't you dare insult me. I did my best. I even tried to hide the fact that if it wasn't for the money, I wouldn't have married you if you'd been the very last man alive! And if you don't want me either, I'm just delighted about it! Do you hear me? You're a domineering, insensitive tyrant, and I shall get down on my knees and beg your father to deport me. No wonder he had to come to England to find you a wife…no wonder!'

During her impassioned tirade, Raschid had frozen. He could not have been more astonished by the diatribe had a chair lifted on its own steam and begun a physical assault on him.

Curled up in a tight ball, Polly squinted up at him through tear-clogged lashes. 'No woman with an IQ above forty would want to marry you and clank about in chains for the rest of her days, trying not to show how h-happy she is when you're thousands of miles away…'

'I believe it is time that you were sobered up.' He bent down, and Polly was off that seat so fast with a piercing scream that she caught him totally by surprise. Having read brutal retribution into that grim announcement of intent, she lost what control remained to her and squirmed along to the far corner of the couch, tugging off a shoe in the blind, terror-stricken belief that she required a defensive weapon.

The cabin door burst wide, the steward and stewardess rushing in. Polly was quite beyond the reach of embarrassment. Stark fear had her cowering, tears pouring down her cheeks in rivulets.

A dark bar of colour overlaid Raschid's hard cheekbones. He spoke at length in Arabic and then quietly dismissed their audience. A hand plucked the raised shoe from her stranglehold and tossed it aside. 'I would not offer a woman violence,' he ground out with hauteur.

'I'm numb, I won't feel it,' she mumbled incoherently.

A pair of arms firmly scooped her drooping body off the seat. 'You will feel calmer when you have rested.'

He carried her into the sleeping compartment, settling her down with unexpected care on the built-in bed. Tugging off her stray shoe, he calmly turned her over to unzip her dress. Cooler air washed her spine. In dismay she attempted to escape his attentions, as he glowered down at her. 'Do you really think that I could be tempted to seize you passionately into my arms at this moment? A hysterical child does not awaken desire within me.'

Having decimated the opposition, he seated himself to divest her smoothly of her dress. Leaving her clad in her slip, he pulled the slippery sheet over her trembling length. Already dazedly recovering from the kind of scene she had never before indulged in, Polly was gripped by remorse. Not only had she affronted him before the cabin staff, she had been unjust. Her resentment would have been more fairly aimed at her parents for cheerfully letting her enter this marriage and blithely ignoring reality.

Could she really even blame them? The pressure on her had been enormous, but she had agreed to marry Raschid. Unfortunately there was a vast gulf between weak resolution and her feelings now that she was on the spot. She swallowed chokily. 'I don't know what came over me... I...'

The steady beat of his gaze was unremitting. 'There is nothing to explain. You were afraid—I should have seen that fear and made allowances for it. But I too have feelings, Polly,' he delivered with level emphasis. 'Financial greed may be permissible in a mistress; it is not in a wife. For that reason I have given you little cause to rejoice in the bargain.'

There was something about him in that instant, some deep and fierce emotion behind the icy dignity and hauteur. For the very first time, Polly suffered a driving need to know how he felt. Bitter? Disillusioned? His anger was gone. What she sensed now, she could not name, but it sent a sharp pang of pain winging through her.

She didn't want to talk about the money. She couldn't face the reawakening of the chilling distaste he had shown earlier. What would be the point of it? The money lay between them and it could not be removed. But for the money she would not be here. Raschid despised her for her willingness to marry him on that basis alone. The whys and wherefores didn't abate his harsh judgement. And the revelation that she loved another man would scarcely improve his opinion of her. Suddenly more ashamed than ever, she whispered, 'I didn't mean what I said.'

An ebony brow elevated. 'I am not a fool, but I ask you this—if that is how you feel, why did you marry me?'

She could not bring herself to play the martyr, pleading her family's need as excuse. Absorbing her unease in the tortured silence, he sighed. Brown fingers brushed a silvery pale tendril of hair back from her warm forehead. 'I had reason,' he said softly. 'To look at you gave me pleasure, and in spite of what you say to the contrary, I could put your aversion to flight so quickly that your head would spin…for when you look at me, Polly, you desire me.'

'That's not true!' Her hostility sprang immediately back to the fore.

The tip of his forefinger skidded languidly along the fullness of her lower lip. His eyes had a richly amused glint now. 'True, my little Polly,' he contradicted.

Her mind was a blank. She was shaken by her sudden explosive physical awareness of him. His sexual impact that close was like a punch in the stomach, yet she did not retreat from it. 'You're not angry any more,' she muttered.

'Be grateful for your visual compensations. I learnt long ago that the perfection Allah denies in the copying of nature is no more easily to be found in human beings, especially in those of your sex,' he stated quietly. 'The inviting smile which falsely offers tenderness and understanding—that I do not require from you. You will be as you are with me. That I will respect.'

He slid fluidly upright. 'We will forget today. I don't believe you knew what you were doing. Had that been obvious to me, I would not have spoken so harshly.'

Reeling from that imperturbable calm and gravity, Polly was agonisingly conscious of the seismic force of the personality behind the cool front. He had not once lost control. She had behaved appallingly, but he had remained cool-headed enough to see her hysteria for what it was. While grateful for his calm, she squirmed from the lash of his superior perception.

A knock sounded on the door. 'That will be the meal I requested. You ate very little earlier,' he reminded her. 'I also ordered a restorative drink for you—before we parted Asif assured me that it was an infallible cure for a hangover. Drink it and then sleep.'

Disconcerted yet again, Polly couldn't even look at him. The stewardess entered, darting a nervous glance at Raschid, who appeared to figure in her mind as a wife beater. Guilty pink suffused Polly's cheeks. He had treated her with a kindness few men would have employed in the circumstances. Dully she reviewed the reckless, thoughtless immaturity of her own showing throughout the day. The contrast did not lift her spirits.

She was wonderfully relaxed when she woke up. Only as she shifted and came into startling contact with a hair-roughened thigh did she realise where she was, and her eyes flew wide.

'Good morning.' Raschid leant up on his elbow. Reading her shock, he laughed. He looked ruffled and in need of a shave and unnervingly, undeniably gorgeous. Black hair, golden skin, blue eyes—a devastating combination. Smiling, he moved a hand lazily and tugged a strand of her hair. 'Come back over here. Or do I have to fetch you?'

'F-fetch me?' she quavered.

He snaked out his hand and settled it on her slim waist, his fingers splaying to her hipbone to propel her coolly back towards him.

'No!' she gasped in alarm.

'Yes.'

'No…I'm not joking!' she cried feverishly.

Raschid laced his other hand into the tangle of her hair and held her frightened green eyes steadily. 'Neither am I, Polly.' He pulled her the last few inches, sealing her into union with his long, hard length. 'And there is nothing to fear, only much to discover,' he promised huskily.

Her hand braced against a sleek brown shoulder, only to leap quickly away again. His dark head bent, the brilliance of his eyes somehow sentencing her to stillness. Taking his time, he brushed her lips with his, and she trembled, lying as rigid as a stone statue in his embrace. He strung a line of light, butterfly kisses over the arc of her extended throat, softly, sensuously dipping a smooth passage across the delicate tracery of her collarbone while his fingers skimmed caressingly over the sensitive skin of her back.

Polly's limbs turned fluid without her knowledge. A strange heat blossomed in her pelvis. She quivered as his palm curved to the swell of her hip and he moved sinuously against her, teaching her the depth of his arousal and momentarily shocking her back into tension. He nuzzled at the tender expanse below her ear and her cheek curved into the pillow, her body awash with fluttering sensations which completely controlled her. With a soft laugh, he finally returned to her mouth, playfully coaxing, introducing her to the myriad textures of his firm lips and sharp teeth and the velvety roughness of his tongue, until the blood drummed in her veins with burning excitement.

Catherine wheels and shooting stars illuminated the darkness of her mind. It was everything she had ever secretly dreamt of, everything she had never expected to feel, except…except… The thought eluded her. Raschid's hands traced the shape of her breasts with erotic mastery, moulding, stroking, inciting. A tiny moan escaped her. A searing rush of almost painful pleasure arched her body up into the heat and potency of the all-male body over hers. Then as suddenly she was freed.

Her glazed scrutiny rested on her treacherous fingers. Anchored in the springy vitality of his hair, they prevented him from further retreat. Strickenly she retrieved them.

He skated a mocking fingertip over her ripe mouth, his eyes bright pools of incredible blue, tautness etched over his flushed cheekbones. 'I am very tempted to enjoy the delights of the bridal chamber with you now.' Straightening with an earthy groan, he looked intently down at her. 'However, that would not be wise. But at least you may now appreciate that you need have no fear of me tonight.'

Pushing back the sheet, he slid out of bed, not a self-conscious bone in a single line of his lean, sunbronzed body. Tonight. A blush warmed what felt like every inch of her skin. She had lain there and actually let him…at no stage had she objected. But on a level with that shockingly polished technique of his, her experience was nil. Raschid could not be compared to the teenage boys, full of selfish impatience, who had grabbed her roughly, attempting to infuse her with a matching passion, only to fail. Never once had she understood what she was supposed to feel during those embarrassing sessions.

Now, in the arms of a male who was virtually a stranger, she found out, and she was in shock. Had he been Chris she would not have been surprised. But he wasn't Chris and he wasn't remotely like Chris. Nor could she ever recall yearning for Chris to touch her. That accidental acknowledgement slid in and jolted her. It was true, she realised in bewilderment. Picturing herself drifting from the altar with Chris, she had then seen them in a dozen cosy settings, but never in one that centred on sexual intimacy. Something in her retreated uneasily from an image of Chris as a lover. Confused by the awareness, she buried it. Hadn't she seen friends succumb to dangerous physical infatuations that burnt out through the lack of any more lasting fuel? Her feelings for Chris had always seemed infinitely superior. She had felt safe. She knew better, she had thought.

And Raschid taught her differently. Carelessly, easily, with the light touch and control of an expert lover, he had showed her what physical hunger was—a wanting, unreasoning ache without conscience, powerful enough to destroy every scruple. She was disgusted with herself. And dear heaven, he was like Jekyll and Hyde! Whatever she might have expected, it had not been that heart-stoppingly sensual persuasion which had effortlessly overcome her resistance. He bewildered her.

He had calmly referred to the wedding night still to come. Panic reclaimed her. What had she done in marrying him? Suddenly she was waking up to the full portent of what marrying Raschid entailed. How could she go through with it? How could she actually go to bed with a stranger? She was not some medieval maiden raised to be bartered in matrimony. Environment had not conditioned Polly to submissively accept her fate without argument.

She was sitting up when Raschid reappeared from the shower-room, towelling his hair dry. Crimsoning at the amount of masculine flesh on view, Polly lost inches of recaptured poise and studied the bed. 'We need to talk,' she muttered.

'I am here.'

Nervously she breathed in. 'Earlier you seemed to make it pretty clear that I couldn't be the sort of wife you want.' She paused. 'Maybe you'd prefer to call a halt now.'

'A halt?'

'An annulment.'

An unexpected laugh greeted her stilted suggestion. 'I presume you are trying to amuse me?'

Indignantly she glanced up. He looked totally unfamiliar

in flowing robes of soft cream. 'Actually I'm being constructive,' she told him.

'Don't you think your desire to be—constructive,' he repeated the word very drily, 'is a little late?'

Polly bit her lip. The suggestion had been born of cowardly impulse. Undoubtedly it must seem to him as if she wanted to renege on the agreement after having collected the profits. 'But you said you wouldn't acknowledge me,' she protested lamely.

'I too may say things in anger which I do not mean. I seriously doubt that you have a drink problem, and even if you had,' his beautifully shaped mouth slanted expressively, 'you are unlikely to find any outlet for it in Dharein.'

'I don't understand you!' Frustration rose in her.

'Our meetings to date have not encouraged either of us to behave naturally,' he returned with infuriating composure. 'And to talk of annulment now when we are married is really quite ridiculous.'

Defensively she stiffened. 'That's the only time you *could* talk about annulment…you don't give a damn how I feel, do you?'

He viewed her narrowly. 'You would like me to be honest? I came to your home with no idea of what reception awaited me there. I cherished no inclination to marry any woman.'

'I beg your pardon?' she cut in.

'I believe you heard me, Polly. Nor can I accept that this news surprises you.'

Hearing was not always believing. He had not wanted to marry her. The information stung and shocked like a sudden slap on the face. A deep sense of incredulous mortification crept over her. 'Then why did you come?' she asked.

'In the hope that you might withdraw as I could not.' Raschid dealt her an unrelentingly sardonic glance, his mouth cynically set. 'But that hope was swiftly laid to rest, wasn't it? However I might have behaved, my proposal would have been acceptable to you and your family. But I am not one to quarrel with what cannot be altered. You are beautiful. *Insh'allah*. It could have been worse.'

As she listened with a slowly dropping jaw, a tide of rage unfettered by reasoning even of the meanest form was building inside her. 'How could you marry me thinking like that? It could have been worse,' she parroted in enraged repetition. 'And how…dare…you get into bed with me!'

Raschid bound a gold *agal* round his headress. 'There may be a certain piquancy to our mutual reservations, but they are unlikely to spill over into the marital bed. There you do not find my attentions offensive.'

'Don't you dare throw that at me now! I had no idea what you were thinking then!' she rebutted stridently.

'I have explained my feelings to you.' The inflection was one of definite reproof, clipped and controlled. 'Now I suggest you dress suitably for your audience with my father. We will be landing soon.'

Sudden moisture gritted her eyelids and she blinked, her anger deflated. Raschid was gone, and she was unutterably crushed by what he had coolly dropped on her. The black joke of the century was on them both. Prince Raschid ibn Saud al Azarin had not wanted to marry her either. Damn him to hell! she thought abruptly. If that was true, why were they here now? Why had he even come to Ladybright? Oh, she wanted to scream! Some outdated code of honour had made him come, had made him refrain from admitting his unwillingness. But now—when he told her it was too late—he had slung it at her with hauteur, as if Polly and her family had gone in pursuit of him with a shotgun. Now she could review his grim and guarded manner at their first encounter. She had fallen hook, line and sinker for an act. The arrogant swine had actually been trying to put her off!

Equating his arrival with unquestioning acceptance of the marriage, she had been too wrapped up in her own anxieties to appraise his attitude logically. But why had he gone through with it? Her thoughts chased in concentric circles, her temper rising afresh. He had the gall to inform her bluntly that her sole saving grace was her face and figure. Suddenly she was dismissed as an individual and reduced to the level of a sexual plaything. It could have been worse—indeed? If it crossed her mind that there was a strong hint of the biter bit in her enraged reaction, she refused to identify it.

'The obvious solution is a divorce as soon as possible,' she pronounced, entering the cabin, her slender curves fetchingly attired in a full-length pale green gown which accentuated her air of spun silver delicacy.

'Don't be a child, Polly.' Raschid glanced up from the papers he was studying at his desk, awarding her reappearance the most cursory interest.

She folded her arms, wrathful at being ignored. 'If the only thing that brought you to Ladybright was that stupid assassination attempt on your father and the crazy promise he made then, I'm not being childish.'

Blue-black lashes swept up like silk fans. 'I cannot refrain from saying that the attempt might have ended in a death which would have been tragic for my country's survival and stability,' he replied abrasively. 'But I will concede that I too consider that promise to be rather…odd. My father is not a man of ill-judged impulse.'

'But, like him, you believe in this honour nonsense.'

'A concept which few of your sex have the unselfishness to hold in esteem. The pursuit of the principle infrequently leads down a self-chosen path,' he delivered crushingly. 'Nor was I made aware of the pledge between our fathers until three weeks ago.'

Polly was astonished. 'Only three weeks ago?'

'There was no reason for me to be told sooner. When I married at twenty, you were still a child. Since my father could not have supposed that an Englishwoman would desire to enter a polygamous marriage—' He paused. 'Although having met you and your family, I would not be so sure.'

It took her a minute to unmask that base insult. She flushed to the roots of her hairline while he spoke on in the same coolly measured tone.

'My father cannot always have believed in that promise to the degree which he presently contends. Had it been otherwise, I would have been informed of it years ago,' he asserted. 'But I understand his motivation and I speak of it now, for it is no secret within the palace. It has long been my father's aim to force me into marriage again.'

CHAPTER THREE

STUNNED by the unemotionally couched admission, Polly sank down on the other side of the desk. 'But why me, if he didn't believe…force?' she queried.

'The promise supplied the pressure. The means by which my father attained this conclusion might not be passed by the over-scrupulous.' Raschid smiled grimly. 'But be assured that before he even met your father, he would have made exhaustive enquiries as to your character and reputation.'

'I was investigated?'

'Without a doubt. You are very naïve, Polly. You cannot suppose that my father would have risked presenting me with a bride likely to shame or scandalise the family.' Sardonic amusement brightened his clear gaze.

In retrospect it did seem very foolish of all of them to have believed that King Reija would gaily give consent to his son's marriage to a woman of whom he knew nothing. Raschid's revelations put an entirely different complexion on her father's meeting with him in London. Assured of her unblemished reputation and goodness knew what else, Raschid's father had calmly manipulated hers at the interview. From the outset he must have known of her father's debts. They could not have escaped detection.

Too much was bombarding Polly too quickly. The amount of Machiavellian intrigue afoot even between father and son dismayed her. But why had coercion in the form of that promise been required to push Raschid into marriage? While he might still grieve for Berah and appear virtually indifferent to her successor's identity, he did not strike her as impractical. His position demanded that he marry and father children; that responsibility was inextricably woven into his future as a duty. Could he be so insensible to the necessity?

'I don't understand—you don't really seem angry with your father,' she said.

'I must respect the sincerity of his intentions. He truly believes that a man without a wife cannot be content. In his view a married man is also a respectable and stable man,' he volunteered, an inescapable harshness roughening his intonation.

'But why didn't you want to remarry?' Polly pierced to the heart of the matter, weary of skating round the edges.

'I preferred my freedom,' he breathed dismissively. 'Since I had spent most of my adult life married, what else?'

'Well, if you're so darned keen to have your freedom back, I'm not holding you!' Polly sprang furiously upright.

'Why this sudden alteration in attitude?' Raschid studied her quizzically. 'What has changed between us except a basic understanding? We stand at no different level now from that we stood at within that church.'

Anger shuddered tempestuously through her. 'Yet somehow you're behaving as if I trapped you into marriage!'

'Nobody traps me, least of all a woman. I made a decision. If I had to remarry to satisfy my father's expectations, why not you?' he traded softly.

'I notice too that, while your father mysteriously emerges from all this as morally above reproach when he's been wheeling and dealing like the Godfather, I'm still being insulted!'

'How have I insulted you?' He vented a harsh imprecation. 'I thought you would be quiet and inoffensive, but the second you left that church you suddenly located a tongue!'

Admittedly Polly had had difficulty in recognising herself over the past twenty-four hours, but the most even temperament would have been inflamed by Raschid. 'Blame your father. Obviously he didn't dig deep enough,' she sniped, nettled by his candid admission that he had deemed her the type to melt mutely into the woodwork. 'I find you unbelievably insensitive!'

'And I find you like every other woman I have met in recent years—demanding.' Exasperation laced his striking features. 'Were you so sensitive in marrying a stranger purely for his wealth?'

Already very pale, she cringed from the cruel reminder. Pride made her voice the comeback, tilting her chin. 'Was that how you viewed your first wife as well?'

He was very still. In the dragging quiet, her heart thudded loudly in her eardrums. The fierce chill of his appraisal forced colour up beneath her skin. 'There can be no comparison. Berah grew up knowing that she would become my wife. Nor was she unaware of the nature of the man she was marrying. You know nothing whatsoever about me.'

Her stricken eyes fell from his. While her reference to Berah had been foolish, she had not been prepared for the charged and telling force of Raschid's defence of her. His fingers were rigidly braced on the edge of the desk. The comparison she had dared to suggest had deeply angered him.

'I don't think you're being very fair,' she argued. 'And I'm not demanding.'

A lean brown hand shifted abruptly. 'Let us have no further arguments. On this subject they lead nowhere.'

'What subject? What are we arguing about? I don't know.'

He lounged indolently back. 'Really?' A dubious brow quirked. 'In the space of an hour you refer to annulment and divorce. This is not, after all, some form of attention-seeking?' he derided. 'You want pretences—compliments, gallantry, romance. I disdain all of those, and I won't play charades. I employed candour with you before today. We each had our price in this marriage. Mine was peace and yours was status and money. Now that that is established, what more can there be worthy of debate?'

'I can tell you right now,' Polly slammed back shakily for want of any other brickbat to hurl. 'Being a princess is not all it's made out to be!'

'You may tell me whatever you wish if you reward me with a still tongue and the sound of sweet silence.'

She retreated to the opposite end of the cabin. He had gone over her like an armoured tank and the track marks of the vanquished were on her back. She had reacted emotionally to a male who did not allow emotion to cloud his reasoning. Or his judgement. He thought that she should have left her family to sink in the horrors of bankruptcy rather than sell herself into marriage. He was delicate in his sensibilities—he could afford to be. Bitterly Polly appraised the outright luxury of her surroundings. Without money her family would have fallen apart. Neither of her parents would have had the resilience to pick themselves up and soldier on.

Yet for all his contempt now, Raschid had been remarkably tolerant about a wedding which could have made a hit disaster movie. In bed—she reddened hotly at the recollection—he had been teasing and warm. But both responses had been logically perfect for the occasion. You didn't calm a hysteric with threats. You didn't coax a frightened virgin with force. Not unless you were stupid, and Raschid, she was learning by painful and clumsy steps, was far from stupid. He was dauntingly clever and dismayingly complex.

Abstractedly she watched him. Even in violent resentment she remained disturbingly conscious of the dark vibrancy of his potent attraction. In combination with looks and wealth that blazing physical magnetism of his must have stopped many women in their tracks. Polly had always distrusted handsome men; they were normally chockful of vanity. Raschid's distinct lack of self-awareness puzzled her. He was stunning, but she had the strangest suspicion that the only time he looked in the mirror was to shave.

Abruptly she denied her view of him by removing to a poorer vantage point. She couldn't understand what was wrong with her. Even when the stewardess served her with a meal, her thoughts marched on. Raschid was beginning to obsess her even as his emotional detachment chilled her. Linked with that raw, overt masculinity of his, that coolness made him an intriguing paradox.

Why had he been so reluctant to remarry? There could only be one reason: a reluctance to set another woman in Berah's place. But Polly found it hard to attribute the longevity of passionate love beyond death and sentimental scruples to that diamond-cutting intellect. What other reason could there be? Accepting that he had to remarry, he had settled for Polly. He liked looking at her; he didn't like listening to her. Then he wouldn't have to listen much, would he? Not with the workload and the travel itinerary he had bent over backwards to outline.

The jet landed with a nasty judder, careening along the runway, the nearest porthole displaying a blur of what looked like desert. Assuming that the airport was oddly sited somewhere out of view, Polly got up. Raschid presented her with a bundle of black cloth. Her blank appraisal roused his impatience. Retrieving it, he shook it out and dropped it over her startled head.

'I can't breathe!' she protested.

'Don't be ridiculous!' Light appeared as he adjusted the set of the suffocating garment. Disorientatingly, he burst out laughing. 'You look very strange, Polly. This *aba* was not cut for someone of your height.'

Yanking up the surplus fabric, she stalked after him. Just outside the doorway, as she was interestedly taking in the sight of a line-up of soldiers and the presence of a small military band, striking up the most unmelodic tune she had ever heard, her foot caught in the hem of the *aba*. Hearing her gasp, Raschid whirled with incredible speed. As she teetered she was abruptly snatched off her feet and pierced by blazing blue eyes. 'You are the most extraordinarily clumsy female I have ever come across!'

'I wasn't planning on wearing a shroud until I went to my coffin!' she snapped back.

His sudden pallor did not escape her. Too late did she understand the source of his wrath. But before sympathy could touch her normally generous heart, outrage took over. Dear heaven, was Berah never out of his thoughts? Here he was carting Polly home, and all she could think about was his first wife!

'Put me down, please,' she demanded icily.

'It's only a few steps to the car.' Indeed it was, and after throwing the unfortunate band an unappreciative glance, he stuffed her inside the limousine like a parcel. In bewilderment she stared out at the huge grey fortress walls rising to sheer heights with no perceivable end only a few hundred yards away.

'Where's the airport?' she queried.

'That is the palace. A jet-strip was built here for convenience. The airport is on the other side of Jumani.'

'That's the city?'

'I am overwhelmed by the interest you have taken in your future home.' His scorn for her ignorance was unhidden. 'Jumani is ten kilometres from here.'

In embarrassment Polly turned to peer out at the gigantic nothingness of the desert terrain stretching in all other directions. It went on into infinity to meet the colourless vault of the sky, a wasteland of emptiness and rolling hills of sand. The isolation was indescribably alien to visual senses trained on green fields and hedgerows.

The limousine whisked them over to the black, shimmering ribbon of road and through the gates of the palace into a vast, cobbled courtyard. Already the heat was making Polly's clothing stick to her damp skin. Raschid's door sprang open immediately. He stepped out to be met by a spate of Arabic from the little man bobbing and dipping rather nervously in front of him. He frowned and swept off.

When he halted as if he had forgotten something ten yards on, Polly just wanted to kick him for striding back to haul her out of her death struggle with the *aba* twisted round her legs. 'That is not a very graceful fashion in which to descend from a car,' Raschid commented drily.

He guided her through the crush emerging from the great domed porch ahead. Glimpsing dark faces and avidly inquisitive female stares, she was ironically relieved to be covered from head to toe.

'I understand that my father wishes to receive us immediately,' he explained flatly. 'You will not speak—I don't trust you to speak lest you offend. On unfamiliar ground I do not believe you are at your most intelligent.'

Burning inside like a bushfire, Polly bit down hard on her tongue. He stopped before a set of carved double doors which were thrown wide by the fearsome armed guards on either side. He strode ahead of her. At a reluctant pace, she followed, to watch him fall down gracefully on his knees and touch his forehead to the carpet. For seventy, the grey-bearded old gentleman seated on a shallow dais at the foot of the room looked admirably hale and hearty. Polly got down on the carpet just as Raschid was signalled up. The King snapped his fingers and barked something in Arabic.

Raschid audibly released his breath. 'Get up.'

Before she could guess his intention, he had deftly whipped the *aba* off again. Polly felt like a piece of plundered booty, tumbled out on the carpet for examination and curiously naked under the onslaught of shrewd dark eyes. Reija passed some remark, chuckled and went on to speak at considerable length. Turning pink, Polly slowly sank down again, but not before she noticed the rush of blood to Raschid's cheekbones. Whatever his father was saying to him was having the most extraordinarily visible effect on him. His knuckles showed white as his hand clenched by his side. A pin-dropping silence stretched long after King Reija had finished speaking.

Suddenly Raschid spat a response. Polly was shocked. A split second later a wall-shaking argument was taking place over her averted head. Father and son set into each other with a ferocity which would have transcended any language barrier. The silences, spiced by what could only be described as Reija's inflammatory and self-satisfied smiles, grew longer. Abruptly Raschid inclined his head and backed out. Polly nervously looked up again.

A gnarled hand beckoned her closer. 'A most unfortunate introduction to our household,' said Reija in heavily accented English. Noting her surprise, he smiled with distinct amusement. 'I speak your language. However, it has often been of great benefit for me to listen rather than to converse.'

Somehow Polly managed a polite smile. Her gormless father had not had a chance against that level of subtle calculation!

'You are welcome,' he pronounced. 'Such pale beauty as yours can only draw my son more frequently to his home.'

It wasn't her place to tell him that he was in for a swift disillusionment. Raschid was about as adapted to having his wings clipped as a bird of prey deprived of a kill. But it was interesting to learn that his father wanted to see him here more often than he evidently did. Reassuring too, she conceded absently. Arguments between father and son were seemingly not evidence of some deep schism in their relationship. Yet she was frustrated by her inability to understand exactly what was going on around her. What had incited Raschid to barely leashed rage and roused his father to only sardonic amusement loudly voiced?

'A man does not drink brackish water when he may sip sweetly within his own household.'

Bemusedly Polly blinked, having been briefly lost in her own thoughts. Fortunately a reply did not seem to be expected.

'It is my hope that you will soon come to consider our country as your home.'

She gulped. 'Yes.'

'To facilitate this you will wish to learn Arabic.' He nodded to himself. 'A tutor will be found for you.'

At least he didn't talk in riddles. She was King Reija's gift to his son—unfortunately bestowed upon an ungrateful recipient. But that, she suspected, was most unlikely to keep the King awake at night. He looked mighty pleased with himself. The same steely obstinacy and ingrained ruthlessness that distinguished the son was reflected in the father.

'Your father—he is well?'

'Yes, Your Majesty.'

'May he live long and prosper.' He waved a hand. 'You may withdraw—the women are impatient to prepare you for the wedding.'

When Polly emerged Raschid searched her eyes almost fiercely. What had caused that argument? she questioned frustratedly. It had driven Raschid into his current dark, smouldering mood. For all his outer detachment, he seethed with intense emotion just beneath the surface.

'He suggested that I learn Arabic.' In an effort to dispel the tension she smiled.

His jawline hardened. 'Do not make that effort for my benefit. It is not important to me,' he asserted harshly.

All over again Polly experienced that lowering sense of rejection. This time, however, she controlled her anger. Reality had finally sunk in. She could evade it no longer. This arrogant, unfathomable male was her husband. If they were at daggers drawn now, it was her own fault; her foolish references to annulment and divorce must have taxed his patience to the limits. She had spouted hot air. Her pride had smarted under a candour that had only equalled her own.

Breathlessly she hurried to keep up with his long stride. He led her down a bewildering succession of corridors. The palace complex was vast, composed of a hotch-potch of two- and three-storey buildings, many of them fashioned round traditional inner courtyards, the various wings linked by passageways and staircases. She would need a map and a compass to get round on her own. As the thick walls echoed with their footsteps, she thought anxiously about the womenfolk awaiting her, glad that her father had been able to fill her in on the distaff side of the family.

King Reija had married three times. His first wife had died in childbirth. His second, Nurbah, was Raschid and Asif's mother. For years she had suffered from a heart condition that had sentenced her to an invalid's existence. Perhaps that was why her husband had chosen to marry again. His third wife, Muscar, had had a daughter, Jezra, who was now sixteen. That alliance had ended in divorce, although Jezra remained within her father's household.

Apart from Jezra, there was Asif's wife, Chassa. She was the mother of two baby girls, and she was only twenty-two. Polly had tried not to look aghast when her father had added that Chassa was expecting yet again, no doubt in pursuit of the baby boy without which no Arab husband could be satisfied.

Shying away from the too intimate tenor of her reflections, she glanced at Raschid and reddened. 'What did you and your father argue about?'

'That is not open to discussion. Suffice it to say that my father and I do not always share the same sense of humour.' His expressive mouth tightened.

Annoyed by the curt brush-off, she said, 'I don't think I want to marry you again. Once was enough!'

He cast her a predatory half-smile. 'But I wouldn't dream of depriving you of the excitements of an Islamic wedding. To deny that to one who, not two short weeks ago, expressed her willingness to live as I live would be inconceivably cruel,' he murmured with silken satire.

Polly trembled with indignation. Raschid mounted a marble staircase slightly ahead of her and then hung back for her to catch up. He was thinking about 'her' again. It was a wonder he hadn't thrown himself into the grave with her. Polly frowned, shaken by the meanness of the thought and the quite unjustifiable annoyance from which it had sprung. Berah had died suddenly, tragically. What kind of man would he be if he did not remember?

At the head of the staircase he stilled. 'I must leave you here. You will find my sister through that door to your left.' His gleaming scrutiny lingered impenetrably on her. Before she could turn away he reached out a hand. 'But first,' he said huskily, drawing her inexorably closer and lifting a hand to lace long fingers with unnerving slowness into the tumbled fall of her hair, 'this.'

In the shadows of the wall he captured her lips urgently. 'Open your mouth,' he demanded, his breath fanning her cheek, and then his tongue hungrily plundered the intimacy she had denied him.

It was as if the ground fell away from beneath her feet.

Her hands clutched at his shoulders for support. She had no control over the surge of hunger that sent a scorching flame to the very centre of her body. It controlled her. Raschid controlled her. In instinctive repulsion, Polly jerked her head back, devastated by the immediacy of her response to him.

'You are quite right.' His eyes were veiled, his mouth taut. 'I forgot myself. This is not the place.'

'I don't think anywhere's the place. If this is a marriage of convenience, why do we…?' She swallowed, apprehensively measuring the midnight blue flare of his gaze. 'You know what I'm saying.'

A winged brow elevated. 'I don't need to justify myself, Polly. Remember that tonight. Patience is not one of my virtues. You chose this,' he drawled with ruthless emphasis.

She whirled away from him through the door he had indicated. Finding herself under the questioning appraisal of a tall, rather plump girl with a strong resemblance to Asif, she blushed.

'You must be Jezra.' Polly summoned up a self-conscious smile.

Jezra pointedly ignored her extended hand. Her rounded face was sullenly stiff, her brown eyes cold. 'I will take you to your maids. Zenobia speaks English, Gada none. But I doubt if you'll be here long enough to improve anyone's vocabulary!'

'I sincerely hope you're right.' As soon as the words left her, Polly regretted them, but she was mentally and physically exhausted. Jezra's hostility, following so fast on Raschid's coldly implacable insistence that she share his bed, was the last straw. 'Look,' she added hurriedly, 'I'm rather tired. Can we begin again?'

Mottled pink had highlighted Jezra's complexion. 'Raschid didn't even want to marry you!' she spat.

'Jezra, please—' Polly began heavily, but the tirade was unstoppable.

'Why should he have? His mistress in Paris, she is twice as beautiful as you—tall and blonde. I hear the men turn in the street to watch her go past. No matter what our father believes, you will not supplant her!' Suddenly the teenager fell silent, her eyes appalled.

Polly had lost every scrap of natural colour.

'It was a lie, a wicked untruth,' Jezra muttered frantically. 'You mustn't repeat it to Raschid.'

The rich blend of colours in the carpet blurred under Polly's strained gaze. 'I've no intention of repeating it to anyone.'

The intense silence throbbed. Jezra cleared her throat. 'I must ask you to forgive me for the rudeness of my welcome.'

She was very pale now, obviously frightened. Polly might have felt sorry for her had she not felt sorrier for herself. 'It's forgotten,' she said flatly.

The final piece of the jigsaw puzzle slid into place, the unknown factor which had evaded her. At last she had a more practical explanation for Raschid's aversion to re-marriage. Small wonder that he was content as he was and his puritanical father had put on the pressure to return his son to a more respectable path. Bile soured Polly's throat. King Reija had supplied Raschid with a blonde on the home front, as if blondes were interchangeable—and maybe they were on Raschid's terms. He did not intend to deny himself the self-indulgence of making love to his bride. Jezra's revelation rocked Polly to her foundations.

The teenager showed her through to an elegantly furnished bedroom. A pair of smiling young girls moved forward. A spill of gorgeous fabric lay across the divan bed. Her wedding outfit? Polly looked bitterly away.

She was a pawn on a chessboard here in Dharein. To

think that she had actually felt ashamed of her inability to enter this marriage with dignity and acceptance: Her misgivings now had concrete proof. Raschid planned to use her as a front for some sordid affair. It was a dirty, devious, dishonourable piece of skulduggery. Chris would never have done this to any woman. Chris was honest and decent.

Locked in her despondency, she quietly let Zenobia help her undress. She slipped gratefully into the cool of a cotton wrap and was guided through to the connecting bathroom before she realised what was intended. Gada was sprinkling aromatic perfume into the water already awaiting her.

'I really don't need a bath,' she said stiffly.

'It will be most refreshing, I promise you.' Zenobia's tiny hands sketched an almost pleading gesture. 'We must wait upon you, *lellah*. Have we displeased you?'

It was easier to submit than to argue. When Raschid lay ahead of her, all else had to pale into insignificance. Her hair was washed five times, left with the texture of oiled silk. Stepping from the bath, she was wrapped in velvety towels. While she lay face down on a divan being gently massaged with rose-scented oil by Zenobia, her heavy eyelids drooped. She slept, awakening with a timeless sense of dislocation. Gada was expertly employing a fine brush to paint delicate henna swirls on her hands and feet. Polly tried politely to object, but ran aground on Zenobia's anxious explanation that this procedure was the custom for the bride.

A chattering cluster of women awaited them back in the bedroom. Jezra stood sulkily off to one side. It was ritual, Polly realised grimly, all of it, from the minute she had got into the bath—hours of age-old ritual to ready the bride for her lord and master. Three elderly women were squatting in the corner chanting what sounded like a funeral dirge. Uneasily averting her eyes, Polly stood while her audience communicated in dumb show.

'Do any of them speak English?' she asked.

'These are Bedouin, *lellah*. They are the women of Queen Nurbah's tribe,' Zenobia explained. 'Very few of them come into the town, but it is tradition that they dress Prince Raschid's bride. They are honoured to be accepted by you as attendants.'

In any other situation Polly would have found the friendly atmosphere contagious, but the strangeness of it all made it another endurance test. She had no idea what they did to her face; there was no mirror in view. She was assisted into the sumptuous silver and blue kaftan. A swathe of crimson silk covered her hair turban fashion and a headdress of beaten silver coins was attached low over her forehead. Only then was she allowed to approach a mirror. A shimmering bejewelled odalisque met her dazed scrutiny. Polly Barrington had vanished.

She was escorted downstairs to Queen Nurbah's apartments, the women following but remaining outside. Raschid's mother was reclining on a daybed, her lined features bearing witness to her poor health.

'I am sorry that I cannot rise to greet you.' Warmth in her creased eyes, she held out a beringed hand for Polly to kiss. 'My doctor insists that I am excluded from the festivities. I am very disappointed. Jezra, the girdle is on the bed. You must perform this service for me.'

Kneeling, Jezra linked a silver belt round Polly's hips and fastened the teardrop sapphire clasp. The women outside stretched out reverent fingers to touch the girdle. At Polly's enquiring glance, Jezra averted her head. 'It is a symbol of fertility,' she explained, surprisingly embarrassed.

Zenobia attached the veil to Polly's face and the procession passed on. In a chamber dimly lit against the darkness now beyond the windows, Raschid awaited her, a tall, still figure, magnificent in dark blue silk robes. His sapphire eyes began at the top of her head and roamed intently down over her. He didn't smile. Whether or not he found it amusing that she should be presented to him as a glittering Arab bridal doll was unrevealed by the impassivity of his bronzed features.

The ceremony was short, witnessed by King Reija and several other solemn-faced men. Hot with mortification, Polly stumbled over every Arabic phrase she had to repeat. Her hand was bound in a length of green cloth attached to Raschid's wrist and released again. She was then hustled back to the door, suddenly alarmingly conscious of Raschid's gleaming gaze following her. Loathing stabbed rawly into her. Consideration and respect didn't cover a mistress.

In a large reception room full of women, a slim, graceful girl with almond-shaped eyes moved to greet her. 'I am Chassa.' She leant forward to kiss Polly's cheek. 'I hope we shall be friends. Don't worry about names, but you must meet everyone.'

After a giddy surge of introductions, an array of colourful dishes were brought to her and the celebrations got under way. Voices, clattering dishes and music reverberated painfully against the headache Polly was developing. She could not get a morsel of food past her sore throat. Chassa sat beside her. She had attended an English boarding school and, optimistically in search of a common acquaintance, she named almost every girl she had met there. Polly struggled to ward off the nagging tiredness which made her feel as if Chassa was talking to her through a glass wall.

At some stage of the endless evening Zenobia touched her shoulder to indicate that she must now leave. Chassa gave her a teasing smile. Polly's spirits sank to her toes. Her stomach turned over sickly. She was borne off by a bunch of bustling matrons on a long trek through shadowy passageways and up a wide staircase to be thrust into an enormous room, dominated by an equally enormous and ornately carved four-poster bed. A wave of giddiness passed over her as the door slammed loudly on the ladies' exuberant departure.

CHAPTER FOUR

HER apprehension of some ghastly form of medieval bedding ceremony removed, Polly breathed again. A carved wooden frieze did justice here as a window. The shutters were drawn back and beyond the frieze swam the milky globe of the moon in violet-hued heavens. Unaffected by the night's beauty, Polly shivered convulsively. A breeze filmed over her damp skin, the chill matching that in her veins. Within these walls the twentieth century seemed a cruel illusion. She had been delivered like a gaudily wrapped present for her new husband to unwrap.

Shakily she trailed off the veil and the headdress. A cloud of musky fragrance was released into the air as she shook out her confined hair. Her temples were throbbing now, and she grimaced. She refused to go through with the rest of this charade. How could Raschid seriously expect her to? At the sound of the door opening, she spun violently, her heart in her mouth.

His luxuriant black hair uncovered, Raschid now wore only a light cream robe. As he approached her, a faint smile softened his firm mouth. His eyes glittered over her. None of her fearful tension was mirrored in his relaxed bearing.

'I am relieved that you didn't undress completely and get into bed to await me,' he mocked, cool palms resting on her shoulders as he studied her with contrasting sombreness. 'You are my wife now.'

Polly's brain was woolly, her head was starting to spin. Dimly she grasped that there was something more than nerves amiss with her. Only willpower enabled her to force the weakness back and stand straight. 'I can't get into that bed with you!' she blurted out.

He dropped down fluidly on one knee and unclasped the girdle. 'I will carry you there,' he promised, snapping free the first of the countless silver buttons, beginning at the very hem of her kaftan.

'I can manage those for myself,' she muttered, stricken by his lack of reaction to her controversial announcement.

Unexpectedly throaty laughter shook him. A hand halted her retreat, tugging her firmly back within reach. 'The hundred and one buttons are mine to undo. With each I glimpse another...' He surveyed her in sudden reflective silence. 'A most provocative custom,' he completed gently.

'For a man,' she interposed tremulously. 'If you think that I intend to stand here while you strip me...'

The lean brown fingers did not hesitate at their self-appointed task. 'This I do not think—I know,' he countered with perfect cool. 'You are nervous, Polly, but you are my wife.'

The repetition of that brutal fact slid through her unnaturally taut figure. Abandon hope, all ye who enter here, she reflected crazily. His wife. All individuality, all rights of self-determination wrested from her by a single ceremony. 'This...this is barbaric!' she whispered.

'Think before you speak. I will not endure insults tonight.' Hard warning chased the previous huskiness from his deep, dark drawl.

Shivering, Polly crossed her hands over her breasts. 'You're not being very...reasonable, Raschid.' Her wide eyes implored his understanding. 'We're strangers! I can't just...'

Rising soundlessly, he uncrossed her defensive hands, his gaze silvery and unyielding. 'You entered this marriage of your own volition, aware that this moment would arrive.'

Oxygen locked in her aching throat. 'I didn't think about it…I couldn't!'

'You will not refuse me.'

'I'm not refusing. I…I…' She faltered to a halt, not really knowing what she was saying but overpoweringly aware of the charge of anger her objections were unleashing in him. He hadn't raised his voice; he didn't need to. The atmosphere was dry as tinder ready to burst into crackling flames.

'I find this emotional display offensive.'

'I expect you would,' Polly muttered helplessly. 'It's not a problem you're likely to suffer from, is it?'

Raschid's hand closed over her wrist, yanking her back from the further retreat she had been unconsciously making. 'You are my bride. What you seek to deny me is no longer yours to deny,' he asserted icily.

She trembled. 'That's medieval!'

'Be careful you do not discover just how medieval I can be.' He sounded the threat with syllabic sibilance, his nostrils flared, his golden features ruthlessly cast. In his proud demeanour he was every inch a barbaric desert prince, the fierce and pagan image of a feudal culture in which it was unthinkable for a wife to disobey her husband. 'You make an impressive start to our marriage, do you not? For what, after all, did you offer me on our first encounter but this?'

Her fingers pressed to the annoying pulse flickering wildly at the base of her throat. The aggression she had incited utterly intimidated her and she felt incredibly weak. 'That isn't the way it was.'

'How was it?' Derision brought violet brilliance to his challenging stare. 'Did you offer me intelligent conversation? Did you try in any fashion to impress me except as a beautiful woman?'

Polly winced from the lash of his contempt. 'I was nervous…embarrassed. I didn't know what to say to you.'

'Yet you cared not what awaited you. You cared only that I took you. You did not even ask me if you would be my only wife,' he reminded her. 'And I told you then that I would bed you.'

'Don't you dare talk to me like that!' She backed to the corner of the bed, her hand clutching at one of the posts for support. She was tempted to throw her knowledge of his mistress at him but too afraid of sending his temper right over the edge. 'Don't you realise how I feel? All you see is…'

'My bride defying me, and I do not like it,' he incised succinctly.

'All you see is an object. Don't you think I have feelings?'

An imperious brow lifted. 'Do you consider mine?'

'You have none.' She leant back breathlessly while he calmly continued to flick loose the buttons. She did not even have the energy to put up a token fight. 'A wedding ring,' she whispered bitterly, 'does not dignify lust.'

The metallic sheen of Raschid's suddenly savage scrutiny made her quail. She loosed a gasp of fear as he moved and swept her up to tumble her down on the bed. 'With that charge on our wedding night you insult me beyond belief. I have tolerated much from you since we left that church; I will tolerate no more.' His intonation was raw. 'I bought you. I own you. That is the pact which you made.'

Shattered, she stared up at him. He met her shocked eyes levelly. The declaration had not been made for effect. *I own you.* Her whole being recoiled from that primal affirmation of possession. As the canopy above her seemed to be revolving, she pushed her hands down on the mattress to lift herself up. The motion took enormous effort of will. She was so cold now that her teeth wanted to chatter. Her silence appeared to have defused his anger.

He came down beside her, reaching up to dim the wall

lights before gathering her into his arms. 'Polly, let us not begin in discord and bitterness. You should not fear what is natural between a man and a woman.'

A draining tide of dizziness tipped her head back, the argent fall of her hair tumbling over his arm. His voice was coming and going like a buzz-saw in her ears.

'Raschid,' she framed hoarsely.

'Listen to me.' His natural assurance emerged even in the low pitch of his roughened murmur. 'It is desire which burns in me. That is not lust. There is no giving in lust— it takes and despoils. That is not how I would initiate my bride into the pleasures of lovemaking.'

Her eyes slid shut as his fingers rested against her cheek. He said something harsh in Arabic, his hand skimming up to her brow, but Polly was already becoming limp, slipping without argument down into the emptiness of oblivion.

'Awake?' A thermometer was thrust in her parched mouth. A strange and yet somehow familiar face, thin and topped by a frilly green hat which contrasted violently with the carrot-red hair, swam into clarity above her. 'Do you know where you are today? Not to worry, you're over the worst. It's not often I've seen that high a fever with influenza.' The stark Glaswegian accent increased Polly's sense of un-reality.

Out came the thermometer at last. Polly tried to move, and discovered her limbs were weighted. Her body was weak as a kitten's. Lethargically she turned her muzzy head. Sunlight was casting lacy shadows through the frieze on to the Persian carpet on the floor. Everywhere she looked, flowers flourished in a riot of colour. Dust motes danced in the air. Her attention wandered back to the nurse. 'How do you come to be here?' She winced at the corn-crake rasp of her voice.

'Noticed I'm not a local, have you? Then you're well on

the mend. I'm Susan MacKenzie.' An almost depressingly cheerful grin came her way. 'I'm on contract with the Jumani City Hospital. I was brought to the palace on the first night, along with every consultant in the building.' She laughed uproariously at the recollection. 'Half the palace inhabitants were crammed outside that door. You didn't half create a panic!'

Polly grew even paler. 'What day is it?'

'Saturday. You couldn't possibly remember much. You've been out of your skull and wandering ever since you became ill. It's a marvel that nobody realised that you weren't well. Still, 'flu can take you very suddenly, and with all that make-up you had on, they couldn't have told just by looking. Talk about the gilded lily!'

Polly's sluggish brain edged back to the wedding and the wedding night. Embarrassment swallowed her alive. By the sound of it, she had given Raschid the kind of night he would never forget! A dramatic collapse on the marital bed seemed a fitting end to a disastrous wedding. Tears lashed her eyelids, but she was too weak to shed them.

'You must be gasping to see your husband,' Susan MacKenzie burbled. 'It might be a while before he appears. Until your fever broke last night he hardly left this room. He's probably sleeping now—he must be exhausted.'

Polly closed her aching eyes. She had made a thorough nuisance of herself. What choice had Raschid had but to play the devoted new husband? And if the tender trap of marriage had inspired him with aversion, the reality of it within days must have left him gnashing his teeth.

An hour later, washed, brushed and nearly deafened by Susan's endless chatter, she was having chicken broth spooned into her. After a nap, she wakened to find Jezra seated by the bed. The teenager immediately grasped her hand fervently, her swollen eyes swimming with tears. 'I am so glad that you are getting better, Polly. Even if Raschid never forgives me for the cruel words I spoke to you in anger, I am glad. Please believe me. I am so glad,' she sobbed, emotion overcoming her.

Polly was soon patting her shoulder and doing her best to soothe the distressed girl. Her illness had infused Jezra with the guilty and superstitious conviction that her revelation had somehow taken its toll. Firmly telling her that that was nonsense, Polly prompted, 'How did Raschid find out about it? Susan said I was rambling. I hope I didn't...'

'I told him. My conscience troubled me,' Jezra whispered. 'He was very angry, and who could blame him? What will I do if he tells our father?'

The unlikelihood of that event curled Polly's mouth. 'I shouldn't worry about that.'

Jezra sighed unhappily and fiddled with her tissue. 'I repeated a dreadful slander. I am ashamed to admit that I believed in it. Now I know how wrong I was to listen to gossip. Raschid is not like that.'

While remaining cynically unconvinced of Raschid's sainthood, Polly smiled reassuringly in the hope that the mortifying topic might be killed between them for good. Perceptibly Jezra brightened. 'It wasn't that I didn't like you, I didn't know you, but Raschid was so unhappy with Berah,' she volunteered in a rush. 'I was afraid that you would make him unhappy as well.'

Her lashes concealing her perplexity, Polly took a charged breath. Raschid's sister was patently unaware that she might be telling her something which she didn't already know.

'All she could think about was babies. All she could do was cry and be depressed,' Jezra muttered scornfully. 'I am sure you are different. My brother is a very fine man.'

The facts had been staring her in the face. She had been too dumb to see the obvious. How could Raschid's first marriage have been happy? A childless marriage in an Arab society where sons were so highly prized as proof of a man's virility could not have been blissfully content. If Berah had not adapted to her infertility, the relationship must have been a severe strain on Raschid as well. But he must have loved her, he must have loved her deeply not to divorce her or take another wife. In his position there could be no other explanation.

When the door opened both their heads spun. Jezra took one look at the motionless figure on the threshold and got up, scuttling out past her elder brother with alacrity. Had Polly had the power of her legs and the innocence to believe she could manage a similar exit, she would have copied her.

Painful heat washed her cheeks. Raschid had never seemed less approachable; his bright eyes were guarded, his expression sombre. 'I am relieved to see you so much improved. Your health has been a matter of grave concern to all of us.'

She bent her head, overtly conscious of the wan and thinned reflection Susan MacKenzie had shown her in her hand mirror. She looked ghastly. And if even she, who had never had much interest in her appearance, thought that, how much worse must she look to him? 'I'm sorry,' she said. 'I've caused a lot of trouble.'

He expelled his breath. 'Is this how I appear to you—as a man who expects his sick wife to apologise for the impossible? I am not such a man. If I were to tax you with any failing—and this must be said in case you are equally foolish on some future occasion—why didn't you tell me how you were feeling?'

With hindsight Polly realised that she had gone through the wedding in an increasingly feverish haze. Until the artificial stimulants of tension and self-discipline had come crashing down inevitably in this same room, she hadn't realised how very ill she was feeling. Awkwardly she endeavoured to explain that to him, her fingers restlessly creasing at a corner of the white sheet.

'You were burning up when I touched you. You must have known that you were ill.' Raschid sighed heavily. 'When you fainted I felt very little different from a man bent upon rape.'

At this startling admission her head flew up.

'I am not so insensitive that I would make sexual demands of a sick woman, whatever you may believe me capable of,' he stressed in a taut undertone.

She evaded his unusually expressive eyes. Reproach was unhidden there. 'I didn't believe that,' she muttered. 'I didn't think…'

From somewhere surfaced the memory of those eyes above hers when she was ill. Beautiful, compelling eyes which had inspired her with oddly lyrical and sentimental comparisons. As it occurred to her that she might have spoken them out loud, she was ready to crawl beneath the sheet. Of course, she'd been delirious. Undoubtedly she had talked senseless gibberish.

Raschid took the seat his sister had vacated. He was very constrained, his smile remarkable only in its brevity. 'I sometimes believe that you think very infrequently where I am concerned—but we need not talk of that night again,' he declared. 'You were clearly not in full possession of your senses. I do not hold you responsible for what you said then.'

A grin suddenly threatened the tight line of her mouth. Hurriedly she squashed it. He looked so deadly serious. He was proffering what she estimated to be on his terms a forgiveness of the utmost generosity. Lunacy must have been upon her—how otherwise would she have dared to fight with him? But perhaps only now did she comprehend how very deeply she had offended him that night.

'We have a great deal to discuss.'

Polly tensed, recoiling from the threat of Raschid openly raising the subject of his mistress and telling her the same lies that he had evidently told his trusting sister.

'However, some matters are better postponed until you are stronger,' he decreed.

He was letting the dust settle on Jezra's inopportune bombshell. A splendid move from a skilled diplomat, Polly realised with bitter resentment. By the time he did raise the subject, the immediacy of drama would be long gone, and in his mind, leaving himself currently undefended was probably as good as a declaration of innocence. It would take some early bird to catch him out!

A lean hand enclosed hers, spinning her out of her fierce introspection. 'I always seem to be approaching you with criticism,' he said.

'I expect you believe that you've had cause.' Polly was in no mood to think guiltily of their catastrophic wedding and its equally trying aftermath from his point of view. That short-lived generosity had steadily receded from her.

'No. It is this failing I have of making assumptions, of jumping the...' He hesitated.

'Gun?' she filled in shakily, outrageously conscious of the thumb absently caressing the tender skin of her inner wrist.

He frowned. 'Why didn't you explain to me that your father was in debt? I had no knowledge of the fact. Your family appeared to be living in comfort and prosperity.'

Polly blinked. 'You didn't know about Dad?'

'When I visited your home I knew nothing about your family. Now I suspect that the bride price went to your father and not to you. Is this not true?' he prompted. 'You gave the money to him?'

Polly didn't recall having anything to actually give. She had a vague memory of signing some papers at her father's request. 'I suppose so, but what...?'

'I understood that the money went solely to you.'

'Me?' she echoed, finally picking up his drift. 'Good lord, what would I have done with it?'

A less guarded smile curved his well-shaped mouth. 'I believed that you became a woman of financial substance by our marriage. In short, I believed that you had married me for your own enrichment, encouraged to that move by your parents. Instead I now learn...'

'How did you?' she interrupted.

'You were most talkative in your fever,' he breathed, abruptly releasing her thin fingers.

She flushed at the confirmation. 'It's not really important now, is it?'

Rising from the chair with the natural grace that accompanied all his movements, Raschid had strolled over to the window. She was surprised that he should turn his back on her; it was a gesture considered very rude by his race. But as she spoke, he immediately turned, presenting his hard-edged profile to her. 'On the contrary,' he murmured quietly, 'I now perceive you as you are. You didn't marry me for personal gain, you obviously did so for your family's benefit. Naturally this must alter my view of you, and you may not wish to hear me say it, but I think very ill of parents able to smile so happily while they barter their unwilling daughter into marriage with a stranger.'

'It wasn't like that,' Polly muttered.

He sent her a winging glance. 'You forget—I was there. Had I been less prejudiced against you, I would have suspected the true circumstances sooner. Your behaviour was self-explanatory. It was your parents who forced you to the match.'

'I made the decision,' she insisted.

'I disagree.' The contradiction was coolly emphatic. 'When one makes a decision one accepts it. To say the very least, you were not in a state of acceptance when you married me.'

Unsure where this was leading, Polly said nothing. In any case, he had spoken the truth. Depressed about Chris and deeply concerned for her family, she had plunged into giving her consent. She had not thought the decision through, she had run away from it. In confusion she appreciated that Chris had not entered her head until Raschid had put him there by association. Recalling her torment at the wedding, she wondered where all that emotion had gone. It did not hurt now. Why? Why didn't it hurt?

Raschid sighed. 'All you must concentrate on now is recovering your strength. I have stayed too long. That dreadfully garrulous woman will assault my ears. Is she ever silent?' he enquired wryly.

She gave him an absent glance. 'No, but she's kind. I like her.'

'Then the purpose was fulfilled. I thought you would be happier with a British nurse.'

'Thank you for the flowers,' she whispered shyly before he reached the door. 'They're beautiful…nobody's ever given me flowers before.'

Chris slipped out of her puzzled musings and her lashes drooped on the flower-bedecked room and the not very cheerful reflection that the floral offerings were worth about as much as the statutory visit Raschid had made. He could not be seen to neglect an ailing wife.

'Only twelve weeks to Christmas, but who would credit it?' Susan MacKenzie stared out unappreciatively at the sun slowly sinking in a blazing glory of crimson and cerise and peach before she returned to brushing Polly's hair. 'I can't wait to get home and be cold and get wrapped up in woollens. Will you miss Christmas?'

Polly's eyes watered. 'Yes.'

'Smile!' hectored Susan. 'You're almost on your feet again. You're suffering from the post-flu blues, that's all. It's only ten days since you were really ill. Then I know you're fed up with this room. That's why you're getting a surprise.'

Polly had had more surprises than she could handle over the last week. Raschid four or five times a day had been a big enough shock to her expectations. Sometimes he stayed only a few minutes, other times he stayed an hour. He never came empty-handed. The bedside cabinet was piled high with paperbacks. If he didn't bring books, he brought flowers or magazines. But half the time he was there, he was broodingly silent, forcing Polly to chatter nervously non-stop.

An intense cloak of reserve characterised Raschid. She could never tell what he was thinking. He had a trick of listening with acute interest no matter what trivial rubbish she was spouting. It had to be a very useful device when he was caught up in boring business meetings, but Polly found it frankly unnerving.

His body language was far from informative. He never relaxed in her company. He paced restlessly like a prowling cheetah confined in a too small cage. He also maintained a distance from the bed that suggested he was in the presence of dangerous contagion.

Polly had gone over and over their conversation ten days earlier, searching for the source of his constraint and his avoidance of the tiniest show of intimacy. But she was essentially in the dark as to the cause. She did suspect that the knowledge that she had succumbed to outside pressures in marrying him had ironically flicked Raschid's pride on the raw. He might have assured her that he now saw her differently, shorn of her brazen guise as a weak-hearted gold-digger, but why did she receive the peculiar impression that a money-grabbing blonde would have been more welcome to him? She frowned. That was just another in a long list of imponderables, and Raschid was full of them.

'You're not very curious, are you?' Susan rattled on. 'Don't you want to know what the surprise is? You're dining with your husband tonight!'

Instead of reacting in blushing confusion, Polly paled. Why on earth would he make such an effort? Guilt? He was leaving for New York again tomorrow. No doubt he was breaking his neck to engage in a passionate reunion with his mistress. He probably had no trouble at all in talking to her. Maybe she even travelled with him. Suddenly her eyes misted with tears and she bent her head quickly over a letter from her sister. It was the 'flu which was making her miserable, wasn't it? She was fed up with herself. These moody highs and lows of temperament were unfamiliar to her.

Maggie had mentioned that Chris had spent the weekend at Ladybright. Polly sighed and set the letter down. Thoughts that would have been heresy to her a month ago had been bombarding her increasingly of late, and she knew why. Her devastating physical response to Raschid had pointed out a glaring lack in her feelings for Chris, forcing her to question them. How could she love Chris without ever having longed to physically express that love? Yet, incredibly, that was what she had done for the past four years.

Had she mistaken liking and admiration and loneliness for loving? The idea that she could have so misunderstood her own emotions dismayed her. But what else was she to believe?

She had missed Chris terribly when he started medical school. She had been hurt and lost as their childhood closeness stretched to a more adult gulf. But those were growing pains, weren't they? Chris had been mature for his age, while she hadn't been, she acknowledged ruefully. A shy, introverted teenager, she had depended heavily on Chris as a friend. Had she stubbornly clung to an adolescent dream longer than other girls?

The lingering remnants of that rosy dream world had died on her wedding day. Of course it had hurt, even though her love for Chris had been a highly idealised and quite impractical thing. In a sense it had been a security blanket as well while no one else attracted her. And all this time she had really cared for Chris as he cared for her. If it had been real love she would not have been defenceless against Raschid.

When Raschid came in she was reading. Glued to the printed page, she didn't hear him. 'Is that enthralling?' he queried.

Glancing up, she did a forgivable double-take. Raschid was wearing an open-necked white silk shirt and a pair of tight-fitting jeans that hugged his narrow hips and long, lean thighs. What he did for jeans would have sold racks of them. Polly's stomach performed a somersault. 'Pardon?' she queried.

'The book.'

'Oh, that.' Carelessly she put it down. 'I didn't know you wore jeans.'

He shrugged rather tensely, skimming a beautifully shaped hand off a denim-clad hip. 'Since you are not strong enough yet to dress, I thought I would be more casual.'

As she began to rise he curved an arm round her and the next minute she was airborne. 'You know, I can walk— I'm not crippled!' she protested breathlessly.

'The doctor said that you were to take everything very slowly. You can't want to risk a relapse. Our climate is not kind to the delicate.' Ebony lashed blue eyes travelled reprovingly over her pink face.

There was a whirring sensation behind her temples. The sunwarmed scent of him was in her nostrils, the virile heat of his flesh penetrating the light kimono robe she wore. The whirring became a thrumming pulsebeat throughout her tautened body. She was unnaturally stiff by the time he stowed her on a tumbled pile of silk cushions in a vast and austere room.

Desire was in her like a dark enemy he had implanted, a hot, feverish intoxication of every sense that left her reeling on the lowering realisation that until she met Raschid she had been part stranger even to herself. While she lay in her bed and he remained distantly polite, denying that her vulnerability existed had been easier. But when he touched her those proud self-delusions shattered. Then, as now, her awareness of him was so pronounced that it was an exquisite pain. And worst of all, some treacherously feminine trait in her gloried unreservedly in the race of her pulses, the dryness in her mouth and the crazy acceleration of her heart. Tearing her attention from him, she squashed those renegade feelings. The power of them terrified her even as they pointed out all over again what she had not felt for Chris.

Raschid folded down lithely and food started to arrive, borne by half a dozen servants. 'Had I known in advance that you would be well enough to join me this evening, I would have located a table and chairs,' he told her.

Dear heaven, had Susan MacKenzie somehow prompted him to this invitation? Polly's cheeks flamed.

'I expect that you have noticed that these apartments are not very modern.'

'I assume Berah preferred the traditional look,' Polly said, woodenly dismissive.

Visibly he tautened. 'Berah and I lived in a different wing of the palace.' He paused. 'After her death I chose to embrace new surroundings.'

Had he set up a holy, untouchable shrine in the old? Polly had long since discounted Jezra's assertion of

Raschid's unhappiness with her predecessor. Four years ago, Jezra had been a child scarcely qualified to make that judgement. His undoubted sensitivity to any reminder of Berah was more revealing. Exactly where did this female in Paris fit in? Then she was being very naïve, wasn't she? Raschid was a very male animal. His sexual needs had not diminished with his first wife's death. A mistress would have been more a necessity than an indulgence, Polly thought darkly. Fortunately she really didn't care what he did as long as he left her alone.

'In comparison with your home, perhaps you find this household rather primitive,' he continued, still only receiving half her attention. 'These things have never been important to me. My needs are few. I have never been much of a consumer of luxury goods. Then I spend little time here.'

What was suddenly freezing her into a polar absence of expression was the amazing sight of Raschid embarrassed and fighting to maintain his usual air of daunting gravity. For some reason he had started noticing that his home had all the warm welcome of Frankenstein's castle. 'Oh, I think this is very comfortable…cosy,' she added in a generous rush, as if they were not seated on a carpet in the middle of an echoing and three-quarters-empty room.

'I usually eat with my father.'

It was a rare titbit of personal information. Raschid never talked about himself. From Jezra Polly had learnt that he had spent the early years of his life in the desert, travelling with Nurbah's relatives, the only allowance made towards his status that of an accompanying tutor. At ten he had gone to a military academy in Saudi Arabia, concluding his education with a degree in business management. The two brothers had enjoyed incredibly different childhoods. King Reija had evidently ruled against the dangers of too great a Western influence being allowed sway over his son and heir. But Raschid's childhood impressed Polly as having been distinctly grim and cheerless, high on character-building discipline and low on parental attention and care-free pursuits. It explained that gravity beyond his years.

'You didn't have to eat with me,' she said flatly, shaking irritably free of her irrelevant thoughts. 'After all, you told me that this would be on the proscribed list. Of course, Asif always eats with Chassa when he's at home. But then, I expect he picked up bad habits, being educated in England.'

At her reference to his brother, his lean features shuttered, his mouth hardening. 'I don't deny that Asif is more Westernised, but he is not someone whom I presently wish to discuss.'

Obstinately she persisted, 'Why? Is he in some sort of trouble?'

He sent her a gleaming glance, refusing to be drawn.

'I found him very pleasant.'

A sardonic brow lifted. 'The art of being pleasant has always been at Asif's fingertips. He has infinite charm with your sex when he chooses to employ it. Now, as you know, I leave for New York tomorrow.' An odd little silence stretched like a bed of nails beneath her nerves. Her smile began to feel frozen on her lips. 'When I return perhaps you will have made alterations here. You have a free hand. I would wish you to feel at home for as long as you are here,' he concluded smoothly.

It was a speech like a scorpion with a sting in its tail. *For as long as you are here.* It reverberated through Polly. Was he making a discreet reference to a divorce in the not too distant future? What else could he be doing? Their marriage as such had not even begun, and already he was fore-seeing its conclusion. A fierce and blinding wave of anger consumed her. 'Exactly how long do you expect me to feel at home?' she demanded. 'Don't please feel the need to talk in polite riddles. If you want a divorce, just say so!'

Raschid did not react to her fury. His eyes remained steady. 'I am not presently thinking of a divorce.'

'What did you raise my hopes for, then?' she slammed back, outraged by his coolness. 'I'd like a time limit to the sentence.'

'Until we tire of each other, then,' he said softly. 'These attractions fade as swiftly as the flowers that bloom in the desert after rain. What is between us will pall just as quickly. It would not be fair of me to pretend otherwise. I do not wish to hurt your feelings, Polly.'

Blindly she studied the glass of lemonade in her hand. How could he employ such brutal, demeaning candour and contrive to do so with that quality of apparent sincerity? Was she ever to understand Raschid? She was trembling with a mass of conflicting emotions. Hatred rose uppermost. Her pride revolted against the implication that she was a purely sexual being, put on this earth for his gratification, an object to be lifted and discarded at whim. He had never planned to give their marriage a fighting chance. He had never envisaged permanent ties. To tell her that openly was to offend her beyond forgiveness.

'You don't have that power,' she parried through compressed lips.

'Perhaps you will now practise the same honesty with me.' He surveyed her with unreadably bright eyes, but the tension in the air was tangible. 'About Chris.'

Her brain in a dazed whirl, Polly echoed, 'Chris?'

CHAPTER FIVE

'YOU called for him when you were delirious. Had you not been ill, I would have requested this explanation sooner,' Raschid advanced harshly. 'Naturally I wish to know exactly what your relationship with this man entailed.'

The mists of incomprehension cleared. Polly's colour fluctuated wildly. Had she called for Chris? While she was ill, had her subconscious mind teemed with the conflict of her unsettled feelings? From beneath her lashes she studied the brooding cast of his features. So this was what had lain behind the constraint she had sensed, this was the subject postponed until she was on the road to recovery. His suspicions roused, he had gritted those even white teeth and simmered over the idea that his bride might not be as pure and untouched as he considered his medieval due. What he really meant was, had she slept with him? The offensively arrogant bite of his demand that she explain herself chased away her momentary embarrassment.

'Polly!'

'My relationship with Chris is nothing to do with you.' Swept by an unfamiliar sense of feminine power, she met his charged stare. 'You bought my disposable future, not my past,' she retorted drily.

In a controlled movement Raschid sprang upright. 'Are you in love with him?' he raked at her. 'I will have an answer from you. You are my wife!'

But only when it suits you to throw it at me, she thought with an inner venom that slightly shook her. In love. In love with love. Was that what she had been? It was still none of Raschid's business.

'Look at me! I will not address the back of your head. But I will have an answer,' he assured her grimly. 'That is my right.'

Angrily she glanced up. 'What's it to you if I am madly in love with him?'

His eyes blazed at her, a formidable and powerful anger written into every taut line of his aggressive stance. 'And with this you expected to establish a relationship with me?' he seethed across the room at her. 'I told myself that I would not judge you unheard again, but I was foolish to doubt my own perception.'

He was like a coiled whip ready to unfurl. She was on dangerous ground. Her malicious intent to confirm his suspicions suddenly lost its strength. Since it must be obvious that Chris had not returned her feelings, wouldn't she end up looking rather pathetic? There could be no vengeful satisfaction in such a conclusion. Realising how she had cornered herself by losing her temper, she said irritably, 'For goodness' sake, I was only joking! Do we need the three-act drama?'

Suddenly alarmingly close, Raschid dropped down in front of her and repeated, 'Joking?'

Polly attempted to retreat. A ruthless hand caught in her hair and blue eyes of feral brilliance flared into her. 'Explain the joke,' he invited.

'Joke wasn't the right word,' she altered in desperation. 'You don't understand…'

His long fingers tightened their hold. 'Make me,' he suggested lethally.

'Chris and I grew up together. He's…he's really just a friend.'

His narrowed stare probed her defensiveness. 'I do not think that is quite the whole story.'

Polly's teeth gritted. 'It's chapter and verse.'

'I believe that you have been attracted to this man,' Raschid countered lazily. 'And perhaps if I had not come along…' The hand at the nape of her neck eased her backwards at the same time as he pressed her down on the cushions by lowering his own weight to keep her captive. 'But it is strange that I should still fail to see the humour of your…er…joke.'

'It wasn't supposed to be a joke!' In raw frustration she struggled to wriggle free.

'Truly diplomacy is not one of your talents.' A tigerish smile slanted his mouth. 'You were trying to make me jealous—you are very transparent, Polly. But how could I be jealous of my wife? You belong to me, you go nowhere without my permission.'

Enraged by his interpretation of her behaviour, she hissed, 'I wasn't trying to make you jealous, and I can't stand it when you say that I belong to you!'

'It is a fact—why quarrel with it?' As her eyes fled fearfully to the door, he murmured, 'The servants won't enter without my command.'

'How about if I scream?' she threatened wildly, her body stiffly refusing to yield to the hard lines of his.

He laughed huskily. 'They will either think that you are very passionate in my arms or that I am beating you. Neither eventuality will bring them rushing through that door.'

The predatory kindling of his measuring scrutiny was not lost on her. She was terrified of responding to him, terrified of a self-betrayal she would find impossible to forgive or excuse. All that Raschid deserved was a display of cool contempt and indifference. He tasted her angrily parted lips with urgent brevity.

She twisted her head away, fighting the leap of her pulses. 'No!'

His fingers framed her cheekbone. 'From the first desire was there between us. A day will come when the very last word you wish to employ with me is no,' he declared.

As he captured her mouth again, skilled and unhurried, then ravagingly sweet and insistent, the taut stasis of her body heated to the abrasively masculine lure of his. She could not deny him. Within seconds she was lost to that violent and intense mingling of sensation and emotion which thundered through her veins like the beat of stormy seas. Her slender length in thrall to the incredibly sensual exploration of his hands, she clung to him. His breath rasped in his throat as he released her, sinking back to narrowly observe her drugged eyes and hectically flushed cheeks.

'And truly it is not a word you use when you most need to use it.' Arrogant mastery burnishing his gaze, his mobile mouth quirked amusedly. 'Then I shouldn't begin what I can't finish. You are not yet convalesced to that degree. But how I wish it were not so!'

Polly pulled the loosened robe clumsily round her again. Her breasts were achingly full from his caresses, a hot, shivery weakness was tremulously besetting her lower limbs. The incisive imprint of him was still on her like a burning brand.

'Must you look at me as if you have been assaulted against your will?' Raschid said drily. 'At least be honest with yourself.'

Her darkened eyes embittered, she whispered, 'You'd be surprised how honest I can be with myself. I know how a whore feels now.'

After an arrested pause, he disconcerted her entirely by flinging back his imperious dark head and laughing with rich appreciation. Indignantly she leapt up—or at least she tried. He spanned her waist with firm hands that imposed restraint. 'Forgive me. It was not very kind of me to laugh at your exit line,' he conceded not quite levelly. 'But sometimes when you intend to be very rude, you are instead very funny. I was supposed to be angry? Shocked?'

'With your experience of that breed of women, I guess not!' she threw in a tempestuous rage. 'But I have no plans to join the ranks. If you had any decency at all, you'd leave me alone. Now will you get your rotten, womanising hands off me?'

An anger that knocked hers into obscurity had wiped the glimmering warmth from his eyes. It dimmed slightly, however, as she hurled the last line at him. 'It is fortunate that I have become well acquainted with your habit of speaking first and thinking second. But I warn you, some day that tongue of yours will take you too far.'

'You aren't going to keep me quiet!' Polly gasped furiously. 'You don't want a wife—you never did. We both know that divorce is on the cards. Since you've been so refreshingly frank, I'll return the compliment. I'm not playing the game, Raschid. I'm not sharing your bed because you've got nothing better to do when you're here. Our marriage is a total farce, and if you push me, I won't fit in with the charade in any way. I'm warning you as well.'

'Don't threaten me.' It was velvety soft. 'Don't ever threaten me.'

Prickles of alarm were running up and down her spine while he silently studied her. His hands slid from her. 'I must confess that I forgot my sister's foolish words to you,' he breathed in exasperation.

What had preoccupied her unceasingly in recent days was the merest triviality to him. Fiercely she stiffened and thrust up her chin. 'Please don't insult my intelligence with the lies your loving sister was happy to swallow!'

'You know me so little still?' The hauteur of his look drove colour into her strained face. 'I might have believed that you had a better knowledge of my character.'

How? He was a law unto himself, a parcel of contradictions. He had a mind with more twists than the Hampton

Court maze, a mind which a scheming Borgia would have envied. A mind which tied Polly up in knots.

'That woman does not exist in my life,' he said coolly. 'I do not pretend to have lived as a celibate, but I would not lie with my wife and then lie with another woman. The concept of that fills me with distaste. I would not be unfaithful within marriage.'

She could not hold his dispassionate gaze. Her head lowered, her brain seething. He had the nine lives of a cat. By the time you had sprung the trap, he had already removed himself to a place of safety. He had dispensed with his mistress. King Reija had played a winning hand. You had to take your hat off to the old gentleman—he knew his son. Enter Polly, exit blonde Parisienne. Convinced that he fully intended to carry on the affair, Polly had worked herself up into a state of righteous indignation. Ignominiously routed, she now only longed for escape. 'I'm tired,' she told him.

'Stay where you are.'

'No, I really feel we've done the topic to death,' she muttered.

A dark brow lifted. 'Though it was not greatly on your mind when you were in my arms, was it?' Raschid hazarded grimly. 'Surely we may deal together better than this?'

A tide of burning moisture stung Polly's sensitive eyelids. She was all mixed up, but she refused to be ashamed of her suspicion. Raschid sought no closer ties with her. She couldn't be blamed for distrust. Not when it was so humiliatingly obvious that the only role she was to be permitted to play was that of mistress within marriage.

He released his breath. 'You do seem tired. This evening has been too great a strain for you.'

Before she could object he had swept her up in his arms. She felt like a toy about to be stowed back on the appropriate shelf in a cupboard, and forgotten. She didn't speak when he laid her down on the bed.

'I will phone you while I am away,' he told her.

'Don't bother,' she retorted from the depths of her bitter turmoil. 'No pretence—remember? And I certainly don't want the reminders.'

'As you wish.'

Even if he had slammed the door it would have made her feel better. But Raschid did not sink to childish displays. He was too disciplined, too self-contained to require the outlet. Dinner had been laden with calamity like the wedding and the wedding night. There was no meeting point between them. He wouldn't permit one. He wouldn't give an inch on the terms he had dictated at Ladybright.

With his essential detachment that supplied him with no problems. Polly was different. She couldn't cope with the knowledge that Raschid expected her to switch her emotions off and let him make love to her. She coped even worse with the awareness that she wanted him, as she had never wanted Chris. The missing ingredient in her response to Chris was all too prominent with Raschid. Sexual attraction.

As the clear call of the muezzin called the faithful to prayer at dawn, Polly was still lying hollow-eyed and wide awake, desperately attempting to calm the fevered rise and fall of her emotions and understand the angry hurt which lay behind her every response to Raschid.

'I'll lend you something.' Chassa rifled a unit with an obliging smile. 'Why didn't you tell me that you had no swimsuit? I must have a dozen.' She dropped a handful on the bed. 'I can't wait until I can wear them again.'

Glancing at Chassa's slim figure in which the evidence of her pregnancy was so slight as to be almost imperceptible, Polly smiled. 'Can't you wear them now?'

Chassa wrinkled her nose. 'I'm always very tired in the first months. It's unfortunate.' Her lustrous eyes shadowed. 'Asif is very active, he loves sports and late nights. I'm not much fun when I'm pregnant, and I shouldn't complain that he's out so often. I'm not very attractive like this.'

'That's nonsense,' Polly protested.

'You are not a man, Polly.' Chassa would not be consoled. Polly changed into the swimsuit, prudently removing her attention from Chassa's tense profile.

Asif might be technically at home, but he was rarely to be found there. In the past fortnight Polly had visited half a dozen times and Chassa had always been alone and grateful for the company. Life with the exuberant Asif was evidently not one of unblemished bliss.

With every day that filtered tranquilly by, Polly had finally conceded that what she felt for Chris was no more than the fondness of a sister for a brother, a fondness that had once been spiced with the pain of an adolescent and quite innocent crush on a childhood hero. She should have realised the difference long before now. It crossed her mind that she had been a late developer in more ways than one.

Raschid was due back at the end of the week. Polly hadn't heard a word from him. It infuriated her that, even absent, he should continue to dominate her thoughts. But what else did she have to think about? An hour learning Arabic every day? Jezra attended an exclusive college in Jumani by day and either entertained friends of her own age group or watched television by night.

'Where are the children?' asked Polly, following Chassa out through her lounge to the swimming pool in the courtyard beyond. As a rule the two toddlers were outside playing.

'With their nurse. They tired me out this morning. I should have invited you,' Chassa hesitated. 'You are very fond of children, aren't you?'

Polly laughed. 'Something of a necessity with three sisters and a baby brother, and your daughters are gorgeous little girls.'

Slipping down into the inviting depths of the pool, she heaved a blissful sigh. The cool lap of the water was wondrously soothing and after swimming back and forth for a while, she floated, grateful for the sunglasses that cut out the blinding glare of the sun reflecting on the water.

'You are a good friend,' Chassa remarked out of the blue. 'You don't ask questions even when you know that there is something wrong. I am glad of your tact.'

Polly sealed her lips on a startled comment. The compliment was unearned. She had not suspected that there was anything seriously amiss between Chassa and Asif; all couples had ups and downs. She was really far too bound up in her own anxieties to be that observant. 'If there's ever anything I can do…' she said quietly.

'You are kind, but it will work out,' Chassa assured her tightly.

What would work out? Once more Polly had that feeling that someone was assuming that she was more informed than she indeed was. It was extremely frustrating. The reflection led her back to thoughts of Berah, whom she still knew nothing about. Her curiosity was only natural, wasn't it? Why shouldn't she pump Chassa? Every time she came here she retreated from the temptation. She cleared her throat. 'Do you mind if I ask you what Berah was like?'

Chassa sat up on her lounger. 'Berah?' she repeated in surprise.

'Raschid never mentions her, and I don't like to ask,' Polly confided truthfully. 'Did you even know her very well? I realise that she died soon after you married Asif.'

'I met her only on a few occasions. When I was a teenager I spent my summers here while my parents were abroad. It was really so that Asif and I could get to know each other a little,' Chassa volunteered wryly.

'But Raschid didn't know Berah before they married, did he?'

Chassa grimaced. 'Prince Achmed is very old-fashioned. Berah was brought up very strictly. She was not educated like you or me—her father didn't approve of educating women.' She sighed. 'You ask me what she was like. She was beautiful, feminine but very quiet, not open.'

'Jezra told me that she was often very depressed.'

Chassa paled. 'Yes, that is true. She became…slightly unbalanced by her craving for a child. She loved Raschid very much—she idolised him. It was very sad,' she said uncomfortably, her gentle eyes troubled, 'but I think that many women have coped with heavier blows. Asif hated her. He said that she changed Raschid forever—I don't know. I have never known Raschid different from the man he is now…' Her sleek dark head turned almost with relief at the sound of footsteps.

Asif strolled out to the poolside, debonair in a fashionable white suit. He was swinging his sunglasses in one hand. When he saw Polly, he struck a theatrical attitude of astonishment. 'I don't believe it! It is Polly the illusion. We hear about you, we talk about you, and how often do we see you?' His grin was ebullient. 'But since your arrival you have been a rare source of entertainment. On that point I can reassure you.'

'Polly is often here. Why do you say these things?' Chassa enquired stiffly, studiously avoiding looking anywhere near her extrovert husband. 'What must she think of you?'

He laughed. 'I was joking. I don't have to treat Polly like a stuffed-shirt guest. She shouldn't need to be told that I'm delighted to find her here. But if I were you, Polly…' As he hitched his immaculate pants to hunker down, his tone became one of exaggerated confidentiality, 'I would vacate the water at speed. You may have noticed that Raschid is not the most liberated of men, and he has this marked tendency to believe that no man can look at you without being inspired by the kind of intimate thoughts which he considers strictly his department. Why else was I barred from paying my respects personally when you were ill? He even objected to me sending you flowers—but I digress…'

'Flowers?' Polly echoed sickly.

'At this very moment Raschid is probably trying to find you,' he continued, unconscious of the brick he had dropped. 'Take it from me, my pool is not where he wants to strike oil.'

Asif had sent the flowers. She could have sunk in her chagrin. Asif's droll delivery further slowed up her thinking processes. 'Raschid's back?' she ejaculated sharply. 'Early?'

She hauled herself out of the water without bothering to wade to the steps. Chassa tossed her a towelling robe. 'I'll send your clothes over later.'

Polly twisted the moisture out of her hair with a nerveless hand. Raschid was five days early and she hadn't heard the jet. How the heck could she have missed hearing it? She fled indoors in panic. He had simply taken the hint about the flowers. Her annoyance was out of all proportion to the embarrassing discovery. A cover-up for the discomfiture of learning that Berah sounded as if she had been the perfect wife aside of her surely understandable grief over her childless state? Beautiful, feminine, quiet, adoring. Polly skidded to a breathless halt inside the bedroom. Halfway out of the robe, she froze in dismay when the door opened.

Crusader-blue eyes flamed over the shapely curves almost indecently defined by the clinging swimsuit. The tightened buds of her nipples were clearly outlined for his appraisal. In a sudden defensive movement, she covered herself again.

'You have been swimming?'

'Yes.' Scorched by the sensual burn of Raschid's outright stare, Polly heard her voice emerge stiltedly. 'I didn't hear the jet landing.'

'We landed at the airport. I had business in Jumani.' His hand lifted to the gold *agal* binding his *kaffiyeh*. Removing it, he cast both aside, his whole attention relentlessly fixed on her as he crossed the room.

Silently he peeled the garment's crumpled edges out of her tight hold and parted them. Slowly he tipped the robe off her taut shoulders to let it fall. Naked desire fired his eyes. A heartbeat later she was in his arms, her stunned protest drowned by the insistent possession of his mouth. Devastated by the smouldering charge of that driving kiss, she trembled violently. He rocked her from her head to her toes with the force of his passion. Her response was intuitive, spontaneous. For a timeless space there was nothing but him, and the world had shrunk to the boundaries of that savage embrace.

Loosening the halter ties at the nape of her neck, his hands impatiently pushed the fabric down to her waist, skimming back up over her narrow ribcage to enclose the tiptilted swell of her breasts. He made a wholly masculine sound of satisfaction. His thumbs drew down over the tumescent nipples he had revealed and her knees buckled, her fingers grabbing at his shoulders for support. His lips broke from hers only as he lifted her and brought her down on the bed.

Her hands flew up to cover her breasts. The glitter of his eyes marked the gesture as he stepped back and began to undress. 'Rewarded with this enthusiasm, I may forgive much,' he breathed huskily. 'Vocal as you were on our wedding night, you would have proved a willing partner had providence not stricken you with illness.'

'That's a lie!' she spluttered, her eyes wide with trepidation.

'I will enjoy disproving the claim. I think playing the shrinking martyr threatened by her husband's lust will be a role you find difficult to maintain when you leave this room again.' Almost casually Raschid leant forward and closed a hand round the slim ankle snaking back as she attempted to escape over to the far side of the bed. In his vibrant amusement, his slashing smile was pure-bred primitive. 'But I confess I had not expected you to make this quite so entertaining.'

Impotently Polly tried to kick. The temper which only surfaced in her with him had taken over. He held her fast, black-lashed eyes of azure glinting with a humour that was more maddening to Polly than anything he had either done or said. 'How foolish of me not to guess. This is in all probability your fantasy.'

'F-fantasy?' she parroted, aghast.

'Your cruel Arab husband spreadeagling you by force upon the bed to have his wicked way with you while remaining indifferent to your pleas for mercy,' he clarified with velvet-dark satire.

Polly was for once open-mouthed and speechless.

His fingers released her ankle only as he gracefully came down on the bed to trap her squirming body in place. 'Are you not to scream at this point?' he provoked. 'Then I see your dilemma. The evil ravisher is supposed to inspire you only with revulsion. I hate to discredit your performance when you have so pronounced a talent for drama, but to date it has not been a performance that convinces.'

His taunts enraged her. Her eyes were molten emerald. Her hand flashed up and was apprehended by fingers with the grip of steel. 'No,' Raschid said succinctly as if he was teaching a very basic lesson to a rebellious child.

Tears of anger and chagrin mingled in her eyes, but anger had supremacy. If the blow had connected it would have been the first violent act of a lifetime. On the other hand, when she was still in the elemental hold of a desire to commit murder she could not be expected to feel ashamed for failing. 'You hateful brute!' she snapped.

His teeth grazed the fingertips of the hand he had imprisoned. The tip of his tongue roamed a tantalising passage down into the centre of her palm where his warm lips circled sensuously. 'We have been married almost a month. I've been very patient.'

'You haven't even asked how I feel!' Polly was shaking and yet her limbs were reed-taut. The erotic seduction of that lazy caress sparked a clenched tight excitement in the pit of her stomach.

'Lively?' he mocked. 'I do not think that your energy level is under dispute.'

'This is disgusting!' she hurled contemptuously.

Eyes a mere glimmer of dense blue gleamed. Raschid bit her forefinger in teasing punishment. 'A man might have to suspend you by the heels over a dry well to receive the truth, but fortunately for you I am infinitely more subtle.' He rolled over, capturing her to the lean, bronze muscularity of his body, one firm hand anchored into the tangle of her hair. 'I think you have spent a long time asleep, Polly, and it is I who will wake you up,' he emphasised, and the purpose marking his compellingly masculine features was no longer even superficially indulgent.

'I can't stop you, can I?' she flashed.

'But you don't want me to stop,' he gibed, his hand smoothly gliding down to divest her of the swimsuit.

He bent his head over the tender flesh he had earlier caressed. His tousled hair was midnight-black against her pale skin. Tormented by the sight, Polly shut her eyes. His tongue lashed the sensitive peaks, his fingers shaping the rounded globes with a gentleness that was her undoing. Then his lips closed there, teasing her into a mindless delirium. His mouth against her breast was an indescribable pleasure, engulfing her in instantaneous heat. Before very long her awareness encompassed only the satin texture of his skin, the rich silk of his hair and the feverish excitement which drove out all rational thought. By then her lips needed no coaxing to meet his, nor her arms any encouragement to hold him.

His hand stroked over her stomach and gently to the very heart of her. It was an intimacy beyond anything she had ever imagined. She twisted against him, instinctively arching in wanton invitation to that intimate exploration. Tiny sounds broke unwittingly from her throat. Tremors of delight surged over her, growing stronger by the second.

Spontaneously she pressed her lips to the smoothness of his shoulder. With an inarticulate little cry she drank in the scent of the sandalwood which clung. evocatively to his skin. His tormenting mouth teased at her throat as she writhed out of control. Sensation heaped upon sensation in an ever-climbing spiral of desire until an agonising ache mounted an unbearable tension in her limbs. Her nails dug involuntarily, pleadingly into the corded muscles of his back.

'Give yourself to me,' he commanded hoarsely.

She raised her lips and he rewarded her obedience with a wild hunger that melted her into honeyed fluidity. He parted her thighs with his and urged her up to receive him. She responded blindly. He entered her without hesitation, and the pain of that alien intrusion partly diminished the frenzy of need that ruled her. But he carried her remorselessly through that barrier, checking her cry of denial with the brand of his mouth. Under the rhythmic stroke of his possession she reached that higher plane she had strained towards in an explosion of ecstasy and fell into that intense, drowning pleasure as if she had been waiting for that moment all her life. Raschid attained that same plateau in silence, only the rough rasp of his breathing and the heavy thud of his heart against her breast betraying him.

He studied her slumbrously, both gravity and a glint of light-hearted indulgence mingling in his shamelessly steady scrutiny. Then he pressed a kiss to her damp temples. 'You please me,' he murmured quietly.

Hard on the heels of dizzy satisfaction came the jolting return to sentience. Those three little words which he lazily bestowed acted on Polly like a clarion call. In that first smarting encounter with self-loathing, she pulled away, only to be deprived of the point by Raschid's abrupt move to accomplish the same feat.

As he left the bed, she clawed the sheet over her nakedness. He was a pagan golden outline in the late afternoon shadows. She pushed her hot face into a cool pillow and the world was still whirling round her. Incredulity and embarrassment held her. He had accurately forecast her surrender, her—why didn't she face it?—her enjoyment. Her own weakness seemed to tower above her in a monolith of shame. Dear heaven, she had lost all control. She had held nothing back.

The mattress gave beside her. 'Polly…my bed is not a burrow and you are not a small furry creature. Sit up.'

She noticed the way in which her bed had suddenly become his bed. Turning reluctantly back, she was bedazzled by the breathtaking river of diamonds and emeralds sparkling white and green fire against his tanned hand. Dumbfounded, she stared.

'I chose it for you in New York.' The metallic coldness of the exquisite necklace chilled her skin, his fingertips light beneath her hair as he fastened the clasp.

A phone call would have been cheaper. Clearing her clogged vocal cords, she whispered, 'It's fantastic!'

'There are earrings and a bracelet to match,' he said off-handedly.

Rewarded for her capitulation as a favoured concubine might have been a century earlier, Polly was nauseated. Her eyes gritted up. Suspicion loomed large. What had Raschid got up to in New York? If she had dared she would have slung it back and suggested that he keep the sparklers for his next mistress.

She wound herself in the sheet, trailing it off the bed, and escaped into the bathroom. In the mirror she looked the same, and yet she would never be the same again. Her fingers rested on the jewels shining with blinding brilliance and shakily she took the necklace off. Desire had stolen her wits. But she had wanted him—oh, how she had wanted him! Angry, bitter, frightened or unhappy, it made no difference. Still she wanted him. What had he done to her? What craziness came over her when he touched her? Buried in the welter of her frantic thoughts, she stepped beneath the cooling gush of the shower. A minute later strong arms encircled her from behind.

'Raschid?' she yelped.

'I can safely promise you that you will not share a shower with anyone else.'

'I don't want to share one with you either!' she blazed back in sudden fury. 'Are you telling me that there's a water shortage?'

'Polly,' he implored unsteadily, 'don't make me laugh.'

He kissed her breathless. Her centre of gravity went spinning off into infinity and her hands laced into his wet hair. Later she didn't remember leaving the shower. Raschid tumbled her down and took her wildly on the soft, deep carpet. She clung to him in a storm of passion, every inhibition banished by more and more and even more of that mindless, self-seeking pleasure. In the aftermath the recessed downlighters on the ceiling above shone down on her like so many accusing eyes. Proprietorial fingers were roaming over her sweat-slicked skin with a tenderness at variance with the sensual savagery he had introduced her to.

It was a dream she wanted censored, a dream she wanted to wake up from to discover that she was not, after all, this woman. But she was—she was this woman, defenceless in a man's grasp, bewitched by a magnetic sexual spell into betraying every principle she had ever believed in.

CHAPTER SIX

'SMILE!' A blunt fingertip playfully scored the tremulous curve of her lower lip.

Snaking free, Polly snatched up a fleecy towel. 'I have to endure everything else, but I don't have to smile!'

Raschid tugged her back with an indolently powerful hand. 'Repeat that.'

Her teeth set together in thwarted frustration.

'Yes, you suffer with such masochistic fervour,' he murmured silkily. 'I cannot wonder at your sudden silence.'

Released, she stalked back into the bedroom to straighten the bed. Listening to the beat of the shower on the tiles, she slid back beneath the sheet. The very bedding bore his scent—evocative, intimate, inescapable. Like an addict Polly breathed it in until she realised what she was doing, and then she wanted to cry. Thinking about Berah, who had reputedly wept the Volga dry, she quickly stifled the feeble urge.

Some time later Raschid inched back the sheet and flipped her over with cool hands. He extracted a lingering kiss before she could rescue her breath to object. 'I can't stay,' he admitted. 'I have a report to give to my father. I'm dining with him. I will try not to be late.'

'Take all night,' she suggested thinly. 'I'm amazed that I was sandwiched into your busy itinerary.'

He laughed softly, his brilliant eyes untamed in their vitality. 'For some things, there is always time.'

Impervious to her mutinous fury, he considerately covered her up again. Angrily she sat up, anchoring the sheet beneath her arms. 'I think I'm entitled to a room of my own. There's a dozen available.'

'But then I would be put to the inconvenience of fetching you.' Calmly he finished dressing, attaching a curved dagger, an ornate silver *khanjar*, to his belt. Straightening, he flipped the edges of his flowing gold-bordered black cloak back over his shoulders. The snap and crackle in the atmosphere appeared to leave him untouched.

'I hate you for this!' Abruptly Polly let loose her pent-up rage and frustration. 'I've never hated anyone in my life, but I hate you!' Her attack throbbed with feeling.

'A category all to myself? I am honoured, and I do understand. It was very selfish of me not to consider your feelings and make it a brutal rape.' Raschid flashed her a glittering glance of sheer masculine provocation and taking advantage of her thunderstruck silence, he pointed out equably, 'You'll be safe in the shower now,' before he departed.

The minute he walked out of the door Polly believed he forgot her existence, just as he had contrived to forget it for the past two weeks. He treated her like a partner in a casual affair. She didn't feel like a wife. How could she? He didn't behave like a husband. But he had warned her how it would be in advance. He had warned her that love and sentiment would play no part in their alliance. And she had accepted those terms—mutely, unthink-ingly, her head buried in the sand.

The instant he left the room, the stimulus of anger mysteriously ebbed away. Behind it lurked a great well of unbearable loneliness. She had made a devil's bargain. It was costing her more than her freedom. It was stealing away all peace of mind, all pride. She needed those pretences he had disdained. What she could not stand was that he should contentedly remain utterly detached from her. It was the ultimate rejection.

It was late when he returned. Polly didn't hear him enter the lounge. He moved like a night-prowling cat. Looking up, she saw him, darkly stilled just inside the pool of light shed by the lamp to one side of her. Her pulses quickened, her breath catching in her mouth. She told herself it was fright.

'Some unexpected guests arrived,' he imparted. 'It would have been impolite for me to leave sooner.'

Polly gave a shrug. Her earlier emotionalism had hardened into a cold and bitter implacability. 'You don't need to explain yourself to me.'

His eyes narrowed. 'I consider it simple courtesy to do so.'

It was Polly who went pink. She gathered up the letter she had been writing, intending to remove herself. Raschid moved a staying hand and sank down on the seat opposite. 'I was most disturbed to learn that you did not leave the palace during my absence. You had only to order a car.'

'Until recently I didn't feel up to much.'

'Surely you might have enjoyed a drive? You are not living in the Bastille,' he said drily. 'It isn't good for you to be shut up after your illness.'

Polly leapt with grim satisfaction into reply. 'Nobody told me that I could order a car, and where would I have gone? Jumani?' she enquired. 'I don't have any money.'

Faint colour barred his cheekbones. 'I should have thought of these things. You have reason to complain.'

'I wasn't complaining, I was merely stating facts.'

'I should have phoned you. You could have reminded me.' He sighed. 'As a rule I am not lacking in manners.'

Incensed by the information that he regarded a couple of phone calls to his wife as a duty courtesy, Polly stiffened. 'It's all right, I didn't really notice.'

Unanticipated humour lightened his features. 'I feel duly

punished now, Polly. For a deliberate omission not to be noticed is a just reward.'

The force of that unchoreographed charisma of his nearly splintered through her cold front. She wanted to smile back. The acknowledgement unnerved her. His attraction was a hundred times more powerful because he seemed quite unaware of it. She could not help comparing him with Asif, whose charm was boyishly calculated and gilded by unhidden conceit. Raschid's sophistication was not Asif's. Raschid might be cultured and cynical, but he would never possess his brother's studied air of bored languor. His vibrancy, shielded by that cool austerity, beckoned to Polly with the burning heat of a fire on a winter's day.

'Tomorrow I will take you into Jumani. There are furniture warehouses there.' He surveyed the shadowy room and the cosy corner Polly had incongruously set up for her comfort with grim disfavour. 'I have never entertained here. I have never even used this room before.'

It was so wretchedly typical of Raschid to reappear the very epitome of well-bred and reasonable behaviour. Gone was the passionate lover, who had taken her by storm and ruthlessly rejoiced in conquest. An odd little shiver, indecently reminiscent of anticipation in reverse, assailed her. Hurriedly she got up. 'Fine. I'm going to bed now, unless you have some objections.'

He eyed her set face unreadably. 'Go to bed if you wish. I have work to do.'

From the door she glanced back. He was motionless by the window, a solitary dark figure in splendid isolation. He didn't need her, he didn't need anybody. But still that view of him unawares tugged wilfully at her heartstrings. She couldn't sleep. It was one in the morning and he was working. Even if he had slept during the flight, time zones played havoc with anybody's system. Polly curled up in a damp heap round a pillow.

Furniture, she reflected incredulously. He talked about her refurnishing when a divide the width of the universe stretched between them. Did he think that all he had to do to keep her in contented subjection was throw a king's ransom in jewellery at her and let her spend a fortune on a home which was not her home and never would be? Did he think that that would miraculously convert her to her lot? Could he really believe that she valued herself so low?

Around dawn she discovered that she was wrapped round Raschid instead of the pillow. There was not a lot of excuse for that in a bed six feet wide. As she began gingerly to detach herself, he turned over and anchored her to his lithe, brown body, murmuring something indistinct in Arabic and then her name. He kissed her, and her toes curled shamelessly. While she was trying to uncurl them, he darted his tongue hungrily into the moist recesses of her mouth and what her toes were doing receded in immediate importance for a very long time.

He sauntered fully dressed to the foot of the bed. Polly's heartbeat tipped against her breastbone. 'What time is it?' she whispered.

'Almost half-past six.'

'Is that all?' Gratefully her eyelids dropped again.

'It's the coolest part of the day. Later it will be too hot for you. I always go riding in the morning. You can join me. That is not a pleasure you have to do without here. Have you inspected the stables yet?'

She didn't want to look at him. As memories touched wilfully and cruelly on her all she wanted to do was curl up and die, preferably without an audience. 'I'm not a very good rider.'

'That's not important.' But he couldn't keep the surprise from his voice.

'Apart from that, I'm not in the mood to go riding,' she muttered. 'Enjoy yourself.'

'You are not making this any easier for either of us,' he breathed. 'You are being childish.'

'It's funny how I'm always being childish when I disagree with you or obtrude as an individual,' Polly said bitterly from the depths of the bed.

Her tiredness put to flight, she tossed for a while before getting up. She was being foolish. She was driving a further wedge between them. Twenty minutes later she arrived breathlessly in the domed porch, just in time to see Raschid swinging himself up into the saddle of a magnificent black thoroughbred. The stallion's sleek lines were pure Arabian, beauty and stamina superbly matched. Feeling she was too late and fearful of a cool welcome, for in all likelihood the invitation had been spurred by politeness alone, Polly didn't advertise her presence.

'How very wifely!'

Startled, she spun. Asif grinned at her. 'Marzouk and Raschid are very impressive. Aren't you joining him?'

She flushed. 'No.'

'He prefers to ride alone.' Then he groaned. 'But now that you are here, naturally that will change.'

'I'm not much of a rider. I don't think I'd hamper him with my company.' She forced a smile, glad she hadn't rushed outside to publish her change of heart.

He swept a cavalier's bow with an imaginary hat. 'I wouldn't be hampered.' His brown eyes roamed appreciatively over her beautiful, laughing face and he sighed. 'You're right—I'm a hopeless flirt. I can't help it. You are much too distracting, Polly. But there are times when distractions are welcome.' He stared moodily out at Raschid cantering through the gates. 'He is a very tough act to follow.'

'Are you in competition?'

He didn't look at her. 'When Raschid was a boy, he trained his own falcon. For three months it went everywhere with him until it was tamed. He didn't mind getting clawed in the process. Our father was very proud of him. In his eyes that's the sort of behaviour that separates the men from the boys. I've still to make the grade, and the most hellish side of it is that you can't dislike Raschid for it.' He turned back to her with a rueful smile. 'For his family, even his unworthy brother, there is no sacrifice he would not make.' He evaded her gaze and sounded a rather strained laugh. 'But when the competition gets too much I can always think of the jeans.'

'The what?'

He pulled open the door, slim and elegant in his tailored riding gear. 'It is what you call an "in" joke, Polly,' he divulged, having recovered his natural buoyancy.

Unable to see anything humorous in Raschid choosing to relax in less formal clothing, Polly soon cast the trivial remark from her mind. Asif's undeniable uneasiness with her for several uncomfortable seconds had concerned her more. Was he afraid that Chassa had made indiscreet confidences? He should know his wife better. Chassa was too loyal to spill the secrets of their marriage.

Returning upstairs, she wandered into Raschid's study. It was really a library, shelved from floor to ceiling with books in several languages. She ran a thoughtful fingertip along the spines of a collection of poetry books. Berah's? Frowning, she passed on, surveying the dull appointments of the cheerless room. Apart from the telephones and the computer it was as early medieval as the rest of the place. Only the bathrooms and the kitchen quarters had been modernised—quite the opposite of Asif and Chassa's wing, which was full of designer furniture and pale, pearlised carpets. Then it was a challenge to picture Raschid against a similar backdrop.

Her hand trailed idly over the back of the chair by the desk. Did he ever think about the woman inside her pleasing shell? Her pride, her emotions, her needs? How were they to live together? How did you begin when the end was already within view? But she had begun. Why did she continue to deny the obvious? She was drowning in a physical infatuation that was terrifyingly intense. Of course she didn't know herself any more. Raschid walked into a room and there wasn't a skin cell in her body which didn't leap to that awareness. She had fought him less than she had fought herself.

Feed a cold, starve a fever; the old saying sang in her head. Could she equate a fever with an obsession? Raschid was fast becoming one. He might infuriate her, he might confound her understanding and he might sting her pride, but at no stage did he do less than fascinate her. She was on the edge of a precipice and the ground was suddenly crumbling from beneath her feet. She didn't want to be starved of him. She was already wondering how long they would have together before his next trip abroad. And if she fell in love with him, what then? Irritably she quelled that foolish worry. The more she looked back at the amount of time she had wasted mooning about over Chris, the more her stomach curdled. Her intelligence was now in firm control of her imagination and her emotions. She was not, she told herself thankfully, likely to be vulnerable in the same direction again.

'You would like tea, *lellah*?'

Zenobia smiled at her from the doorway. Reddening, Polly set down the gold pen she had absently lifted, studying it, questioning how it had got into her hand. 'Yes, that would be nice,' she said vaguely.

She kept her nose in a newspaper over breakfast. Raschid fingered through his mail and watched her in exasperation. After they had eaten, an air-conditioned limousine ferried them away from the palace at speed. They travelled along a wide thoroughfare banked by young trees being industriously watered. Taking in the size of an impressive building near completion, Polly asked what it was.

'A second hospital. It is due to open in a few weeks.'

'I'd love to see it.' Her mouth compressed. 'But I suppose that would be out of order. It wouldn't do for anybody to hint that you had a wife animated by intelligence.'

'I am not sure that it is intelligence that is animating you at this moment. I will see what I can arrange.'

As they topped the brow on a rolling hill, Jumani spread out before them. The glass of tall office blocks reflected the cloud formations. As they drove through the city her bad humour melted away as her attention roamed in eager darts. Modern skyscrapers vied with wedding-cake mosques and graceful minarets. Green expanses of parkland gleamed at intervals between the buildings. The pavements were busy and the inviting window displays she glimpsed as they sped past belonged to retail outlets that were many and varied.

'How does civilisation look now that you have got over the wall?' Raschid enquired silkily.

'It's lovely. Is that a shopping centre?' she exclaimed.

His eyes gleamed. 'Yes, Polly. Jumani has several.'

It happened slowly. He began to smile, and it was like no smile he had ever given her before. Like the sun after the rain, it was brilliant and warm.

A herd of dinosaurs could have been running amok in the city traffic—Polly would not have noticed. That smile that was neither cynical nor merely polite passed through her with the paralysing force of an electric current.

The day was an entertaining whirl. She enjoyed the tour of the warehouses and the excessive attention they received. She found herself laughing a lot, relaxing as she had never relaxed before in Raschid's company. They had lunch in a private room in a luxury hotel in the city centre; men didn't take their wives into public dining-rooms in Dharein. Raschid was not entirely at ease during the meal while the manager and waiters swarmed about them. Polly suspected he was breaking new ground. And deep in her tangled thoughts she was vaguely conscious that she would do almost anything to waken that charismatic smile again.

That evening they had barely finished dinner when Raschid's secretary, Medir, made an apologetic intrusion to mention an important phone call. Restive on her own and pleasantly relaxed, Polly decided to go for a walk in the palace gardens. In the shelter of the steep walls pepper and tamarind trees shaded fragrant oleanders with heavy pink blooms that scented the night stillness. Strolling back, she was in a brown study, and she gasped in dismay when a dark shadow moved into her path.

'Good heavens!' Clasping a helpless hand to her palpitating heart, she stared accusingly up at Raschid. 'Could you make a little more noise? You scared me—I thought I was alone out here.'

His mouth slanted. 'You are far from alone. Seif and Raoul have not been more than a few steps from you since you came outside.'

Dazedly she followed the direction of his hand and registered two more shadows over by the wall. Raschid's bodyguards.

'I am sorry if I startled you, but then you are not very observant.' His manner was teasing.

'What were they doing following me?'

'They are there for your protection.'

Before she could drily enquire if walls half-way to heaven were not protection enough, the unmistakable sound of voices raised in argument filtered down from the balcony above them. Polly recognised Asif's voice immediately.

'I believe we should go back inside,' Raschid drawled.

'All couples argue,' she said uncomfortably.

'Few as much as they do.' It was grim.

Polly frowned. 'Well, I hope you're not blaming her. She's very easygoing.'

'You don't understand the situation.'

'Educate me, then.' A silence that was deeply mortifying stretched in answer to her request.

'Don't get involved,' Raschid murmured finally. 'I voice that warning kindly.'

She felt snubbed, firmly slapped down for daring to imply that she might be sufficiently accepted as part of the family to be trusted with a confidence. In the darkness her cheeks burned. She liked Asif and Chassa, but she was neither the interfering type, nor in this case was her curiosity of the morbid variety. Picking up Raschid's tension, she had impulsively tried to share whatever was worrying him.

'Chassa does not enjoy the best of health when she is pregnant. No doubt tempers become short,' he continued smoothly.

He was only covering up; there was more to it than that. Assuming that Asif was equally keen to have a large family, surely he was guilty of selfish neglect? As Raschid curved an arm round her to guide her back indoors, Polly went suddenly still in the charged hold of an explosive acknowledgement which demolished her composure.

Where on earth would she be if she became pregnant? Already that was a possibility. She was astonished that not a single word had ever been spoken on that subject. Was Raschid under the impression that she had taken some step to avoid the danger?

'What is wrong?' He glanced down at her narrowly.

'I've just thought of something you haven't thought of.' An anger she didn't quite comprehend raced up hot and swift inside her. 'Although I must admit that on every other count you were ahead of yourself—with one strange exception. What happens to our strictly timed marriage of

convenience and extreme practicality if I become pregnant?' she demanded shakily. 'Or is there a wheel within
a wheel there as well? Some nefarious plan, perhaps, to
gain an heir without the encumbrance of a wife? I imagine
that would suit you very nicely.'

In the unkind clarity of the overhead light Raschid's pallor was pronounced. His burnished eyes blazed dangerously
bright, but his response when it came was very quiet. 'That
would not be within my power, Polly. I can give no woman
a child. You stand in no danger of becoming a mother while
you live with me.'

Shock sent a wave of giddiness over her. Her fingers
tightened painfully on the stair rail. In that instant Raschid
had turned her over and inside out. She had not been prepared; she had never even suspected. The shock stupefied
her into silence.

'I am sorry—I have embarrassed you.' His proud bone-
structure was etched hawklike beneath his golden skin,
black lashes half obscuring silvered eyes that even now
possessed a cruel capacity to interpret her every fleeting
expression. 'The manner of telling was unforgivable. Unfortunately you took me by surprise.'

Afterwards she didn't recall climbing those stairs. In
stricken confusion she blamed herself for blundering clumsily in where angels feared to tread. Having noted the unusual aspect of Raschid overlooking any eventuality, might
she not have made that last step in deduction for herself?
Or would she have? Berah had been firmly fixed in her
mind as the partner unable to have children. Only now did
she see that she had had no evidence on which to base that
assumption. Secure in her misapprehension, she had repeatedly missed the point of all that she had learnt about
his first marriage.

He stood straight and still by one of the tall lounge windows and met her uneasy gaze unflinchingly. 'You must

wonder that I should have concealed this fact at our first meeting. Had the marriage been of my seeking and had I viewed the tie as one of permanency, I would naturally have told you. Then I did not consider it a necessary explanation. But for some time I have wished to raise the matter with you. Before I went to New York,' he quoted unemotionally. 'But you took yourself off to bed early, and I must confess that when I returned yesterday, it was my belief that you must already be aware of the fact.'

Polly was being overtaken by a hideous premonition of what his life must have been like with a wife desperate to have a baby. 'I wasn't,' she told him.

'That was obvious. Perhaps you thought that the fault lay with Berah. No, the failing was mine, not hers,' he asserted. 'But I am not, after so many years, over-sensitive to this fact now. *Insh'allah.*'

His dark-timbred drawl was the merest shade unsteady. All the over-sensitivity that ferocious pride of his denied was written in his jewelled eyes. Could she have turned time back and remained in ignorance, Polly would have done so. A floodtide of guilty tenderness pierced her deep. In its wake a nameless emotion as fierce as the desert heat clawed pain into her. But she could not reward his hard self-discipline with an emotional response. With that thought she lifted her head and said quite naturally and without a hint of sympathy, 'It's not really something that concerns us.' She paused before continuing, as continue she must, for that terrible curiosity would not leave her alone, 'But I would appreciate knowing a little more about Berah. Of course, if you don't want to talk about her, I'll understand and respect that.'

A muscle jerked tight at the corner of his mouth. 'There isn't much to tell. For an Arab woman, children are an integral part of marriage. She will measure her own importance in terms of the sons she gives her husband. Berah could not adapt to childlessness. It was not to be expected that she could do otherwise. Her sole interests revolved round home and family. Unable to have what she most desired, she was naturally unhappy.'

'When did you find out?'

'We had been married for two years. Berah had seen several different doctors, and then I…she did not want to tell me when the discovery was made. It was a heavy disappointment,' he confessed curtly. 'A marriage can have no meaning without children.'

'These days couples actually decide not to have children,' Polly protested lamely.

Raschid dealt her an inscrutable glance. 'Not in an Arab society, and there is a difference, is there not, in a freely made decision? In a man such a failing…'

'Will you stop that? Fault—failing. Will you stop talking as if it was something you could have helped?' The involuntary censure sprang from her—she could not retain it.

'I am sorry that my terminology should offend.'

'Oh, I didn't mean that, for goodness' sake!' Very close to tears, she stumbled to a halt. She hated herself for forcing Raschid to answer her questions. For a charged minute, she even hated him for confessing a very private and personal sorrow in the heroic and stoic tradition of a sinner awaiting the casting of the first stone. But above all her conflict dominated a near-overwhelming need to be physically close to him. Denied that, she could only sit there in miserable silence.

'My brother had to become a husband long before he wished for the responsibility. Chassa and Asif have paid high costs of their own. Asif was a very poor candidate for an early marriage, but stability only comes with future generations…' A knock sounded on the door and Medir appeared on command, wringing his hands in his usual deprecating fashion. 'Excuse me,' said Raschid, and swept out, at last releasing her from that terrible rigidity of expression and bearing. Her shoulders slumped and slowly she breathed again.

He reached for her in the night when she was pursuing sleep without success. Finally he offered her the physical contact she had craved. Of their own volition her hands linked round the strong column of his throat, her fingertips delving into the feathery strands of his hair. Tonight, inexplicably, she was wild for him. The driving spur of a hunger she could never have expressed in words pulsed in her veins. Like the sea tide that beats eternally on the shore, it was powerful, irrefutable and tenacious. The same elemental force seemed to energise that stormy fusion. Afterwards Raschid kept his arms wrapped tightly round her. 'I wasn't gentle,' he breathed. 'Did I hurt you?'

As she uttered a shy negative, the tension in him gave. A deep and abiding sense of peace cradled her. She buried her face in his shoulder, loving the scent and the touch and the feel of him, but sleep was far from her. Unbidden rose an image of a little boy with black hair and bright blue eyes, and she crushed it guiltily in her imagination. Raschid had lived ten years with the knowledge of that impossibility. But wasn't it strange that the wife who had reputedly loved him so deeply should have selfishly wallowed in her own disappointment without caring about the damage she was inflicting on him? What kind of love was it that had ensured that Raschid remained as painfully sensitive now as he must have been then? Anger stirred in her and that pain she could not comprehend kept her awake.

Conversation over breakfast was practically non-existent. Stealing a glance at the distant cast of his hard profile, she found it extraordinarily difficult to equate him with the passionate lover of the night hours. All that was light-hearted, warm and volatile in Raschid was strictly confined to the bedroom. Beyond that door he was courteous and aloof.

Last night she had almost flung herself at him. Now she cringed from the memory. Perhaps it was imagination, but Raschid seemed a thousand miles further away from her this morning.

Uncertainly she cleared her throat, and he looked up. She couldn't quite meet his eyes. On the other hand, she would not surrender to her own discomfiture in front of him. 'What are we doing today?' she asked brightly.

'I'm afraid I have work to attend to. You must make your own amusement.' He got up.

The silence crushed her like a giant stone. Her head bowed. She was humiliated by the assumption she had made and the chill of the snub she had invited.

He paused at the door. 'Why don't you ask Chassa to go somewhere with you? She would enjoy the diversion.'

'When I require your advice on how to get through the day, I'll ask for it,' she whispered.

Emptiness yawned inside her. When had she forgotten the rules? Their marriage was a temporary expedient. Was Raschid worried that she was in danger of forgetting the fact? He had a depth of percipience she had found uncannily acute on more than one occasion. He was highly attuned to fluctuations in behaviour and atmosphere. He watched, he waited and he deduced. An unwary word or gesture rarely escaped him.

Had it not been for what he regarded as a fatal flaw he would have dutifully remarried long ago. He would have selected someone suitable, of course. Some little twittery, submissive creature who knew her place. He wouldn't have chosen Polly. The more she thought along those lines, the more humiliated she felt. He was tearing her self-respect to ribbons. She despised herself for responding trustingly to yesterday's misleading warmth. She despised herself more for craving a smile—a stupid, worthless smile from a selfish brute who endowed her with invisibility the minute dawn broke.

In the afternoon new furniture was delivered. Polly was noisily shifting it about the lounge when he came towards her. Her heartbeat went haywire and she hated him for it.

'Why aren't the servants doing that?'

She straightened with an arctic smile. 'Because I'm en-joying doing it myself. Sorry, did the racket disturb your concentration?'

'As it happens, no. I wanted to speak to you.'

Polly lifted a footstool. 'Carry on.'

His eyes flashed. 'Put that down.'

With exaggerated care, she obeyed. Rapier-taut, he breathed. 'I owe you an apology for this morning. I am sorry if I distressed you.'

'Do I look distressed?' she demanded acidly, and turned away to plonk herself down on a seat. Once again he had disconcerted her. She could feel the tears gathering.

'I do not know how I ever thought that you were quiet,' he told her.

'The fox condemns the trap, not himself.'

'William Blake,' he identified softly. 'How sweet I roamed from…' As Polly studied him in astonishment, he shrugged. 'Poetry is much loved by my race.'

She bent her head.

'I wasn't considerate this morning,' Raschid went on.

'And of course we must stick to the letter of the law, mustn't we?' she muttered bitterly.

'No,' he contradicted. 'We have to live together, and this situation demands adjustment on both sides.'

So they had a situation now, not a marriage. She couldn't breathe, and she sniffed. With a sigh he knelt down in front of her and gently rescued the cushion she was crushing between her hands. 'You are upset. I shouldn't have mar-ried someone…'

'I'm not upset! I just don't like anybody looking at me when I'm crying!'

A shadow of that rare smile skimmed his mouth. 'Am I to leave while you compose yourself?'

'Don't be silly.' Irritably Polly wiped at her damp eyes. 'But I really don't want to hear one more time about how you didn't want to marry me. How you can say that and then...' She faltered to a blushing halt.

'Make love to you?' he interposed. 'You are very innocent, Polly.'

'No, I'm not. I'm getting educated all the time.'

Raschid sighed, 'I am a man like any other...'

'Don't worry, you're not on a pedestal!' she snapped tearfully.

His eyes glittered in driven frustration. 'You are my wife, my very beautiful wife, and it is my right...'

'To demean me by using me?' Polly inserted jerkily.

He pressed a finger to her quivering lower lip. 'That is crude, and what I have to say to you now is not easy, but I don't want you to be hurt.' He slid upright again and moved a nebulous hand. 'You must not begin imagining that you have become—' unusually, he hesitated, 'attached to me.'

Fixed by that remorseless azure gaze, she was a butterfly on the end of a twisting pin. 'I really don't think I want to hear any more of this.'

'It would only make you unhappy and it would only make me uncomfortable. I couldn't respond to those feelings. I don't have them to give. There, it is said, and you can be offended with me if you wish,' he completed harshly.

Rage had glued her tongue to the roof of her mouth. 'Attached to you?' she retorted, wondering if the parasitic choice of term was accidental or subconsciously deliberate.

'To what aspect of your truly entrancing nature could I become attached? I'm in no danger of...'

'If it is true I am glad of it, but it is not unusual for a woman to become confused about her feelings for her first lover.' As Raschid cut her off in throbbing mid-speech his narrowed eyes gleamed over her fiercely.

Polly had leapt up in her fury. 'Oh, don't give me an open-ended invitation like that to ventilate my exact feelings, Raschid. It might prove seriously damaging to your ego!'

'Sexual pleasure is not restricted to those in love, Polly,' he bit out.

'All the way to Dharein with its strict moral code to find a husband preaching promiscuity!' she derided.

Dark colour had sprung up over his cheekbones. 'It was my intent to say that within a marriage where there is respect and understanding there is no shame in enjoying physical intimacy,' he returned icily.

Her chin went up, although she was shaking. 'I was taught that emotions were the distinction that lifted us up out of the animal kingdom. I'm surprised that you're not suggesting that I take a lover so that I can field-test your convictions for myself!'

Eyes an incredulous blaze of shimmering blue clashed with hers. 'The penalty for adultery in Dharein is still death.' It was a primal and savage snarl to match an anger strong enough to drain the outraged colour from her cheeks. 'But were I ever to have cause to suspect your fidelity that penalty would seem a happy exit from this life.'

The violent aggression she had incited arrested her vocal cords and her heartbeat. He released his breath in a hiss and stared at her. 'It seems that I have yet to learn appreciation of your jokes,' he enunciated through clenched teeth, the menacing cast of his hard features easing only slowly. 'But that was a provocation which would rouse any man to anger.'

Her knees were disgracefully wobbly. 'Excuse me,' she mumbled, and fled before her queasy stomach could disgrace her.

Fortunately a few gulps of fresh air out on the balcony beyond their bedroom settled her back to normality. When a hand touched her shoulder, however, she nearly leapt in the air in fright.

A firm hand steadied her. 'I believe you should abandon this tendency to refer to other men as if you are still free to think of them.'

His eyes still had a banked-down glitter. Backed up against the balcony wall, Polly was absently relieved to have a wholly clean conscience in that direction. 'Was it true what you said?' she asked.

He shifted one of his exquisitely expressive hands. 'Divorce is easy for both sexes in our society. The rights of women and children are well protected by the law. They were enshrined there centuries ago. There is little excuse for those...'

'But it does happen?'

'It has been some years since such a case has been presented, but the law still stands.'

'Well, I think...'

'I would point out that while our penal code is harsh, infringements are fewer than those in more liberal countries. Nor do our women walk in fear of sexual assault. Polly, let us discuss something on which we are less likely to argue. I don't want to argue with you.' Staring down at her vibrantly beautiful and intransigent face, he gently pushed a straying strand of hair back from her cheekbone, employing the familiarity that was almost second nature to him now.

She spun bitterly and violently away from that confident

hand. 'I'd like to be on my own. I'm sure you have work to do.'

His jawline clenched. 'I came to ask you if you would like a tour of that hospital. I have arranged it.'

An anguished bitterness consumed her. Was this one of those adjustments he had mentioned? The necessity of sacrificing the occasional hour to her entertainment outside the bedroom door? Of humouring her with the pretence that he respected her as an intelligent, thinking human being? She saw herself yesterday, utterly riveted by the spellbinding charge of his full attention. She saw herself last night, slavishly eager in his arms. And she recoiled from both degrading images. This was a fever which required starvation at every possible opportunity.

Raschid had spelt out brutal facts. She ought to thank him for the short sharp shock treatment. If this agony of pain she was enduring, if this dreadful urge to claw, scratch and bite she was experiencing was the death throes of some embryonic love, she wanted no part of it, and she would have no part of such colourful fancies. There and then she made that pact with herself. The stubborn determination which was the backbone of her character underlined the decision.

In her conviction that she loved Chris, she had wished unhappiness on herself. Raschid was just as unobtainable. Did she have a masochistic streak that rejoiced in suffering? Well, if she had, on this occasion it was not about to find even a tiny outlet.

'I don't really think that that would be my style.' She produced a bright smile. 'But I hope that won't cause offence.'

'And I hope that you know what you're doing,' he intoned coldly.

CHAPTER SEVEN

THE limousine sped through the palace gates and shot to a halt in the courtyard. Polly took a deep breath before she climbed out. Zenobia came hurrying anxiously to greet her as if she had been lying in wait.

'It is late, *lellah*,' she said breathlessly. 'You have been out for so long, and Prince Raschid returned soon after you left.'

Since Polly had planned that nifty timing she had the grace to blush. Zenobia moved to take the single package which was all her mistress had to show for an entire morning in Jumani. For three weeks a silent war of attrition had been raging between Polly and Raschid. His five-day absence at a meeting of OPEC in Geneva had proved a much-needed breathing space for her fast fraying nerves. But now he was back.

If she could, she avoided him. If she couldn't, she took refuge in a cool, offhand manner. Neither practice pleased. To a feudal male who took for granted that he should be the very centre of his wife's universe anything less was an insult. At the heart of his detachment would always dwell that chauvinistic ambivalence. But Polly had no plans to play the doormat. After all, wasn't she just riding out her time here in Dharein? Hadn't he been the one to lay down the rules? If he was now discovering that philosophy and action had little in common, the problem was his, not hers.

'I think,' Zenobia's dusky face was strained, 'Prince Raschid was concerned that you were away, *lellah*. So unfortunate,' she muttered.

Polly's eyes gleamed. Raschid wouldn't show her that

115

he hadn't been pleased. He would be as aloof and unfailingly polite as he had been before he left. Why not? Her paltry sense of satisfaction was short-lived. For every dismissive word, every deliberate avoidance, she had paid a thousandfold when the sun went down. He punished her for her defiance with exquisite finesse and ruthless expertise during the hours of darkness.

Heat suffused her unhappy face. As long as her heart hammered crazily to the intoxication of his kisses, she had nothing to congratulate herself on. Her stubborn elusiveness by day and her bitter attempts to withstand his seduction at night had not turned him from her physically.

She was watering her lush indoor plant collection when he appeared.

'Oh, hello,' she tossed in his general direction, dealing his tall, superbly masculine figure on the threshold the most sparing acknowledgement. But the inescapable weakness a glimpse of him always brought was invading her body, pulling every tiny muscle taut with sharp awareness.

She didn't hear him cross the carpet. The first she knew of it, the dainty watering can was wrested from her and her feet were leaving the floor. He crushed her mouth under his, his tongue thrusting a fierce passage between her yielding lips with a passionate, searing urgency that currented through her with a lightning-bolt efficiency.

'Hello…Polly,' he derided.

Giddily recovering, she shrieked, 'Put me down this minute!'

'As you put the phone down on me yesterday?' he gritted.

She was totally unprepared for the towering rage which made a mask of his darkly handsome visage. 'I didn't put it down. I was about to get in the bath, and I told you that!' she argued, breathlessly involved in a struggle for release that was as undignified as it was unsuccessful.

Her eyes flew wide as Raschid kicked open the door of their bedroom.

'And that…it came before me?'

'Everything comes before you!'

'I will teach you manners if it is the last thing I do,' he swore, dropping her from a height down on to the mercifully well sprung bed.

Polly bounced back against the headboard, her green eyes ablaze, maddened by his treatment. 'You touch me now and I'll never forgive you for it!'

He sent the door crashing shut with a powerful hand and swung round. 'I hear and I tremble,' he scorned. 'The next time I return you will be waiting for me.'

'Behind the door with a brick, in all likelihood!' she snapped.

'And you will have something more to say to me than "Oh, hello",' he mimicked, and yanked off the gold *agal*, a predatory glitter illuminating his wrathful stare. 'What fashion is that in which to greet your husband? You have sulked long enough. I won't stand another day of it!'

'I don't sulk!'

He sauntered over to the bed like a sleek cat stalking an already cornered prey and calmly began to remove his clothes. 'I am master in my own household.'

'You can't do this to me!' she raged, violently thrown by his sudden unforewarned change of tactics.

He lowered his lean, sun-darkened body down beside her, pulling her to him with determined hands. His eyes roamed almost savagely over her. 'If it pleases you…I missed you in my bed,' he breathed less roughly. 'Feel your body against mine. It speaks of welcome, and that is what I will have. I think you missed me too.'

'Do cows jump over the moon?'

Disorientatingly laughter tremored through his long, muscular physique, making Polly unbearably aware of his potent masculinity. 'Ah, Polly, what a talent you have for making me laugh when I'm angry! I should have lost my temper with you long ago.'

There were tears in her eyes. She was trying so desperately hard not to react to him. 'Don't,' she pleaded, fast reaching a stage where she was no longer too proud to plead.

Raschid's lips whispered provocatively over hers. 'You want me,' he murmured, 'and there is no shame in that. For five days all I have thought about is this moment and the pleasure we will share.'

And this was now and tomorrow was another day. That insidious philosophy suppressed that terrible, aching despair, and she surrendered as she had feared she would all along. Five days stretched out over aimless hours and lonely nights could be a lifetime.

'I think cows do jump over the moon.' Raschid's slumbrous gaze tracked mockingly over her when all passion was spent.

They didn't, they went into orbit. Shifting away from him, she fiercely denied that misleading after-intimacy of togetherness and muttered venomously, 'When I'm free I could make a fortune selling my story to one of the tabloids. I've got just the title! *I was an Arab sex slave.*'

The lazy arm which had predictably reached out to prevent her retreat tensed. With an appreciative laugh he dipped his mouth to the smooth curve of her pink cheek. 'I think you are as likely to do that, *aziz*, as walk naked down a street.'

Damn you, don't you ever take me seriously?'

'A sense of humour helps.' Coolly employing his superior strength, he turned her back to face him. 'Do I have to repeat what I said earlier? From now on, you behave,' he spelt out.

'I'm not a child!'

Slowly he rested his dishevelled dark head back on the pillow and looked steadily back at her. 'Only children play hide and seek.'

'Because they want to be found,' Polly countered shakily. 'Well, I'm afraid there was no such ego-boosting motivation behind my wish to spend as little time as possible with you. Now if you're…finished…I'm getting up.'

His hands swept up to close round her slender forearms. 'You are not going anywhere, and you will listen to me. Do you think that the ridiculous lengths you have gone to in avoiding me have not aroused comment? Asif has a phrase,' his brilliant blue eyes glittered up into the pale oval of her face, 'fighting dirty…'

The blood rushed hotly to her face. Not once had it occurred to her that her conduct might embarrass him. Stubbornly engaged in what she deemed a private war of survival, she had forgotten the prying eyes and listening ears surrounding them.

'Perhaps you think I enjoy having my father enquire if I cannot control my wife?' An unhidden flash leapt in his eyes. 'He finds it very amusing. I don't, and while an English gentleman might turn the other cheek, I will not. Push me and you will discover that to your satisfaction if not to your pleasure.'

'Let go of me!' Polly breathed.

'Am I hurting you?'

'That's not the point!'

'That is exactly the point,' Raschid overruled. 'I am sorry if I wound your pride, but better that than any more lasting damage.'

She stiffened. 'If you're threatening me with violence…'

His nostrils flared. 'No man who is truly a man needs to hurt a woman to make her see reason. If I have to hold you to make you listen to me, it is because you spend so much time running away from reality,' he asserted drily. 'While you are my wife you will behave as I expect my wife to behave, and whatever differences we have are not to be set up for public debate. Is that understood?'

Polly quivered with temper and chagrin. 'I hate you!'

'That wasn't the question.'

'You lousy bully!'

'A bully would have cut out your tongue and shackled you to the foot of the bed with a chain by now,' a disturbing quirk matched the sudden humour in his eyes, 'but what a very dull life a bully would lead with a Polly cowed into submission! I believe you understand very well what I have said and I don't think you will repeat those errors.'

'I wonder where you get that idea!'

Slowly he smiled. 'It didn't work, did it? And it is not very comfortable to avoid someone all day and then go to bed with them at night. I believe you must now see the point of the relationship I was trying to establish with you, now that it is being made clear that you cannot embarrass me into sending you home.'

Was that what she had been doing? 'You don't want a relationship, you want a bed partner,' she condemned.

Raschid was inexorably drawing her down on top of him. 'If that is true, I have yet to find one. So far I have taken a human sacrifice to bed and awakened to sullen silences—not to mention the disappearing wife act.'

At this Polly's lips opened on a soundless oh of outraged disbelief.

He smiled. 'But I live in hope of the sacrifice becoming a partner.'

'I want to get up!' she repeated unsteadily.

His response was husky and soft. 'Lie to yourself, *aziz*, but never lie to me.'

Her head twisted away. 'I meant what I said.'

Tumbling her over, he smoothly reversed their positions.

Gazing down at her, he indolently laced a brown hand into the wild disarray of her bright hair. 'Your obstinacy may rival mine, but not, I think, your endurance. Or your powers of self-denial. Exactly where would you be if I didn't throw you on beds, *aziz*?' he demanded with lethal satire.

Pinpointing her deep sense of floundering inadequacy, he held it ruthlessly up to the light. He hurt her as he had never hurt her before. Her susceptibility to his smallest caress was indefensible. 'You…bastard!' she muttered.

A formidable cool sharded his intent stare. 'Even if I should find adoration distinctly boring, how I dislike to hear such language upon my wife's lips.'

You liar! Did Berah bore you? She was tortured by the memory of the male who had talked of his first wife in a tone the reverential reserved for an early Christian martyr, the male who had sensitively removed to new surroundings to evade distressing reminders. Berah had touched him deeply. Berah had awarded him all that an Arab prince was brought up to expect from a wife—in public and in private. Her love had been acceptable. Her love had been returned. Jealousy laced with pain wrenched at Polly. 'You won't be receiving adoration from me!'

Without hesitation Raschid released her, casting her bewildered face a hard, glittering smile. 'However, there are other things that I will have,' he declared. 'There you are, Polly. Just this once I give you what you say you want— your own company and an empty bed. But why is it, I wonder, that you should lack the glow of a woman receiving her heart's desire?'

Her pallor was pronounced, her pulse suddenly a thunderbeat. Her heart's desire… Oh, lord, help me! she thought. In that bemused instant of savage rejection and jealousy, she saw. She saw what she had blindly fought for and, conversely, blindly fought against. It was not solely that lean, sunbronzed body that roused the indecently insatiable hunger of her senses. No, it was so much more. That quick and clever brain, that potent aura of leashed animal vitality, that quicksilver humour which could flash out disconcertingly from behind the gravity, that... She could have gone on endlessly, a new convert glorifying her idol. She loved him, head over heels over sanity. Logic had nothing to do with it. Love, she appreciated dazedly, wasn't something you could control or decide not to feel.

'Ask me, admit that you want me, and I'll come back to bed.'

Wrenched from stricken self-analysis, she looked at Raschid weakly. Oh, why does it have to be you? she thought. A lithe, unashamed pagan, already provocatively aware of his physical power over her. She recognised that change in him—that overt, predatory awareness of his sexual magnetism. She could have sworn that it hadn't always been there. But it must have been. Wasn't blindness one of her worst failings? And wasn't perception his strongest talent? How long would it be before he guessed that this wasn't the full extent of his power?

In the silence he sent her a wolfish smile, amused now, outrageously confident. With it went a look of outright possession. 'It may not be today, it may not even be tomorrow, but you will make that admission eventually,' he told her.

'I hope you have the patience of Job!' The snappy retort came to her with the saving ease of habit, but he left her sunk in depression.

Even desire didn't threaten his cool self-dominion. He was as content to sate his high sex drive with Polly as he would have been with a mistress. He was just as safe from emotional involvement. All this fine-sounding talk about wanting to establish a relationship was a subtle countermanoeuvre aimed at driving her metaphorically to her knees and moulding her into the required image of wifely behaviour.

It wasn't worth any more than that wretched swimming pool being created for the past ten days at phenomenal expense and incredible noise out in their courtyard. Had she asked for a swimming pool? Even hinted? It was pretty hard to pretend that you didn't notice a swimming pool being built, but Polly had managed the feat. And now in the midst of a running battle she discovered that she didn't want to fight Raschid any longer, but she shrank from the danger of him realising how she really felt about him.

In the middle of the night the call came, shrilling through the veil of her slumber, causing her to mutter crossly, but late phone calls for Raschid were not unusual.

'I'll take this on another line.' Before she drifted back to sleep, she wondered that he should have spoken in English.

It was still dark when he shook her awake. He was fully dressed, his features tautly cast. He gripped her hand firmly, his eyes were steady. 'You must be brave, *aziz*,' he urged. 'I have bad news to relate. Your father has had a heart attack—a serious one. He is in intensive care.'

'No!' Her mind rejected it entirely. Her energetic, jovial father, lying on the boundary between life and death? Impossible! But beneath Raschid's level gaze, she lost that fragile, futile confidence. 'Dear heaven!' she whispered.

'As soon as you are dressed we will be on our way to England. Zenobia has already packed for you, the arrangements are made. I didn't wish to waken you before it was necessary.'

Polly gasped, 'That call…it was for me! Mother…'

Raschid sighed. 'It was not from Anthea. It was Mrs King, the housekeeper, who contacted me. Your sister Maggie also spoke briefly to me. I understand that your mother is so distraught that she is in bed under sedation. Your family are greatly in need of you.'

Her mother had collapsed—of course she had. She had always leant heavily on her husband. With his life in the balance, she would go to pieces, regardless of how that reaction would affect her family. 'The children must be terribly frightened,' she muttered worriedly.

'Quite so, and though it is very hard for you, that is why you must be strong—for all their sakes. Your father is alive,' he emphasised. 'Hold to that. He has tremendous zest for life, and that must be in his favour.'

They landed to a grey, wet London evening. The waiting car ferried them the hundred miles to the local hospital, where the consultant was carefully non-committal. There was, they learnt, a danger of a second attack. Polly was allowed to glance in at her sleeping father. His ruddy face was drained and caved in. She rammed back an undisciplined sob of fear as Raschid's arm moved bracingly round her. He had been so marvellous, immensely calm and reassuring and sensible. It was second nature for him to advocate the setting aside of personal feelings to consider others more vulnerable.

Maggie rushed down the steps of the house and flung herself into Polly's arms. The household was in chaos. 'Why couldn't Uncle Peter and Aunt Janice have been here?' she sobbed. 'Mummy thinks Daddy's going to die!'

Polly also regretted the absence of Chris's parents. Had they been in England they would have come to Anthea's assistance, but they were in South America where Peter Jeffries, a high-flying executive for an international consortium, was engaged on important business. They weren't free to fly home to support Anthea through her ordeal, and Polly sighed, fearing that her mother would find her presence of little comfort.

The following days were ever after a blur for Polly. A flood of well-wishers, denied access at the hospital, called at the house. Anthea exhausted Polly with her constant demands for reassurance and her pettish refusals to accept it. Her visits to her husband's bedside always resulted in an emotional breakdown when she came home again. Unable as she was to accept a female in a supportive role, the task of soothing Anthea fell upon Raschid. His phenomenal patience with her mother's hysteria shamed Polly. In her heart she knew that he deemed Anthea a pretty, self-orientated and utterly useless woman, who was failing her children at a time when they most needed her.

On the same day that the consultant cautiously pronounced that Ernest appeared to be out of immediate danger, Raschid was recalled to the Middle East by an attack on a Dhareini tanker in the Gulf. Polly was in the nursery, where she had been spending most of her time trying to keep up her siblings' spirits. She was reading a story to Elaine with Timothy sleepily curled up on her lap when Raschid came to break the news to her.

In the dull glow of the gas fire his constraint was noticeable. Putting Timothy into Maggie's reluctant arms, she followed Raschid from the room. 'Many casualties?' she asked.

'The number is not yet certain.' His angular cheekbones stood out in sharp relief. 'They have been airlifted to the nearest hospital. I am afraid that this means that I must leave.'

'Of course. Those poor men…their families.' Polly's voice broke, and shamefully it was not out of shocked compassion alone. For a selfish moment, she could not bear the knowledge that they were to be separated.

Timothy's cantankerous wails flooded the landing as Maggie flounced out. 'He just won't settle for me. He wants you.' Uncomfortably she glanced between Polly and Raschid, for they were several feet apart.

Her brother fastened chubby arms victoriously round her neck and subsided. Over the top of his curly head, Polly took in Raschid's absorption in a section of unadorned wall and the rigidity of his profile. He really was upset. In fact, she had never seen him so upset about anything that he wouldn't even look at her.

'It may also be some time before I can return,' he related woodenly. 'Excuse me, I must take my leave of your mother.'

Her heart was heavy as lead. Mrs King was packing for him, and she insisted on helping. When she came down to the hall Raschid was leaving the drawing-room. She could not help but feel neglected at the inordinately long time he had devoted to her mother while she had wasted time upstairs, believing he would return there.

'I must go now.'

Uncertainly she drew level with him. He inclined his dark head, a silvered coolness in the scrutiny he sent fleetingly over her. 'I will keep in touch,' he told her.

'I'll miss you.' It was dragged from her.

He elevated an ebony brow. 'I think you have much to keep you occupied here.'

And that was that. He strode out of the door, down the steps and into the car. He didn't touch her. He didn't look back once. He took his leave of her with no more emotion than he would have used with a servant. He left her behind, and she was white-faced and sick inside. He made her painfully conscious that, for all his patience and kindness, he had not even kissed her since they left Dharein. Generally she had been too tired and too busy to refine too much on that restraint. But once or twice, yearning for that comfort that only intimacy with a loved one could bring, Polly had been very tempted to drop hints—only to be forestalled by the embarrassing fact that she didn't know how to be subtle or even clumsy in that direction when Mrs King had put them in a room with single beds.

She pressed a shaking hand to her lips. They had had so

little time here alone together; she had spent long hours with the children to keep them from under her mother's feet. Raschid hadn't come looking for her, though. In retrospect it seemed to her now as if he had been steadily withdrawing from her ever since they arrived.

'Really, darling,' snapped Anthea when her daughter reached for a second scone, 'I'm not surprised you're putting on weight!'

Encountering Janice Jeffries' sympathetic eyes, Polly flushed. 'Actually I've lost some,' she said.

'Nonsense! The buttons on that blouse are pulling.' An astonishingly coy look banished her mother's irritation. 'That was always my first sign. Don't be prissy, Polly. Are you pregnant? You can tell me—I am your mother.'

Freezing, Polly studied her plate. 'No, I'm not.'

'Then I suggest you cut out the sweet things.' In disappointment Anthea became sharp.

Janice, whose weekend stay was due to conclude that afternoon, tactfully turned the conversation. 'I understand that you're leaving on Thursday, Polly.'

Anthea sniffed, 'Everybody's abandoning me!'

Chris's mother laughed. 'Ernest will be home on Tuesday and Peter and I will be down the weekend after next. Polly must be missing her husband. She'll soon have been here a month.'

Anthea frowned. 'Good lord, is it really that long?'

Leaving the two older women chatting, Polly went for a walk outside. In two weeks it would be Christmas. It was very cold. She dug her hands into the pockets of the old coat she had taken from the gunroom. The emergency here was over; it was her own personal crisis that raged on. Raschid hadn't phoned in five days. Contact had slowly wound down in frequency as her father's health steadily improved. Raschid had not once prompted her return. She had finally made her own arrangements. She would just darned well turn up—Hey, remember me, I'm your wife!

Her strained face convulsed and suddenly she was crying. It was happening just as he had said it would happen. Her attraction had faded. Raschid might not be ready to think of divorce yet, but he was in no hurry to reclaim her. When she heard steps behind her, she stiffened in dismay.

'I thought I'd give our mothers an extension before I broke up the party,' teased Chris as he drew level. He peered at Polly's turned-away profile. 'Here, what's wrong?'

In embarrassment she shook her head, praying that he would leave her alone again. On his couple of visits to Ladybright before his parents' return from abroad, she had been uneasily conscious of his searching glances, his efforts to take their conversations into more personal channels. But some things weren't for sharing. One of them was the conviction that Raschid was making the most out of a cast-iron excuse for their separation. Even his father could not question a daughter's attendance on a sick parent.

'It's that damned odd marriage of yours, isn't it?' he persisted curtly.

A choked sob escaped her. When she would have turned away, he prevented her by closing his arms round her. 'Oh, Chris, don't be nice,' she begged. 'It'll only make me worse.'

His hold tightened uncomfortably. 'He can't force you to go back to him!'

'But I want to go back,' Polly said in surprise.

'You don't need to pretend with me.' As he stared into her lovely, tear-drenched eyes, his features tightened. 'Polly, I...'

'I'm not pretending.' Her hand was braced against his shoulder, trying to press him back. Even as she dazedly read his intent expression, it was too late. He was kissing her. For a stunned second she was still before she jerked her head angrily back. 'For goodness' sake, Chris!'

Abashed and awkward now, he let out a groan. 'Hell, I'm sorry. I got a bit carried away.'

In her high heels she could see over his shoulder. A hundred yards away beneath the trees lining the rear entrance to the estate, a dark male figure was stationary. In bemused horror Polly blinked. Raschid was already swinging away to retrace his steps. Her pulses had no time to go off on the Big Dipper ride he usually inspired.

'I could kill you!' she launched fiercely at Chris before she set off across the sodden lawn in pursuit. When she breathlessly reached the driveway, the silver limousine was still parked. Raschid was lodged by the open rear door, darkly magnificent in a navy suit and inhumanly still.

'You will have your divorce,' he pronounced flatly.

The cold menace of his chilling stare killed the words of explanation bubbling on her lips, and when she moved forward, he slashed a hand through the air, forcing her to a halt. 'Do not return to Dharein. I will neither see you nor speak with you again.'

The blazing, earth-shattering row Polly had anticipated was nowhere in sight. Tried and sentenced without a hearing and dismissed with a snap of his aristocratic fingers, she was in shock. Before she could recover, Raschid slid into the car and slammed the door. Her eyes were maintaining a glazed contact with the receding car when Chris reached for her. Raschid hadn't even been angry enough to lose his head, she was thinking numbly. Possibly he had seen what he wanted to see—the excuse to end their marriage.

'Polly, I don't know what to say,' Chris muttered tightly. 'Ever since your wedding, when I realised you weren't a kid any more, I guess I've had this feeling that I missed the boat, but I didn't mean to come on to you. Holding you like that…well, you're very tempting and I just lost my head for a moment.'

Barely listening, she mumbled, 'It's not contagious.'

Anger flared briefly within her. Had Raschid no faith in her at all? No trust? No respect? If only she had slapped Chris like some outraged Victorian maiden! Raschid had been too far away to see her annoyance, hear her angry words.

'What are you going to do?' Chris pressed. 'I feel terrible. This is my fault.'

Polly shrugged jerkily. 'It's just a stupid storm in a teacup. Forget about it,' she advised tautly. 'I'm flying back in a few days anyway.'

He sighed. 'If there's anything I can…'

'Nothing.'

'How do you intend to cover his departure?'

'I don't think he'd entered the house and the car was parked out of view. He could see us from here,' she pointed out, tight-mouthed. Raschid had spied on them, he hadn't advertised his presence, and what had he been doing arriving by the back entrance? A kiss, and she was in the divorce court. How dared he condemn her out of hand!

Stalking through the front door, she walked into a bower of flowers. Maggie got up from amongst the beribboned baskets of white roses. 'These came half an hour ago. Aren't they gorgeous? Raschid does have style.'

'Raschid sent them?' Polly gulped, and swallowed. If Chris hadn't been standing there guiltily ill at ease, she would have sobbed her heart out in absolute despair. It was incredibly hard now to recall that she had once believed she loved Chris.

'Who else?' Maggie eyed her sister's drawn pallor curiously. 'He may not phone much, but he knows how to employy the language of flowers!'

*   *   *

'If everyone would remain seated please,' the stewardess called unexpectedly while Polly was trying to don her *aba* without elbowing the passenger beside her.

'Is this lady… Her Highness?'

As Polly triumphed over the *aba* she recognised Seif and Raoul, dwarfing the stewardess in the aisle. Startled, she stared. Both men bowed low, then Seif motioned a hand. Why were Raschid's bodyguards collecting her off her commercial flight? He hadn't tried to prevent her return, and she had clung feverishly to that favourable omission. She had phoned the palace. Medir had told her that Raschid was unavailable. Pressed pitilessly on a third call, he had revealed that Raschid was in the desert at some place called Jebel Kaddish. Polly had duly announced her arrival time at Jumani airport.

Outside the heat of midday engulfed her. 'Where are we going?' she asked.

'To the plane.'

'We've just got off the plane!'

No answer. Her anxiety level was reaching elephantine proportions. They led her on a long trudge round the airport buildings. A curious little craft sat there, a cross between a helicopter and a seaplane without floats.

'I wish to go to the palace,' Polly declared tautly.

'Princess go join Prince Raschid.' Seif made idiotic stepping motions into the empty cargo hold facing her, much as though he was trying to coax a bashful sheep into a truck. 'Long flight, must leave…pronto,' he produced with a gold-capped grin.

She boarded with her case. Where her wishes ran contrary to Raschid's Seif and Raoul became uniformly deaf. A rough bench seat adorned by an incongruous cushion was indicated by the pilot. The two guards remained on the tarmac. Raschid was still in the desert. Did he want to see her somewhere more private than the palace? Or did that whistling pilot have instructions to push her out without a parachute above cloud cover? Polly, get a grip on yourself, she told herself. You're facing a battle royal, not an execution!

CHAPTER EIGHT

WITHOUT a view the flight was endless. The pilot chain-smoked, making conditions doubly unpleasant. When they landed Polly stumbled gratefully out into the open air. The plane was overhung by a massive black outcrop of jagged rock that protruded like broken teeth into the sky. It screened them from even a whisper of a breeze in the intense heat. Jebel Kaddish was a desolate landmark, surrounded by a barbarously bleak and magnificent landscape of dunes. In the changing light the sands gradually shaded from beige to ochre as they marched in undulating succession into the horizon.

A shout burst from the pilot and Polly spun round. She had to shade her eyes to see the tribesmen, precariously perched on camels, travelling towards them at speed. The dust they were churning up almost obliterated her glimpse of the rider on the black stallion in their midst. As they approached they spread out and finally reined in, encircling the plane. Steady-eyed Bedouin with thin, weathered faces, they were a ragged collection, yet they possessed the intrinsic dignity of a proud people in their erect carriage.

Marzouk pranced, reacting to his rider's fierce tension. Burningly blue eyes slammed into hers. Beneath the *aba* she couldn't breathe; she couldn't break that savage stare either. The pilot broke it, hurrying forward to bow low and engage with gusto on the ritual and lengthy greetings that betrayed his desert origins. Mortified by Raschid's failure to acknowledge her, Polly studied the ground with burning cheeks.

A tribesman dismounted and took her case to strap it on

to a lone baggage camel while a second led another camel forward and with a practised flick of his cane made it kneel. On its back it bore a basketwork litter draped with bright cloth. Raschid at last walked Marzouk over to her and sprang down.

'Look, I didn't expect a welcome mat, but—' she began huskily.

Without a word he scooped her up and settled her into the litter, indifferent to the ill-tempered camel's vicious attempts to snap at him. His prompt response to his wife's reluctance provoked many covert smiles, and Polly's anxious eyes brightened with indignation.

The camel lumbered upright and the world lurched sickeningly. As they moved off at a steady pace, the swaying movements of the litter sentenced her to motion sickness. It was some time before she realised that by relaxing her body and keeping her attention off ground level, she could banish it. By then the only sounds were the crunching footfalls of the four-legged beasts of burden and the riotous clamour of her own heartbeat.

They came upon the camp suddenly over a rise, a cluster of around twenty black tents and bush fires sending up smoking grey spirals. Darkness was falling now with astonishing speed and her muscles ached in every joint. The logic behind bringing her here evaded her, but she was very grateful that the journey was over.

As she clambered stiffly from the litter, two manservants she recognised from the palace bowed low. Raschid trailed her unceremoniously past them into the shadowy depths of the nearest tent and pressed her round behind an interior wall of intricate leather and beadwork. Rugs and quilts were heaped there on a low rope bed, and she sat down immediately. Her legs were shaky supports.

'Remove the *aba*. Only the elderly women mask their faces here.'

Obeying, Polly glanced up, wet tendrils of hair clinging to her brow. And neither the searing intensity of his stare nor his dangerous stillness could quell the treacher-ous rush of excitement seizing her. It was a dark en-chantment that stripped her of pride and principle. If she had ever been strong with Raschid, she had never been weaker than she was now. The silence tortured her. 'Say something!'

A lean hand clenched to show the white of bone. 'Keep yourself from my sight!' he said icily.

She scrambled up, blocking his exit. 'At least hear what I have to say!'

'Cry it to the wind. You are as likely to hear an answer there,' he gritted in caustic derision. 'With every hour that passes you will regret the insolence and the false confidence which encouraged you to disobey me.'

A creature recognition of cold threat enforced her retreat. And he was gone in a flicker of movement with the sound-less grace of a hunting animal. Nervously Polly looked around. Her surroundings were basic. She was not sur-prised. The servants were a necessary sacrifice to status, but Raschid wouldn't flaunt his wealth here. In a corner she espied a radio apparatus and two elaborate bronze oil lamps. Beyond the dividing wall she found tinned goods and sacks and a second doorway. She knew that the very front section of the tent was reserved for the all-male bas-tion of the traditional coffee hearth where the men enter-tained. From outside drifted the aromatic enticement of cooking food.

He couldn't ignore her presence indefinitely, could he? Yet he must want to do just that. The most expensive bride in the Middle East had given the poorest satisfaction. In one way or another she had fought him every day of their marriage. He could have strung her along, he could have pretended it was forever and by now she would have been eating out of his hand. But while she acted on her emotions,

Raschid acted according to his principles. He would not have lied to her.

How much had her bloody-minded behaviour before he saw her in Chris's arms contributed to his distrust? Oh, how childish she had been! Out of her depth and trying to keep her head above water, she had used the only means of defiance at her disposal. In some ways, she acknowledged unhappily, it had almost been a game to her while she tried to raise a real live emotional reaction from Raschid. But where did all that inappropriate groundwork leave her now? He didn't want her here. So what's new, Polly...? Her thoughts were bitter. But he would believe her, surely he would? If he didn't...no, she refused even to think of that eventuality. This was just a stupid storm in a teacup, she reminded herself. It was just that he hadn't realised the fact yet.

Mahmoud brought her a savoury meat and rice concoction and a frothy cup of milk, and she ate hungrily. He reappeared with a shallow dish of water in which she was evidently expected to wash. Doing her best, she dressed again, frowning over the tightness of her waistband. Her mother was right and the scales were wrong. She was putting on weight. As a long shadow darkened the magazine she had taken out to read, she glanced up apprehensively.

'You should be in bed. Before dawn we break camp.'

'Can we talk now?' Already Raschid was removing his clothes in quiet, economic movements.

'I have no desire to talk.' In the soft light shadows obscured his expression.

Tension formed an iron band across her temples. She had already opened her case, but little within was suitable for a desert sojourn. What might have been comfortable would not be deemed respectable among nomads, whose women were shapelessly if colourfully covered from head to toe. Pulling out a lawn nightdress, Polly hesitated, her fingers coiled tight in the fabric. 'I was crying and he was comforting me. He kissed me...I didn't kiss him.'

He grated an Arabic profanity, his teeth a feral white slash against his sunbronzed features. Frustration and strain summoned tears to her eyes. Granted more privacy than tent walls, she would have dared his anger and persisted. Edgily she began to undress again. Never had she been more conscious of Raschid, never had skin seemed more indecently naked.

Impatient fingers wrenched the nightdress from her grasp and flung it aside before she could drop it over her head. As she collided in shock with incandescently blue eyes, the brand of fear she could taste flooded her mouth. 'No...!' she shuddered in stricken understanding.

Raschid doused the lamps, plunging them into darkness. He found her with ease. There was no place to go, no room for evasive action, and if she cried out, the whole camp would hear her. Whatever she did, it would not turn Raschid from his cruel purpose. He was in the merciless grip of a murderous rage which had smouldered unabated for over five days. The icy mask of disdain he had shown her at Ladybright had been a façade, no more indicative of his real feelings than a smile would have been.

He laced a hard hand into the silken fall of her hair. 'Let me show you how I would treat a whore,' he invited with soft, biting menace. 'If I thought of you as my wife, I would kill you with my bare hands. Yes, you succeeded, *aziz*. Celebrate your hour of victory now, for the glory will be brief. You twisted my guts with jealousy, and for that education, I am ungrateful.'

'There's nothing between Chris and...' His hand clamped over her lips.

'I doubt if he'll want you back when I am finished with you. That lingering and so appealing innocence of yours will be gone. And then he would have to wait a very long time. For as long as it amuses me you will remain in Dha-rein, and when I wish, I will lie with you,' he swore with muted savagery. 'You have no rights. I grant you none, and I thank you for revealing your true self. I have you on my terms now, and I will yield you no quarter.'

Polly was paralysed by the raw force of his invective. A sleeping tiger had been kicked into wakefulness and un-caged. She had yearned for the power to pierce his detach-ment, but not with the violent, destructive drive of emotions that had splintered his control. For that sin and for this vengeful act of subjugation he intended, Raschid would never forgive her. He would despise himself for using force with a defenceless woman. Her brain functioned frantically as he joined her, his lean body achingly familiar, but the hands sweeping her shrinking flesh were coolly set to shame, not to pleasure.

'I…I need to go…outside,' she stammered in despera-tion.

Releasing his breath in a hiss, he folded back. Barely able to credit the success of her gambit, Polly blindly fum-bled for some clothing and footwear, pulling on what she suspected was his discarded woollen *tobe*.

'Don't get lost.'

For once, intuition was letting him down. Until he cooled off, Polly had no other objective inside her panic-stricken head. Raschid was not presently accessible to reasoned per-suasion.

Fortunately their tent was set some distance from the others near the edge of the camp. As a dog barked she quickened her step. Her energy level was on an adrenalin boost. Moonlight cast a black and white photographic clar-ity on the desert, and she ran like the wind. Glancing back to check that her flight had gone unnoticed, she hurried on again without looking—and stepped into mid-air. She went head over heels down a slope that had lain concealed by shadow, sand gritting her mouth and her nose, but she didn't cry out. At the bottom, winded, she got up and shook herself, her heart thumping fit to burst.

It seemed common sense to travel along the meandering valley of low ground between the dunes rather than exhaust herself trying to climb. Besides, she wasn't planning on straying too far. The air was surpris-ingly humid, lacking the frost she had expected, and she settled into a half trotting, half walking pace in the eerie, supernatural quiet. Raschid would look for her, and by the time he found her— lord knows, a herd of camels couldn't have left clearer tracks—she prayed that he would have calmed down. Should anyone else be involved in her disappearance, he could say that she had lost her bearings. Nobody would suspect that it hadn't been an accident. Well, what else could she have done?

Raschid was half out of his mind with jealousy. A dark, profoundly sexual jealousy, new to his experience, had ripped the lid off his outer skin of cool to reveal the passionate turbulence of the emotions beneath, and the strength of those emotions had shattered her. If he had felt like that, why had he left her with Chris in England?

Without warning the entire surrealistic landscape around her was brilliantly illuminated by a forked flash of lightning. A fine mist of sand sprayed her shocked face as a wind came up out of nowhere and the first drops of rain sprinkled down. Above her the black velvet heavens were suddenly ripped asunder by spearing arrows of blinding light that jetted down into the ground with a ferocity that terrified her. Like a strobe disco display magnified a thousand times, the elements began to go mad.

The rain now fell in a lashing blast, plastering fabric wetly to her limbs, stinging her exposed skin. Instinctively she crouched down, trying to protect herself from the incredibly heavy downpour. When an animal leapt at her, she was knocked flat, and since she hadn't seen what had attacked her, she screamed so loudly that she hurt her throat. The dog stood over her whining, while its panting mate raced up and licked at her hand.

Raschid barked a command and the dogs retreated. The noise of the thumping rain prevented Polly from hearing what he slung at her. Water streamed down his face as he lifted her and practically threw her up on to Marzouk's back. Her instant of unholy relief at first sight of him was limited by the realisation that he had put his saluki hounds on her trail. He had hunted her down like an animal.

It was a nightmare trek back to the camp. Her teeth chattered convulsively, her skin numb from a cold that penetrated to her bones. Raschid had to carry her into the tent.

'If I took a whip to you now, no man would blame me!' he roared at her above the storm. Ablaze with dark fury, he dropped down to strip the sodden *tobe* from her shivering limbs.

'You put dogs on me, you brute!' she gasped.

He produced a towel and began to rub it roughly over every complaining, squirming inch of her. As her circulation revived, the exercise became painful. Unsympathetically he glowered at her. 'What were you waiting out there for?' he demanded. 'Noah's Ark? You lie in a *shoeb*...a dry torrent bed. Didn't you see the water pooling? Within minutes it would have flooded. In winter there are flash floods in the desert. My own people have drowned. The storms come suddenly and it's not always possible to reach higher ground!'

'Stop shouting!' she begged.

He rolled her dexterously into a quilt and tugging her forward, towelled dry her dripping hair. 'Another few minutes and the salukis would have lost your scent in the rain,' he bit out rawly. 'You could have died. Your tracks would have been washed away and the sands above you would have slipped down to conceal your body. Allah be praised that you are saved and that no man lost his life in pursuing the most stupid, reckless…' At that point words seemed to fail him and he subsided. Rain-washed violet eyes framed by spiky wet lashes surveyed her pallor with grim satisfaction.

In the electric silence, he slowly breathed in and screened his eyes. 'I shout at you, but the blame is mine,' he asserted in a roughened undertone. 'In threatening you, I have shamed myself more than you have shamed me in the arms of your lover.'

Polly's eyes ached. Her hand crept up uncertainly on to the brown fingers resting tautly on his thighs. 'He's not my lover—I was telling the truth. It was an emotional moment and Chris made a mistake,' she cited unsteadily. 'But if you won't believe me, if you won't listen, what more can I do to convince you?'

Raschid's hard-set profile was unresponsive. He looked at her small hand and it retreated immediately. He got up. 'You should not have returned,' he said very quietly. 'But what choice had you? I placed you in an intolerable position with your family.'

'Where are you going?'

'I must attend to Marzouk.' He vanished back out into the slackening rain before she could utter the heresy that his horse was more expendable than he was and he was still soaking wet.

An opportunity to vent some of his pent-up anger had made him more approachable, and even in anger he had automatically taken care of her needs. What agonised her was the suspicion that, guilty or innocent, she was no more welcome. Then that scarcely fitted his behaviour. Jealousy suggested…what? Caring? She grimaced. It was more likely to be the reaction of a very possessive male, enraged by the slur on his masculinity and the insult to his pride.

He had walked away from her in England. Yet he had arrived that day with flowers and an evident intent to surprise her. It didn't make sense.

To say the very least, Raschid's behaviour had been erratic since they had received the news of her father's heart attack. Then, when he had talked of a more normal relationship, he had withdrawn from her in every way. He had stayed away, maintaining a contact of skeletal cool...and then the flowers. If there was an explicable pattern there, Polly was darned if she could see it.

She wakened to grey light and the bloodcurdling roar of an angry camel. Around her the covers were undisturbed. Raschid hadn't slept beside her. As soon as she sat up, a slender Bedouin girl appeared with water for her to wash. She must have been sitting outside the tent listening for the first sound. Giggling shyly at Polly's halting attempts to communicate, she gave her name as Hirfa. It took considerable dumbshow to request her need for a pair of scissors. Polly put on her loosest dress and then cut the top off the *aba*, dropping the butchered garment over her shoulders to cover her bare legs. She was pleased to have solved the clothing problem so easily.

When she finally left the tent, half a dozen chattering women converged on it. The camp had almost vanished but for the tent roof under which Raschid's oversleeping wife had rested. The men were congregated round the fires drinking tea in relaxation while their wives and daughters laboured to pack every possession.

Nearby Raschid lifted a hand, motioning Polly over.

'Join us,' he invited. 'Do you want some tea?'

In some surprise she sank down beside him. His companions were noticeably quiet at the unconventional development. 'It's cool, isn't it?' she remarked, a conversational opener that only had Mahmoud dispatched to fetch her a rug she didn't need.

At Raschid's signal, the teamaker served her first with the next round. Smiles were in evidence as Raschid said something.

'What did you say?' Polly wanted to know.

'Never mind. You are accepted because I accept you here.'

Acceptance was a dubious honour. The strong tea, thick with sugar, was served without milk and most of the men were smoking. The fumes were taxing on her sensitive stomach, and she dimly wondered why; smoke had never bothered her until recently. But, listening to the melodic rise and fall of voices, a kind of peace embraced her. The confrontation over, perhaps the talking would come soon.

'I thought desert travel was all down to trucks these days,' she confided when some of the men had drifted away.

'This is deep dune country,' Raschid explained. 'The four-wheel-drive which may traverse this terrain has not yet been invented, and even if it was, these Bedouin could not afford it. There are no roads in the interior—the sands would soon swallow them up. In summer when the tribe stay by the borewells they use old trucks to transport water to their livestock, but they leave them with settled relatives or sell them when it is time for the winter migration. I agree that this background is not for you.'

Polly tensed. 'I didn't mean that.'

He shrugged. 'At this time of year I usually spend some time in the desert. When we had been apart for so long, I could not let you return to the palace.'

'I'm quite happy here,' she assured him.

'Conditions are spartan,' he said flatly.

'I don't mind.' Polly was starting to get annoyed.

His narrowed eyes rested on her. 'Perhaps I do.'

'Perhaps you just don't want me here!'

He sighed. 'You are over-sensitive this morning, and that

is also my fault.' He sprang up and moved a rueful hand. 'Everyone awaits us.'

Cocooned back within the litter, she reflected on his calm, uninformative manner. Was he thinking over what she had said? Having mastered his temper, was he now seeing reason? At least he was speaking to her again. Great, Polly, you can read a lot into that, she thought. Why aren't you angry with him? You have every right to be angry.

The long, winding cavalcade trailed steadily out into the desert wastes. As the burning crimson orb of the sun ascended, the brilliance of the colours shed on the sands fascinated her. Occasionally strange formations of volcanic rock interrupted the vast landscape, but as the sun reached its zenith, the glare sapped the earth beneath of life. Polly was nearly asleep sitting up when the caravan came to a sluggish halt.

Moving her cramped limbs was agony, and Raschid came to her assistance. As his arms released her, her head swam dizzily. Everything blurred into formless shades of grey and she passed out cold.

Woozily meeting the stark azure eyes above hers, she mumbled, 'I'm sorry, I just don't know what...'

The concern harshening his features eased. 'This journey is too taxing for you.'

An improvised shelter had been erected to provide her with shade. Self-pity overcame her and the tears welled up. She was hot and sweaty and miserable, and Raschid was giving her a look that said she must have been feeling ill to faint and why hadn't she mentioned it sooner? But she hadn't been feeling ill.

'Don't cry. Of all the female weapons I abhor, tears are the most unfair,' he muttered. 'And it is worse that it is not a weapon with you.'

Since there wasn't a weapon in her armoury that she wouldn't use to hang on to him, the exasperating gush continued. What was wrong with her? Of late she had emulated a wet weekend all too often and all too easily.

'Polly…I beg of you.' Presented with a tissue, she guiltily mopped up.

Unnerved by the brooding gravity of his appraisal, she looked away, and he sighed. 'In marrying you I have caused you great unhappiness.' His deep, dark drawl was very low-pitched. 'Sometimes, as the sun at noon, you can make me a little crazy…or a lot crazy, like last night. Unlike you, I do not share my feelings easily, and some, believe me, are more wisely kept private. But I must ask your pardon for doubting your loyalty. I did not have sufficient cause to condemn you unheard.'

She was weighted by the funereal atmosphere. 'It's forgotten,' she hastened to tell him.

'You are too forgiving. I have not treated you as I promised.'

Polly had to gulp inelegantly into the tissue to fend off another flood. By then Raschid was already rising and helping her up. 'The tent is prepared and you must rest. I had hoped that today we might travel on to Aldeza, but you are too tired. You have still to sleep off your jetlag.'

'What's at Aldeza?'

He said something in incomprehensible Arabic and his mouth tightened wryly. 'The Palace of the Fountains. You will be comfortable there at least.'

She awoke to soft, artificial light. Once more Hirfa magically appeared. Unfortunately Polly couldn't understand what the girl was asking her and she left again. When she returned with Raschid, Polly was wretchedly conscious of her bedraggled appearance.

'Hirfa wishes to know if you want a bath,' he explained.

'A bath?' she echoed.

He laughed huskily. 'We are near a well. I bathed earlier. Even if the legendary luxury of an Arab prince's desert dwelling must fall far short of popular and romantic expectation,' he added wryly, 'at least you may be clean.'

An antiquated tin bath was carted in. It took buckets and buckets of lightly steaming water to fill it. Embarrassed by the labour involved, Polly only stopped feeling conscience-stricken when she was free to luxuriate in water for once more than an inch deep. It was heavenly! She thought of Raschid's smile, his laughter. Later, she mused dizzily, with a wicked little shiver of anticipation, later he would make love to her. Even as she dried herself, her skin moistened and her cheeks warmed. She was a prey to the thousand erotic images imprinted on her memory bank.

But dinner was not to be the cosy twosome she had innocently pictured. After helping her to dress, Hirfa ushered her outside. In the centre of the camp, a large fire was burning. Round it the men were gathered. On its environs the womenfolk were cooking on small fires and in between the children were running about, noisy in their excitement.

As she settled beside Raschid he explained that since they were leaving the camp in the morning, he was playing host to thank the Bedouin for their hospitality. Private conversation was impossible, and when the men rested back to smoke and recite the long, tall stories and legends that richly endowed their spoken heritage, Polly bowed out, recognising that her presence was acting as something of a dampener. She drifted back to the tent and got ready for bed.

It was ages before Raschid followed suit. Shyly she kept her eyes closed while he undressed. When he slid in beside her, the minutes slowly passed and he made no move to touch her. She had feigned sleep too well.

'I'm awake,' she muttered, then flushed.

'Count chickens,' he advised shortly.

'It's sheep, not chickens.'

'Sleep, Polly.' The message was succinct.

Rejection bit deep. Although pride urged her to silence, she could not maintain it. 'Are you still suspicious about Chris?' she asked him.

'No.'

Stiff with hurt and bewilderment, she whispered, 'Then why—?'

In the gloom Raschid moved. A match was struck and a lamp shed unwelcome clarity on her hot face. 'It is wiser this way.'

Stunned, she dropped her head. 'Yet when I wanted it this way, you wouldn't hear of it.'

'I was wrong.' He seemed to be measuring his words carefully, and well he might have done, for her temper was starting to rise. 'I am not afraid to admit myself at fault. The money…it was less than nothing to me. I should have let you sleep alone. I won't take advantage of you in that fashion again.'

Evading visual contact, Polly bit her lower lip. 'And if I were to say that you wouldn't be…er…taking advantage…?'

'My answer would still be the same.' As she flinched, his hand pressed her flat, forcing her to meet the charged glitter of his eyes. 'Do you think that I no longer want you? That is not the case. But once you said that I demeaned you, and I did. How could I not? Our marriage goes nowhere. It can go nowhere,' he spelt out harshly. 'We have no future together.'

'You never saw one!' Polly was torn by an agony that was almost physical.

His fingers slid slowly from her shoulder. 'No, I did not. You love children, and I—I have been through that war once with a woman, and I know too well its end. Even with love it could not work.'

In the chaos of those early days at Ladybright, it hadn't occurred to her that Raschid was seeing her with children for the first time. But even registering that rare betrayal of his vulnerability, she was beaten back into a passion of pain by his concluding statement. He was talking about Berah—Berah, who exerted the same deep hold on him in death as she had alive, and that was the real reason in her opinion why he had no room for Polly in his life.

'I don't want to hear about her. She was weak and selfish, and she wasn't a saint.' As anger and hurt clawed cruelly at her, the last remnants of her control came crashing down. 'And she's ruined you for anybody else!'

Perceptibly he curbed the anger hardening his facial muscles. 'I know you mean no disrespect. Had you any real understanding of how desperately unhappy she was, you wouldn't speak like that. She did not ruin me. If anything, it was I who destroyed her. I watched her change from a contented and uncomplicated girl into a bitterly insecure and disturbed woman.'

'But I…am…not…her!' Her throat was thick and full. 'And I love you.'

A profound silence enclosed the involuntary spill of her words. She shut her eyes tightly, physically willing the clock to turn back and reclaim her confession.

'You are distraught. You do not know what you are saying.' Raschid's withdrawal was instantaneous, a cold wind across tender flesh.

She was too bitterly upset to heed the warning. 'Don't I? It may be an emotion foreign to you in relation to me, but I know how I feel!'

Dark blood had burnished his high cheekbones. Slashing a hand down in finality, he reached for his woollen *tobe*. 'No more. In the morning you will regret this.'

'All I regret,' she framed with a shaky sincerity that had its own dignity, 'is falling in love with a man who is afraid to feel anything for any woman. What did she do to you?' she continued painfully.

A tremor racked him. He lifted his clear, compelling eyes from the ground and challenged hers fiercely. She knew that he hated her for witnessing his naked emotion and probing clumsily at wounds that had never healed. After four years he couldn't even bear to talk about Berah. In inflicting pain on him, Polly suffered doubly, for she felt his pain as if it was her own. In stark fear, she had lost her head, for if he shut her out of his bed, he shut her out altogether. Her heart belonged to him, but it was an unsolicited gift he had cast aside without hesitation. Then who wanted to find love where they felt none? Her love had no intrinsic value. What had she believed she might awaken with her foolish admission? Pity would have heaped coals of fire on her.

What did she do to you? He hadn't answered. Polly could have answered for him. She had died.

Some timeless period on in that endless, hellish night, Raschid returned. In silence she lay there until dawn spread a grey pall of light. She must have slept then, for the racket of rotor blades rudely awakened her and the heat that had damply slicked her limbs told her the day must now be well advanced. As she sat up, she was disconcerted to find Raschid seated at the corner of the bed, his probing scrutiny mercilessly pinned to her.

'The plane…?' she queried.

'Aldeza is a half-day's ride from here. By air it will take less than half an hour.'

She fiddled with the fringed edge of the rug. 'You're still speaking to me.' It was a limp attempt at humour.

'Strange as it may seem in the light of recent events, we are not, I hope, undisciplined children.' The cool controlled politeness with the edge of satire she dreaded was back. A tortured sense of frustration consumed her. The barriers were erected again with a vengeance.

* * *

At first glimpse Aldeza stole Polly's breath away. At the second it stole her heart. An exotically beautiful white marble palace of crowned domes and slender minarets, it shimmered a dozen tranquil reflections in the stilled waters of the silent stone fountains dotting its superb frontage. On every side lush gardens of shaded arbours and trellised walks beckoned and vibrant roses of every imaginable hue flourished against the oasis of greenery. The Palace of the Fountains was a polished jewel enhanced by an exquisite setting.

Built four hundred years ago by an ancestor of Raschid's, the hilltop palace had lain empty for over fifty years. Polly couldn't understand why nobody in the family had previously mentioned its existence to her. Surely they must visit this beautiful place? Before they entered the building, she darted over to a glorious climbing rose and snapped off a single, unfurling bud.

'Why don't the fountains work?' she asked.

'I believe they must have fallen into disrepair. That can be rectified,' Raschid assured her.

'Oh, don't make that effort on my account!' she snapped.

Doors stood wide on a huge, deserted entrance hall, lined by carved pillars. An army could have marched before them. Mosaic tiles in every shade from lapis lazuli to deepest emerald patterned every surface with spectacular effect. 'This is out of this world,' Polly said reverently, cricking her neck and turning slowly. 'I've never seen anything...'

'Quite so reminiscent of an Arabian Nights fantasy?' As he watched her, an irreverent grin banished his austerity. 'At last I have pleased!'

Resenting his ability to tease her when she was employing conscious effort to conceal her absolute misery, she moved away. 'Why is it empty?'

'The situation is remote and not easily accessible. In the days before hunting was prohibited, my father would bring parties of guests here. But now Aldeza has become a white elephant. When the family desire a change of scene they head for the Costa del Sol and the nightlife. We have a villa there.' He paused. 'Did I tell you that Asif and Chassa are in Spain at present?'

'No.'

'I believe that their problems are at an end,' he remarked.

Polly folded her arms. 'Good for them. Who last lived here?'

She could feel his frown on her back. But his family were not her family, and he had slapped her down on the one occasion she had dared to believe otherwise. She would not be drawn now to invite another snub.

'My grandmother, Louise. She lived here alone for many years.'

She spun. 'Louise? That's not an Arabic name.'

Raschid looked at her in surprise. 'She was French. I thought you would have known that.'

'It never fails to amaze me what you imagine I might magically know without being told,' she said tartly.

'Or me of what you might learn did you but ask.'

Her teeth gritted. 'I am asking. How did you acquire a French grandmother?'

'Her father was an anthropologist, who came here to write a book on the nomadic culture. Louise worked as his assistant. My grandfather, Salim, only met her once to fall violently in love with her.' His firm mouth curled dismissively. 'Much happiness it brought to either of them!'

'It sounds romantic to me,' observed Polly.

'They broke up within two years and spent the next fifteen living apart. Does that sound romantic?' Raschid threw her a sardonic smile. 'But of course I would not know what might fall within that category, would I?'

'You said it, and if he was one bit like you, I'm not...'
The curious sound of a stick tapping across the tiled floor
whipped her head around.

CHAPTER NINE

A WIZENED little old lady, shrunken by age into a bent bundle of black cloth, was approaching them, flapping a hand to harry the servants hurrying behind her. As she creaked down low before Raschid, he tried unsuccessfully to persuade her from the attempt, but down she went, jabbering in shrill excitement, her blackbird-bright eyes avidly pinned to them both.

Under the voluble onslaught of her emotional greeting, Raschid grew oddly tense. His brow furrowed, a curious expression set his hawkish profile for a split second before he produced a distinctly strained smile. Fingers of colour had overlaid his complexion when he turned to Polly. 'This is Ismeni. She is very old, and her mind wanders now. Would you give her that rose you carry?' He answered her bewilderment with a charged glance. 'She believes it is for her because she imagines you to be Louise. The poor creature is quite convinced that we are my grandparents,' he related under his breath.

'She's *what*?'

'Dispute will only distress her, but indeed it is a melancholic misapprehension on which to begin our stay,' he told her.

Tickled pink by his discomfiture, Polly suddenly smiled and bent to bestow the rose on the weeping Ismeni. A clawlike hand clutched hers and dry lips pressed to her knuckles. Raschid gently raised the old lady. Snapping his fingers, he summoned two of the servants, stonily studying the floor nearby, to attend to her. To Polly's amusement, Ismeni drove them back with a staccato stream of commands and

153

bustled round again to usher her and Raschid personally into a lofty-ceilinged salon, adorned by some very fine pieces of period furniture.

'Why did she want the rose?' whispered Polly. 'There are thousands of them outside.'

'Louise planted them. Roses have special significance for Ismeni. Her former mistress allowed no one to pick them.'

'Lord, I feel like a vandal now!'

A disorientating smile slashed his lips. 'Not at all. The gift of a rose from my grandmother must have been a signal honour. Why am I whispering? You are contagious, Polly.' Then he raised a brow. 'Or is this the result of being welcomed as the resurrected? Ismeni must see a doctor, though I doubt if much may be done.'

'At least she seems happy.' Polly sat down on a delicate gilded sofa with all the comfort of a rock-face. 'Tell me the rest of the story,' she pressed. 'I assume that Louise had blue eyes.'

'Yes. She was fair, though not as fair as you.' His gaze strayed to the glistening veil of silver hair tumbling round her shoulders, lingered ruefully on her attentive stillness. 'It isn't a happy story. Salim was young and hot-headed. He persuaded Louise to marry him after only a handful of meetings, but religious and cultural differences soon divided them. After my father was born, Louise came here to live. She came on a visit and she refused to return.'

Polly frowned. 'What did he do to make her do that?'

'What did they have in common, Polly?' Raschid shrugged noncommittally. 'She hated the way of life here. She was educated, well travelled and independent. She had enjoyed a freedom which was denied to her in marriage. She couldn't adjust to the cloistered existence of the harem. She was also a devout Catholic, and the continued practice of her faith did not recommend her to female relatives who already resented Salim's choice of a foreign bride.'

'I wonder how much of an effort he made to help her adjust.'

'Who knows? My grandfather was greatly angered when she refused to return to him. He took a second wife,' Raschid divulged grudgingly.

'My goodness!' gasped Polly.

'Mirsa, my uncle Achmed's mother,' Raschid supplied. 'Undoubtedly there was a desire for revenge in the speed with which he made that marriage, but he was quite within his rights according to his faith. If he wanted to punish Louise he must have suffered for the impulse, for she never forgave him for it.'

'How could she have?' Polly demanded hotly.

Raschid sighed. 'When my father was six, Mirsa died in a cholera epidemic. In the intervening years my grandparents had scarcely spoken. When he came here, she remained in the harem and he would see his son and not her. But after a suitable period of mourning, he approached Louise and begged her to return to him as his wife. She refused him. There was no forgiveness in her heart.'

'How could there have been? He spends six years with another woman, fathers a child and then condescends to ask her back?' she interrupted.

Exasperation clouded Raschid's gaze. 'He could not abandon Mirsa after marrying her. He still loved Louise. It must have cost him much pride to make that approach when she had deserted him in the first instance. It was my father's belief that my grandmother still cared for him. However, they did not enjoy a reconciliation. When he was here, she kept to her own apartments. She died of a lung infection, and it is a fact that he grieved very deeply on her death and he did not remarry,' he completed drily.

Moisture was clogging Polly's vision. She grimaced over her silliness, but it really was the most miserable story. 'It was all his fault.'

'I knew it would make you sad, but why it should also make you argumentative, I do not know. Must we engage in partisan sympathies with two people who died even before we were born?' He studied her ruefully. 'Doesn't that strike you as a trifle fanciful?'

Embarrassed by her sentimentality, she got up and wandered restively across the room. But she was thinking of Louise, making a stand at Aldeza in what must have been a cry for help and rewarded for her defiance by her husband's cruel resort to another woman.

'For goodness' sake, Polly, they couldn't live together. They were unsuited,' Raschid pronounced with finality.

An edged laugh fell from her, and she whipped round, her luminous eyes embittered. 'Like us? Isn't that how you would describe us? Once he'd tired of her, he didn't give a damn about her feelings, and I bet that every inch of the way he laid down the law on exactly what suited him. And altered his arguments accordingly! Are you telling me that you can't see parallels, Raschid?'

He sent her a driven glance from shimmering blue eyes. 'In the mood that you are in, I will not argue with you.' Icy constraint marked him. 'You are not yourself.'

But she was what his handiwork had made of her. He had forced a need into her very skin that did not neatly vanish at his command. He had roused emotions that even she could not control. And now she was to switch off and meekly accept the status quo, swallowing the face-saving lies he had considerately put within her reach.

He didn't want to take advantage of her; that falsehood had been proven. They had no future because he couldn't give her a child. That was her decision, not his. That he had not even given her that option proved his insincerity. Their marriage had been just a game for Raschid, a cruel sexual game for a highly sexed male. He had used her— he had admitted it. Now he didn't want the messy complications. Damn you! she thought, you're tearing me apart! He was standing there mentally willing her to match his composure and his control called up the devil inside her. Polly was swept by an incensed and bitter urge to smash it.

'You won't argue with me?' With one hand she lifted a vase and slung it across the room, where it shattered noisily against the wall two feet to the left of him. He hadn't moved an inch. Dazed by her wanton destructiveness and the violence which had suddenly forced a passage through her, she licked her lips. 'Now we've got something relevant to argue about...'

Anger and disbelief vibrated from him. Her breath loosed in a sobbing sound. 'I'm sorry,' she muttered.

'Come here,' ordered Raschid.

'No!'

Her judicious refusal seemed to land a second after he reached her. If she had wanted a reaction, she was getting it now. He had her cornered. Stepping sideways, she met with steel-clad fingers braced against the cold wall. 'In all my life,' he gritted, 'no man and no woman has ever raised a hand to me!'

'I wasn't aiming at you!' she protested.

His hands clamped round her wrists. He wasn't listening. 'With the exception of you.'

In one inexorable motion he dragged her against him. His aggressively masculine proximity inflamed her already stirred emotions. Whatever he might have intended to say was forgotten when he stared down at the breathlessly parted invitation of her lips, the unwitting softness of her eyes. Later she didn't know how it happened. One minute he was glowering down at her, the next his mouth was plundering hers with an explosive hunger that demolished her shaky defences.

Rage and wild ecstasy were one in that embrace.

Passionately she yielded to him, melting into boneless acquiescence against his hard male contours. He kissed her until a thunderbeat of crazy excitement had her trembling in his hold, and then he jerked back, thrusting her away from him. Bright sunlight hid his virile figure from her bemused stare. At the far end of the room a servant entered with a tray of refreshments.

'Forgive me,' Raschid ground out in a stifled undertone.

Polly could not forgive him. She hadn't seen the servant, dismissed by a mere motion of his hand; all she had tasted was the raw vehemence of Raschid's repudiation. The drag in the atmosphere was intense. She was drained like a defeated bird who has beaten its wings too long against the bars of a cage. Last night in a fit of emotional insanity she had confessed her deepest and most private feelings, and had set the stage for her own humiliation. To rise above that awareness now in receipt of another rejection was impossible for her. It was over, it had long been over; he had tried to tell her that diplomatically last night. How many times did he have to hurt her before she would accept the truth? You couldn't make someone love you, you couldn't make them care.

'I don't think you really understand how I feel. Perhaps I did not express myself well last night, but you must believe that for a long time I have considered only what was best for you,' he breathed starkly.

Disgusted at this piece of hypocrisy, Polly refused even to look at him. 'Will you get someone to show me to my room?' she said coldly.

He uttered her name as though it was torn from him. Only when the dead silence had ticked painfully on did he fulfil her request. He didn't argue her retreat—he had to be relieved by it. Tact and exquisite manners were not enough to drain the discomfort from dealing with a wife who did not want to let go and who had the most embarrassing habit of opening her mouth to say exactly what she thought.

Half an hour later she lay in the barbaric splendour of a sunken tiled bath, an escape from the excessive attention of several twittering female servants. This was an old-style harem, accessible by a single corridor and sealed behind grilled windows, *mesharabiyah* screens and an iron-barred gate. An unearthly silence had reigned through the intersecting and richly ornate rooms. They had crossed an echoing expanse, an eerie green marble grotto of still water and shadowy archways. Thinking of Louise sentenced to solitary exclusion here from the outside world made Polly shudder. At least she would be going home eventually, she thought in miserable self-consolation.

She dismissed the servants hovering in the bedroom. The bed was enthroned on three shallow marble steps and on it rested an ensemble that would not have shamed a Twenties film starlet. Surveying the shimmering silk nightdress and the ridiculously extravagant azure satin wrap with its silly feathered trimmings, Polly squirmed. It had been dug from the bottom of her case and pressed. Just three weeks ago that over-the-top glamour had caught her wistful eye in the window of an exclusive lingerie boutique near her father's hospital, and in a weak moment she had splashed out. For Raschid. Cruel reality had shredded her embarrassing daydreams but, since she didn't know where the rest of her clothes were, she had to put the outfit on.

A meal was brought to her while she rested on a tasselled ottoman. By then she had examined her surroundings. She was in Louise's rooms, falsely occupying apartments that Ismeni appeared to have conserved to the best of her ability. Faded sepia photographs adorned the elegant writing desk. A tiny bud vase there contained the rose she had given the old lady. An opened drawer had revealed yellowing notepaper, envelopes inscribed with spiky handwriting and tied with ribbon. On the dressing table monogrammed silver brushes awaited a ghostly hand. It was decidedly creepy.

Shortly after nine Ismeni appeared bearing a tiny cup of hot chocolate. With gnarled hands she turned down the bed and lovingly smoothed pillows embroidered with tiny roses. She became agitated when Polly tried to communicate with her. Polly had to steel herself to get into Louise's bed. A shiny crescent moon speared pearly, indeterminate shadows into the room and the quiet folded in. Twenty minutes later Polly rebelliously threw the covers back and got up. Dammit, she didn't have to play up to Ismeni's batty delusions to this extent! The old dear wouldn't know if she sneaked off to find another bed, because frankly the hair was starting to prickle at the back of her neck. The unhappy Louise's spectral presence had got a death-grip on Polly's imagination.

Leaving the room, she almost tripped over the bundle sleeping across her doorway wrapped in a rug. Shoe-button eyes came alive, and Ismeni gave her a toothless grin. Startled into a gasp, Polly was guiltily put in mind of one of Macbeth's witches. Tottering upright, the old lady seemed unsurprised to see her. Bowing low as if a command had been issued, she started down the dark corridor in the most peculiar stealthy fashion without putting on a single light.

After a moment's hesitation Polly followed. Traversing the grotto room, Ismeni disappeared into the shadows where she opened a door, motioning Polly to precede her. Glimpsing a narrow, curving staircase, her curiosity fairly caught by now, Polly went ahead—then flinched when the heavy door thudded shut behind her, sealing her into Stygian gloom. In vain she struggled to open it from the inside. Incredibly, there was no handle.

'Ismeni!' she yelled frantically.

There was no answer. Unable to see an inch ahead in the musty darkness, she had to feel her passage clumsily up the climbing wall. There were thirty-two precariously narrow steps. At the top her palms met solid wood. In claustrophobic panic she pushed with all her might, and the panel swung out with a noisy creak. Her own momentum catapulted her forward into the dark room, and she stubbed her bare toes painfully on something and went down with a crash and a very unladylike epithet to clutch her throbbing foot in inexpressible agony.

Sudden light illuminated the scene. Aghast, she stared at Raschid, who had leapt out of a chair by the window. If Polly was astonished to see him, he was equally astonished to see her. His hand dropped back from the tall Persian lamp. He stood there poised, his shirt hanging unbuttoned and loose from the jeans sleekly outlining his long, straight legs, his brown feet bare.

Recognising Ismeni's gruesome mistake with scarlet-cheeked chagrin, Polly mumbled, 'I must have taken a wrong turning somewhere.'

Raschid was strangely unresponsive. His brilliant blue eyes fanned over the opulence of her attire. His lashes fanned down. He seemed to breathe in very, very slowly before he unfroze and strode over to crouch down beside her. 'My apologies. You…er…startled me. Your foot… nothing is broken?'

Above her averted head an anguished twitch threatened his steel-set mouth.

'I'm sorry if I disturbed you,' muttered Polly.

Absently he plucked a cobweb from her feathers. 'I was not in bed. I went for a ride and…came back.' His voice fractured and slurred as she released her grip on her foot and the over-large wrap lurched off one pale shoulder to reveal the utter transparency of the whisper-thin garment underneath. 'You came to me…and it went wrong,' he murmured with husky suddenness. 'I know how this feels.

You must not be embarrassed. It was very sweet, and I am very touched.'

On the brink of glacially disabusing him of the notion that, not content to trail him home to Dharein, she had decided to lay siege to him in his bedroom as well, Polly looked up, connecting with the electrifying intensity of his eyes. Her heartbeat accelerated as if he had turned an ignition key. His forefinger unsteadily skimmed an untidy strand of silver back behind her ear.

'And also it is very exciting,' he muttered thickly.

Her brain was in limbo. That straying hand was gliding a tantalising path down over the column of her extended throat and she wanted to move into the warmth of that hand. The potent male scent of him intoxicated her. 'Ex…citing?' she echoed.

'An invitation from one so shy.' Lean fingers banded round her slender forearms to tug her relentlessly closer. 'Your generosity shames me. My pride would have kept me from you, but now that you are here…'

'Yes?' she croaked.

'I cannot refuse you when night after night I have ached for you.' His voice was uneven, sibilant. 'And to what avail? I cannot deny you. *Insh'allah.*'

The tip of his tongue traced the sensitive curve of her lower lip, and she shivered violently. *Insh'allah.* If the Lord wills it, so it will be. *Insh'allah.* This happens because it is already written. Raschid captured her hands, guiding them down over warm, bronzed flesh, roughened by a crisp haze of dark hair. Beneath her tentative caress he shuddered, venting a shaken groan of satisfaction. He threw back his head, his darkened eyes fiercely searching. 'Is this what you really want?'

A torture chamber would not have extracted the admission that she had not arrived under her own steam. 'You've…er…changed your mind?'

Her nervous question elicited a rueful laugh. He pulled her to him, sealing her soft curves hungrily to his male heat. 'Polly, I have never been in doubt of what I want. I have only doubted what was fairest to you, and never more than when I saw you in another man's arms—a man whom you have always been ready to love, a man whom you might have married had I not come into your life. It did not seem unlikely to me that you should turn to him when I had neglected you, and I wanted to hate you for it,' he breathed roughly into her hair, 'because I did not feel I had the right to tear you from him. But now I find there is little of the martyr in me.'

Slumbrously he studied her as he got up, lithely carrying her with him. Silk sheeting cooled her back, as he laid her down as if she was fashioned of spun glass. All that she grasped from that hail of sudden words was that his jealousy of Chris had been much more deep-rooted than she had ever suspected.

'You are sure?' he repeated.

As she nodded, still a little dazed by what was happening, his tautness evaporated. He smiled, and her pulses went haywire. He bent over her and the thrumming in the air sizzled with pure electricity. 'When you are near or far,' he confessed, 'I burn for you, night and day. No woman has ever had that power over me.'

Sadness entered her briefly. Berah reigned on upon her pedestal, divorced from earthly pleasures. The incandescent chemistry of the bedroom was Polly's only weapon. A few weeks ago she would have scorned it. An inner voice jeered at her present frailty. Was this how she would hold him? With the desire that could make him swerve from cool logic in a moment's temptation? Quote fatalism in smooth excuse for his inconsistency? She wouldn't listen to that voice. He didn't love her, and that wasn't fair, but there were many unfair things in life. This would be enough, she told herself squarely. This time—it would be enough.

His mouth dipped to caress the tempting pink-budded breast invitingly shaped by silk. Her fingers speared deep into his black hair, holding him to her, for she was racked by an intolerable hunger. Almost roughly he found her mouth again, his hands hard on her hips as he raised her to the thrusting evidence of his arousal beneath the tight denim. Passion flared white-hot and uncontrollable and sealed them together. What followed was the most indescribable physical pleasure Polly had ever experienced.

A rapped-out Arabic command awakened her. Peeping sleepily over Raschid's restraining arm, she was just in time to see Ismeni vanish through the same concealed panel she had entered by the night before.

'That woman, she is crazy!' Raschid declared with a distinct lack of charity. 'She actually crept in here to try and waken you up and trail you out of my bed—then she argues with me. Why should I care about my wife being found in my bed? Where else should she be? Why should I hide this?'

Polly blushed fierily. 'I hope you didn't upset her.'

'Upset her? When I told her that you were staying, she smiled smugly at me. So why did she argue?'

Polly was having some very strange ideas about what Raschid's grandparents had got up to in the dead of night when everybody else thought they weren't speaking. It was time for confession. Polly remained mute. Raschid had succumbed to that wildly seductive siren who had shamelessly thrown herself at his head last night. Now was not the time to stand up and be counted as a fraud. Exciting, she savoured blissfully. She would give Ismeni the most enormous bunch of roses. 'She still thinks I'm Louise,' she said.

'Are you seriously suggesting that my grandfather kicked his wife out of bed at dawn like a concubine...'

'How do you know he didn't?'

'By what I know of my grandmother he would not have survived to see the sun come up,' he whipped back drily. 'In any case, they never lived here together.'

'But he visited.'

'They were separated,' he reminded her.

As silence fell, uncertainty reclaimed her. The old lady's early-morning visit had taken the spotlight off their renewed intimacy. Suddenly she was afraid that Raschid might regret the night that had passed.

Veiled eyes tabulated her fluctuating expression. 'There's something I must say...' he began.

'Don't!' she rushed in nervously.

'You cannot inhabit an ivory tower forever.' As his mouth quirked, his thumb gently mocked the protective down-sweep of her lashes. 'I won't talk of our parting again, but that option must always remain open to you.'

In astonishment her eyes flew wide, drowned in the proximity of dense blue. 'You think I need that option?'

A powerful wave of emotion stirred her. In a few words Raschid removed her deepest fear. He settled back against the tumbled pillows and shifted a sinuous shoulder, sudden constraint marking his firm mouth. 'Who can foretell the future? We must be realistic,' he murmured. 'You are very young now, but some day you will want a child. That desire will take you as surely as the dawn follows darkness, and human nature being what it is, what you know you cannot have you will want all the more. But in denying what is between us, I was trying to avoid that dilemma, I was making the decision for you.'

'That wasn't your right,' Polly muttered shakily.

'I don't want you to be foolishly blind, *aziz*.'

She didn't know how to answer him. What he said was

true. It would be some time in the future when she really came to terms with the impossibility of ever bringing her own baby into the world. As she sat up a twinge of nausea irritated her and automatically she lay back again, lost in her serious thoughts. Whatever regrets or pangs might seize her some day, she would keep them to herself. Thanks to Berah she would have to keep them to herself completely. Berah's failure to accept the situation had left Raschid vulnerable, and Raschid, to put it mildly, did not cope very well with the ignominy of vulnerability. He was much more likely to walk away from any relationship which might expose that weak spot. Was that savage pride of his all that had kept him from her? Oh, how much she wanted to believe that, but in her heart she could not believe it. He had had the power to deny her because she did not have the power to inspire the uncritical love and loyalty he had awarded Berah. Why was she upsetting herself like this? She had enough love for both of them, and, aware of his tension, she muttered something trite about crossing that bridge when or if they came to it.

'You know, there's something that I've always been curious about,' she admitted, eager to leave that other subject behind. 'What did you and your father argue about on our wedding day?'

A sudden, unexpected smile banished his serious aspect. 'Is that important now?'

Her bosom swelled with chagrin. 'It was about me, then,' she condemned. 'You were complaining about having to marry me, weren't you?'

He burst out laughing. 'Polly, your imagination is an unfailing source of entertainment! Very well,' he capitulated with veiled eyes, 'I shall tell you what I was told that day. There was never an assassination attempt on my father's life, and the promise made was not made with serious intent.'

'There was never an assassination attempt? But that's impossible!' Polly exclaimed.

'Your father mistook one of the guards for an assassin.' The faintest tremor roughened Raschid's explanation. 'When he dragged my father to the ground, the guard concerned shot at him, believing that he was assaulting mine.'

'But it can't have happened like that,' she argued shakily.

'I am afraid it did. My father was naturally relieved that Ernest sustained only a minor injury. Fearing that a serious diplomatic incident might result from the misunderstanding, my father allowed Ernest to believe that he had saved his life, and he made that pledge in part jest.'

Setting the incongruous truth beside her memory of her father's overweening delight in recounting the story of his one hour of heroic valour, Polly was almost overtaken by an irreverent tide of mirth. 'Dad must never find out the truth,' she whispered tautly.

'When your father requested an interview with mine, he assumed that he was coming to request that the promise be fulfilled, and it was then that he had enquiries made into your background,' Raschid went on. 'Having an undutiful son determined to remain a widower, and being impressed with what he learnt of you, he turned the situation to his advantage.'

'It was very cruel of him to tell you the truth...' Suddenly she went off into gales of laughter, unable to hold it any longer. 'Oh, I wish I'd been there!' she gasped. 'I'd love to have seen your father's face when mine hurled him down on the ground...he must have been absolutely raging!'

'I confess that at the time I was not very amused.' Laughing now himself, Raschid caught her to him, rakish eyes brightly appraising her. 'But now I would concede that he chose you very well.'

He possessed her parted lips in a blindingly hungry kiss,

glancing down at her to murmur mockingly, 'By Allah, I have missed you, but you will not have the advantage of distance again. When next I go abroad, you will come with me. You have become indispensable to my comfort, *aziz*.'

Polly touched the heights of happiness in the following week. Every morning they went out riding, and under Raschid's patient tutelage she lost the nervous unease on horseback which had been instilled in her by her father's neck-or-nothing expectations when she was a child. The third morning they returned to the soft rush of water. The fountains were playing again. Raschid had had the ancient plumbing overhauled to please her.

She was enjoying a kaleidoscopic desert sunset from the vantage point of the terraced gardens one evening when he came to find her. The grey gravel plain surrounding the palace's hilly basalt setting was bathed in illusory gold and scarlet. The bleak, enduring mystery of the wilderness possessed a savage beauty and an endless, fascinating variation of colour, shape and texture that reminded her potently of Raschid.

'You look very pensive,' he commented.

He had had work to do this afternoon. The plane had come in, bringing the mail, and then for some reason it had come back again later. When Polly had walked outside, Raschid had accompanied her on a walk through the gardens. She suspected that he was afraid she had felt neglected, left to her own designs for a few hours. Now here he was again.

Gracefully she arose from the stone seat. 'I was just relaxing,' she said.

'Or were you thinking that it is Christmas Eve and you are far from home? No snow, no holly, no roaring log fires, no stocking,' he teased, rather unfeelingly, she felt, for she was hopelessly sentimental about Christmas.

'I'm a little old for a stocking,' she muttered repressively.

'I suppose you are.' Raschid flashed her a slow smile. 'I almost forgot—we have visitors.'

'Visitors?' Polly exclaimed in dismay.

He gripped her hand when she would have parted from him in the hall. 'You will do very nicely as you are.'

As he guided her determinedly into the salon, she faltered in her steps several feet into the room. Her dazed scrutiny climbed the height of an eight-foot pine tree shimmering with starry lights and glittering baubles. The carpet beneath was heaped with gaily wrapped parcels. Somewhere in the background the strains of 'Deck the Halls,' erupted loudly.

Strong arms encircled her from behind. 'Have I only made you homesick? I would have invited your family, but your father is not fit enough to travel yet.'

Her eyes filled and she swallowed thickly. 'You did this for me?'

Raschid turned her round. 'It is a small thing if it makes you happy.'

The pleasure of having overwhelmed her showed in his eyes alone. His head descended in slow motion and she stretched up instinctively for his lips to encircle hers, something vague about visitors receding into her subconscious as wildfire raced through her veins. He lifted his head, still holding her close. 'I love you,' he whispered half under his breath.

She didn't look up. She didn't believe him. She wished he had kept quiet, although it was herself that she ought to blame. By thoughtlessly hurling her love at him, she had made him uncomfortable, she had made him feel that he had to respond. And with such conviction he did it too, she reflected, torn between pain and amusement. He dropped it in a constrained, unsophisticated aside. He didn't lie very well.

Somebody coughed noisily. Raschid jerked back from her.

'Would you like us to go out and come in again?' Asif grinned from the doorway with Chassa by his side. 'Then again, I'm not that easily shocked.'

Chassa smiled at Polly's astonishment. 'I hope that you don't mind that we've invited ourselves to Christmas lunch?'

'How could she? We brought it with us, along with a Swiss chef. Airsick, by the way. Just as well he has got until tomorrow to get his act together,' Asif laughed. 'Chassa dressed the tree. Have you any idea how much trouble it was to transport that tree out here?'

Warmly embracing Polly, Chassa whispered, 'Don't listen to him. Raschid arranged it all, and we have had a lot of fun helping him to surprise you.'

It was a wonderful evening. Delighted by the efforts Raschid had made on her behalf, Polly felt her pleasure was increased by the awareness that she really was accepted as a part of his family. Chassa bubbled with an effervescence which Polly would never have associated with her a brief five weeks ago. She was a different woman, while Asif, once he had finished showing off, seemed curiously quieter. But whatever had strained their marriage had clearly been dealt with and set behind them. Chassa glowed with the confidence of a woman who knew she was loved.

When the other couple left them alone at midnight Polly could no longer resist the heaps of presents. Raschid had even arranged for her family's gifts to be collected in London and flown out. By one o'clock she was in a welter of torn wrapping paper under his indulgent eye, dazed by the extravagance of all that he had bought her and hard put to it to understand how he had contrived to do so with only a telephone at his disposal.

'All I've got for you is an anthology of poetry, and it's not even wrapped,' she confided shakily. 'I wasn't sure if I was even going to give it to you. I thought you might think I was being silly.'

Laughing, he gathered her up in his arms. 'You are my Christmas present, but if you are about to start crying again I shall leave you under the tree!'

'I'm so happy,' she sniffed, and it hit her then, a piercing, frightening arrow of foreboding as if she was offending some jealous fate by daring to be so happy. 'I don't think I ever want to leave here.'

The stark fear in her eyes had covertly engaged his attention, to etch a faint frown line between his brows. 'What is really wrong, Polly?' he asked.

'Wrong?' she gulped, staving off that horrible feeling that had briefly attacked her and knowing that she was being ridiculous to pay heed to it. Tensely she laughed. 'I was just trying to work out where I'll ever wear all that jewellery!'

'There is a State banquet next month and there is Paris next week,' Raschid murmured into her hair. 'But that was not really what was worrying you, was it?'

Cursing his perception, she buried her face in his shoulder. 'I can't help wondering how Dad will bear up to a festive season without parties,' she lied. 'I hope he'll be sensible.'

'I'm sure he will be. We'll find time to visit again soon,' he promised, his tone ever so slightly cool. But Polly didn't notice. She was thinking what a silly fool she would be to let insecurity plague her, and she looked up at him with a bright smile.

CHAPTER TEN

IT WAS the day after Boxing Day when Polly bounced ex-
uberantly out of bed to go riding and instead keeled over
in a dead faint at Raschid's feet. Bedlam had broken out
when she resurfaced. Zenobia, who had been flown out with
the clothes Polly had required several days earlier, was
down on her knees weeping. Raschid was biting out harsh
comments to some unfortunate out of view and from the
corridor outside came the babble of excitable voices, sig-
nifying the gathering of the servants scenting a drama.

'Lie still.' Before she could sit up to sheepishly announce
her recovery, Raschid was pressing a restraining hand to
her shoulder. 'You are not to move until the doctor arrives.'

'Where are you going to get a doctor from?'

He sighed. 'I had already arranged for Mr Soames to see
Ismeni this morning. Now he will see you as well.'

'But we're supposed to be leaving today,' Polly argued.
'And I don't need a doctor.'

'Have you no respect for your health?' he demanded. 'Be
grateful that I have!'

Expelling his breath, he sat down beside her. 'You scared
the heart from my body. Repetition had not accustomed me
to this habit of yours,' he said, attempting a taut smile. 'But
don't worry. I am sure it is nothing serious.'

His restless pacing over the next few hours told her his
imagination was roaming at large over a list of killer dis-
eases. But it didn't occur to Polly that she had anything to
worry about. Feeling vaguely out of sorts once or twice
was surely excusable with all that had been happening in
recent weeks? She didn't like to say that to Raschid in case

he felt that she was blaming him for it. Perhaps she had let herself get overtired, something like that.

When the doctor arrived, Raschid announced that he would stay. Polly objected and, emanating disapproval and reproach, he left them. Mr Soames was familiar and cheerful, but he threw her completely with his third question. When had she last been bedevilled by that particular female curse? It seemed shrouded in the mists of time. Raschid had been in New York...but that had been months ago. It couldn't have been that long, it simply couldn't have been...

Mr Soames cleared his throat. 'Haven't you suspected the cause for yourself, Your Highness? You're pregnant.' Taking her pulse, his examination complete, he missed the arrested paralysis of her face. 'I would say ten to twelve weeks, and...'

'I can't be...I can't be pregnant! It's just not possible!' Her interruption was a strangled squeak.

His beetling brows rose in concert. 'There's no room for doubt, Your Highness. Your condition is too well advanced.'

The intermittent nausea which had bothered her and then vanished came to mind...her disappearing waist. She gulped, welded visually to the older man's cool professional confidence. 'Honestly? I mean...I really am?'

The poor man probably wondered if she required a long-overdue chat about the birds and the bees. He had no idea why his announcement should reduce her to dazed incoherency. She drifted out of the rigidity of deep shock on to a euphoric plane and nodded like a vacant marionette while Mr Soames gave forth about sensible diet and regular rest and the excellence of Chassa's obstetrician. She didn't hear a word. Under the sheet her hands slunk covertly over her stomach. The hows, whys and wherefores could not preoccupy her. Somebody had made a mistake. Or whatever had been amiss had miraculously come right. Polly was in no mood to question a miracle.

A baby. She felt ten feet tall. His baby! Exultancy claimed her. She was flooded by the dizzy joy of what this news would mean to Raschid. Then a shadow briefly fell over her rapturous, sun-filled outlook. Would he mind that it was her and not Berah? No, of course he wouldn't mind. He would be simply floored by the shatteringly wonderful discovery that he was about to become a father. She couldn't wait, she just couldn't wait to tell him and see his reaction.

Having abandoned all hope of receiving an intelligible sentence from his patient, the doctor opened the door to usher in Raschid. He beamed benevolently. 'Nothing to worry about. The most natural thing in the world, and she's in excellent health. Your wife is expecting a baby.'

Overhearing the announcement, Polly was shot from her blissful anticipation. She sat up, agonisingly disappointed by the man's thoughtlessness. Raschid's back was turned to her. It must have taken him thirty seconds to speak, and she didn't catch his response, for he was showing the doctor out again. Impatiently, expectantly she awaited his return. He'd be in shock—naturally he would be.

Raschid shut the door almost clumsily behind him. He lodged by the window, his dark head slightly averted. Too overcome to look at her? Then suddenly he moved. He smashed a clenched fist with punishing force against the carved window frame. Something cracked. If her life had depended on it, Polly couldn't have produced a vocal sound.

'When were you going to tell me?' He faced her now, ashen in complexion, every harsh lineament of his bronzed features rawly defined. Silver eyes beat into hers, metallic arrows dipped in the poison of violent repulsion. 'How do you look at me still? Have you no shame?'

'Sh-shame?' she echoed.

'You think perhaps that I am so stupid that I might believe that it could be mine? Or did you think I would be so desperate to believe that I would credit that the impossible could be possible?' He could hardly get his tongue round her language, but every cruelly destructive word hit its deadly target. 'Then I grant you reason to doubt my intelligence. Though you have never told me the whole truth about him, I believed you when you said he hadn't touched you, and now…to be presented…with the proof of your…' His English failed him altogether as he struggled for mastery of himself.

Polly had turned to stone. Her backbone was ice, her eyes blank as an accident victim's. Blood dripped from his bruised hand; he could have bled all over the carpet and she could have watched in numb inaction. Something indescribably breakable had snapped inside her. Something indefinably precious had been wrenched from her. The loss of faith, hope and charity was the least of the damage.

'It's your baby.' She hated him for forcing her to make that demeaning contradiction. By the simple expedient of mentioning just how pregnant she was, she could have vindicated herself. But a freezing cold and alien anger was hollowly filling her. Would Raschid have done this to Berah? Would he have doubted her fidelity? Would he have flatly and finally pronounced that he could not be the father of her child? All the bitter resentment that Berah's unassailable position in his heart had ever aroused in her had a stranglehold on her now when her wondrous gift was repudiated with sordid and unforgivable condemnation. He was hanging himself, and a twisted, unfamiliar part of her earned an embittered satisfaction from a ringside seat on the execution.

He was breathing fast and shallowly. 'I am neither desperate nor stupid. Sterility is irreversible.' He turned away from her. He was shaking, and then he turned back. 'Comfort!' he thundered at her, his eyes razors on her pinched profile. 'Now I know what you feared—the consequences of your treachery. Is this why you came to my bed willingly here? Did you already suspect your condition? I see this all now…in its foul clarity!'

The depth of calculation he laid at her door stunned her. He didn't want to believe because he didn't want her baby any more than he had ever really wanted her. Had he cared for her at all, he would have wanted to believe no matter how hard it was to believe. Tremulously holding on to her composure, she whispered, 'I don't think that we can have anything left to say to each other. I'll be on the first flight home.'

'Home?' The savage impact of his repetition struck her like a blow from a mailed fist. 'You will never see him again, you will never go home!' He swore that like a blood oath in the hot stillness of a seething silence. 'Until I have decided how to deal with you, you will stay here.'

Polly wouldn't defend herself. Exoneration was within her reach at the mere recall of the doctor, but she wouldn't do that unless she was forced to it. The longer Raschid harboured his filthy suspicions, the harder he would fall when the truth came out, as inevitably it must. But it would be too late then for him to develop an interest in fatherhood. Nothing would change the way she felt now. This was her baby, and by hook or by crook, she would take it home to England with her. Raschid could do whatever he liked. She was finished with him. Furthermore, getting upset wasn't good for her now. She had her baby to consider. Impervious to his unbelieving stare, Polly carefully settled herself back against the pillows and rearranged the covers, ignoring his lowering, dark presence.

When he swept out, she stared into space for a long time. Then she rolled over and the hot tears coursed down her cheeks. If there was a prize for consistent stupidity, it ought to be hers. Raschid had been determined to give their marriage a front of contented respectability. He had found the magic formula by making a fuss of her for a few days. How easily she had been deceived! How amused he must have been by the speed of her surrender! The bitterness infusing her was venomous and vengeful. It was like no feeling she had ever experienced before. It was implacable.

Stifling her tears, she refused to recognise the enormous pain bottled up behind her anger. Stonily she listened to the dulled whine of the plane taking off, relieved at least that Chassa and Asif had left the day before. Now she was on her own. Suddenly she sat up again as it dawned on her that Raschid had to be sharing the flight with Mr Soames, who was as likely to refer to the baby as Raschid was unlikely to show his emotions. She smiled a not very pleasant smile. There was a strong possibility that Raschid might be back before nightfall.

But nobody came. It was the next day when she learnt that Ismeni had passed peacefully away in her sleep the night before the doctor arrived. Polly learnt quite accidentally. She had been using Raschid's room, and when she went down into the harem she walked into a hive of activity. A crate was being packed with Louise's surviving possessions. Polly's shocked response to a death which surprised no one else made Zenobia anxious.

'This lady, she was very, very old and not well in the head,' the little maid murmured uncomfortably. 'The doctor said it was her heart.'

The desktop was piled high with a mound of yellowing envelopes. As a hand moved to them, Polly gasped, 'Leave them. I'll deal with those.'

Heaping them in a box, she left the servants to their work. Upset by the news of the old lady's death, Polly could not bear to stand by and watch them dismantle Ismeni's shrine to her beloved mistress. But no doubt the servants, long hampered by Ismeni's authority, were keen to springclean a majestic suite of rooms which had probably lain unused until Polly's arrival. Since the palace had enjoyed only occasional use as a hunting lodge, there couldn't have been many important female guests here over the years.

Raschid had laughed when she told him about the untouched room, and he had laughed even harder when she confessed her foolish fancies. She had had no fear of ghosts while she slept in his arms. You weren't happy here, Louise, and I am, she had thought. Had the djinns that whispered out in the lonely places of the desert overheard her vainglorious boast? Just like Louise, she was discovering the dangerous folly of loving unwisely. And just like Louise she had been left at the Palace of the Fountains in splendid isolation.

Upstairs in the salon she flicked through the letters she had saved from the wastepaper basket. Indecipherable Arabic penned by the same hand covered every envelope, and there were dozens of them. Polly replaced them neatly in the box. Someone in the family ought to examine them in case there was something of importance in them. As she set the box aside the hum of a helicopter coming in to land disturbed the quiet. Expecting Raschid and having coolly kept away from the windows, Polly was sharply disconcerted when Asif was ushered into the salon.

'Are you your brother's messenger?' she demanded glacially.

Asif looked at her momentarily as if she had lost her wits. 'Raschid does not know I am here. He wouldn't thank me for interfering like this, and I hope that we can keep this visit of mine between ourselves,' he breathed tautly.

Polly frowned. 'I can't think of a single reason why you should have come to see me.'

He took a deep breath and then dug out a cigarette. Lighting it, he inhaled slowly. 'Look—it was I who was having the affair with Francine, not Raschid,' he said abruptly. 'You know what I am talking about, you don't need to pretend. Jezra told you about her. It is the only thing that I could think of which could have caused this trouble between you and Raschid.'

Dealt the unexpected and, what was more, the most embarrassing of the unexpected, Polly felt her passage slowly down into a seat, her stunned eyes pinned to his flushed face. 'You were having an affair?'

'It is over now. You have no need to look at me like

that,' Asif muttered defensively. 'When Raschid returned without you, he looked even worse than he looked when Berah died. If he has been stupidly honourable and chosen to be secretive for the sake of my marriage, then I must speak up.'

She swallowed, wondering how to tell him that he was barking up the wrong tree. 'Asif, I really…'

He straightened his shoulders. 'You must believe me, Polly. At least let me explain. She was a secretary in our Paris Embassy. I was infatuated with her. I moved her into an apartment, using Raschid's name without his knowledge,' he admitted heavily. 'When rumours reached my father's ears, Raschid was forced to cover up for me.'

'You have a fine, upstandingly moral brother!' she interposed in disgust.

Taken aback, he stared at her. 'It wasn't like that. He did it to protect Chassa. He did it to stop me doing something foolish and breaking up my marriage.' His gaze flickered from hers as his voice dropped in volume. 'And he did it because I fear our father's anger. He is very fond of Chassa, considerably less fond of me. He also expects all of us to maintain strict standards and guard against scandal. I had been in trouble before, and my father is not a forgiving man. For a long time I have been working with Raschid to persuade him that Chassa and I need not live here all the time. If he had learnt it was I who was involved with Francine, all hope of that freedom would have been gone for good.'

'I understand.' Polly's shocked anger on Chassa's behalf was softened by a brief spasm of pity for Asif. He had abandoned his dignity in his mistaken belief that this woman Francine was at the bottom of her separation from Raschid. He had no idea of what was really wrong, and she had no intention of telling him.

'And you believe me?' he pressed impatiently.

Hurriedly she nodded. 'Yes, I believe you.'

'I have trusted you with a confidence that could destroy

my marriage,' he breathed. 'Chassa doesn't know about Francine and she must never know about her. I love my wife, Polly. I have come to my senses, and I will not risk losing her again. I am asking you to keep this a secret.'

Now that Polly had the entire story, she was quite convinced that Asif's request was unnecessary, for she suspected that Chassa had known all along that there was another woman in her husband's life. Chassa had also assumed that Polly would be in Raschid's confidence. Ironically, Polly was grateful that she had not been. The awareness of Asif's infidelity would not have relaxed her in Chassa's company. She forced a soothing smile. 'Naturally you can rely on my…discretion.'

'I knew you would be an understanding woman.' His fear allayed, he smiled brilliantly at her. 'With a sensibly short memory. If you have falsely accused Raschid, you had better make the first move.'

'Indeed?' she murmured expressionlessly.

His wandering attention had fallen on the box of correspondence resting on a small drum table. He lifted one of the envelopes and without hesitation extracted the notepaper within while saying, 'Be generous, else you will wait forever. You could get blood out of a stone quicker than you could get my brother to an apology, and after all, he has made a lot of firsts for you…'

'What?'

Fixedly studying the letter in his hand, he glanced up absently and then grinned. 'Furniture warehouses, flowers, meals in hotels, the swimming pool. Do you think my brother makes a habit of these things? He's about as modern as my father, but recently he's been behaving out of character. You've led him quite a dance, Polly,' he said cheerfully. 'I've never enjoyed anything quite so much as I have enjoyed watching Raschid having to pursue a woman for the first time in his life, and he's basically rather shy…'

Polly reeled. 'Sh-shy? Raschid?'

Asif was back with the evidently fascinating letter. 'Deep down. Of course, the military education and my father soon put paid to that, but he's anything but a womaniser. Never had the opportunity until that demented woman died, and after eight years of her, I expect he had gone off the notion...boy, is this hot stuff! Whoever would have thought it?' he muttered, heading on to a second letter with appetite. 'Where did they come from?'

'Your grandmother's desk.' Polly wasn't interested in the letters. 'What did you mean by demented?'

'I really shouldn't be reading these,' Asif commented. 'But I know what I'll be doing on the flight back. Wait until my father sees them! It's the dates when they were written that have the shock value.' He was tugging out more letters to examine them.

In frustration Polly said, 'Will you forget those stupid letters for a minute? What did you mean by demented?'

He stared at her. 'Do you know what these letters are? They're love letters written by my grandfather, and he was obviously getting replies. I always understood that my grandparents separated long before she died, but they must have made it up, even though she stayed here.' Finally appreciating that he did not have her full attention, he frowned. 'What do *you* mean by what do I mean by demented? Didn't you know that she ended up in one of those clinics for the mentally disturbed?'

She had turned pale. 'No, I had no idea she was really ill.'

'Raschid didn't tell you? It's not the sort of thing anybody wants to talk about, I guess,' he conceded dubiously. 'Berah was diagnosed as a manic depressive a couple of years before she died. Raschid went through hell with her.'

Polly's surprise was unhidden.

'If I'm not very charitable about her, it's because she threw herself down those bloody stairs in front of Raschid, and I know what that did to him, and I lived with what that did to Chassa,' Asif murmured roughly.

Polly looked at him strickenly. 'She committed suicide?'

'It wasn't anybody's fault, least of all Raschid's. She was supposed to be in the clinic. It was her father who took her out of it. Achmed would never accept that she was really ill, and when he realised that my father was trying to persuade Raschid to divorce her...well, obviously he didn't want that,' he said. 'He went off to Switzerland, decided off his own bat that she was normal and brought her home so that she would be there when Raschid returned from New York. What he didn't know was that Chassa was pregnant. Berah heard the servants gossiping and she'd been off her medication for twenty-four hours. Raschid was always her audience. She died in his arms.'

Polly felt sick. Ashamed of every carping thought she had ever had about Berah in her ignorance, she whispered tearfully, 'He didn't tell me.'

Asif sighed. 'Don't blame him for that, Polly. Nobody wants to remember a nightmare. He would never have divorced her. She was as obsessed by him as she was about kids. When she died, Raschid blamed himself, although he had done everything possible to help her.'

She sucked in air chokily. 'He blamed himself because he couldn't give her a child.'

Asif shifted uncomfortably. 'I don't believe a child would have made any difference. That instability must have been in Berah. It would have come out in some other way even if there had been children. I hope that Raschid accepts that now. He suffered enough with her when she was alive.'

Polly was fumbling for a handkerchief. Shorn of the smug sense of martyred piety which had buoyed her up from Raschid's departure, she wanted to put her head down and cry.

'I ought to be going.' Uneasily Asif lifted the box and she pulled herself together long enough to see him out to the plane.

How could she have believed that Raschid was not suffering too? Only now would she let herself acknowledge the agonised pain he had struggled blindly to contain in front of her. She could have turned that whole confrontation round, but she hadn't. Hatred could lie a hair's breadth from love, and she had hated him for his lack of faith. She had wanted him to suffer. She had wanted to punish him for not loving her as he had loved Berah.

He had cause to condemn her for consistently avoiding telling him the whole truth about Chris. Raschid wasn't stupid; he had suspected that there was more. She had fostered a fertile breeding ground for his suspicions to leap back to the fore. She should never have let him leave her believing those terrible things; two wrongs did not make a right.

It was early the next day when she heard the plane. Instinctively she knew that Raschid was on it. She was still in bed and she jumped up, calling for Zenobia and instructing her to say that she would be upstairs in fifteen minutes. But Raschid didn't wait. Polly was brushing her tangled hair when he appeared. He halted six feet from her, and she looked even though she didn't want to look. Senses parched of his vibrancy overwhelmed her poise, sapped her control as she set down the brush and took a seat on the ottoman behind her.

A little pale, very tense, his left hand bandaged, he was informally clad in black jeans and as physically arresting as a panther rather sheepishly at bay. Incandescent eyes travelled over her with aching slowness and she needed no words to tell her that her explanation, her proof was not required. That look was extraordinarily expressive. If only he had given it to her two days ago! she thought with helpless bitterness.

'I expect you found out while you were gathering your evidence for a court case. You would have needed a doctor's report,' Polly attacked.

Raschid had changed colour at her taunting words. He moved. 'Polly, I...'

'Don't you dare come near me!' she said fiercely.

Shorn of his usual sweeping aplomb, he hovered, and she bent her head, determined not to be swayed by the sight of him. She could not compete with Berah's shadow. She could not be second best. The intensity of her own feelings for him demanded more, and after all she had gone through, being accepted simply because she could give him the child he had thought he could never have, wasn't enough. 'You can skip the apologies, the heartfelt regrets and the smoothie persuasions,' she whispered painfully. 'You can have access, but I really don't think we could ever live together again.'

He shifted. 'Try to imagine how I felt.'

'Stay where you are!' Polly snapped shakily. 'I'm being sensible, and I'm never sensible when you get close.'

He drew his hand from behind his back and laid a single white rose on the carpet along with a small pink furry teddy bear. 'I am at your feet with them,' he muttered hoarsely.

Polly surveyed the offerings in horror. Her throat closed over. She had underestimated the depths to which he would sink in a tight corner. Her hand flew up to her convulsing mouth. Her eyes watered accusingly. 'I am not touched,' she spluttered. 'Do you hear me?'

He took immediate advantage of her emotional disarray by striding forward to match the declaration he had made with the action. His arms enclosed her tightly and he buried his head in her lap. 'Forgive me,' he implored gruffly. 'If I could not believe in a miracle, it is because I have never experienced one before. I would give all that I had to steal those accusations I made from your memory, but I cannot. I can only ask you to try to understand that for ten years I believed that I could not father a child. I never doubted it, and I never forgot this fact. It haunted me with Berah, and it haunted me even more after her death.'

Black silky hair, dark as a raven's wing, was brushing her clenched hands. She ached to touch him, to hold him. It was a craving that stormed through her every defence. The harsh sincerity of his plea was more than she could withstand. Her hand crept up on to his taut shoulder as she whispered, 'You hurt me so much. I was so happy, and then all of a sudden it was like a bad dream.'

Raschid looked up at her with anguished azure eyes. 'It should have been beautiful, and I spoilt it—but ten years, Polly,' he repeated, 'it is a long time. When he said you were pregnant it almost destroyed me.'

'Your first thought was that I…'

'My first thought was that I had driven you into his arms,' he interrupted, roughly insistent. 'I was so shocked that I could see no other explanation.'

Polly reddened. 'It wasn't all your fault,' she said rue-fully. 'When I married you I did think I was in love with Chris, and when I realised that I wasn't, I just wanted to forget about it. I'd made myself so miserable for so long…well, it left me feeling rather stupid.'

He buried his mouth heatedly in the centre of one of her palms. 'I had seen the bond of affection between you at the wedding,' he breathed, lifting his head. 'I did not suspect you then. He was flirting with you, but you were not flirting with him. It must seem very arrogant of me, but I did not really believe that you might love him until I saw you with him at your home. Then I wanted to rip him asunder… slowly.'

Polly gulped. 'It was just one of those things. He didn't mean to kiss…'

'We have talked enough about him,' Raschid interrupted with a subdued flash in his clear gaze. 'He is unimportant. It is Berah we must talk about. It was only when I was on the plane that it occurred to me that she could have lied.'

'Lied?' she echoed.

He gave a harsh laugh. 'Yes—lied. At first it was hard for me to accept that she could have done that. Two years into our marriage she had shown very few signs of her illness. I had no reason to suspect that she could practice such an appalling deception, but I should have suspected later. I should have, but by then I had other problems with which to concern myself. I have never been honest with you about Berah. I always felt the need until now to defend her memory from criticism.'

'I can understand that. Asif explained…'

As Polly compressed her lips in dismay over the admission, Raschid sighed. 'It is all right—I know he was here. Having given my father those letters last night, he could not hide where he had been, and he told me exactly what he had told you. It was not all true. Asif likes to exaggerate.'

He released her hand and stood upright. 'Berah did not commit suicide. She fell, Polly. She was extremely distressed, crying, hysterical. It was an accident. I am not denying that she had suicidal impulses, but if she had wanted to die, she would not have chosen such a method. She fell,' he said again. 'But that did not make me feel that I had failed her any less. When I left you here, I flew to London.'

She frowned. 'Why?'

'To see the specialist whom she had seen,' he explained, a muscle jerking tight at the corner of his mouth. 'It was not to check up on whether or not you could be telling me the truth. I had to know. I had to know for my own peace of mind whether or not Berah had lied or somehow misunderstood, and when I spoke with that man, the irrational guilt of years left me.'

'It must have been very upsetting for you to discover that she could have done that to you,' Polly remarked brittly.

Bleakly Raschid looked back at her. 'No, it was the most wonderful thing I had ever heard in my life. It set me free of my conscience.' He moved a broad shoulder jerkily. 'You see, I never loved her. I cared for her, she was my wife, but I was never able to love her as she loved me. She would never meet me as an equal. She would not mix with other people, and she took a dislike to every member of my family. Although she was quiet with me, she was vicious with the servants. Of course she was not well, but I did not know that when we were first married. The time when I might have learned to love her went past.'

Pale with a mixture of guilt and regret, he watched her anxiously, and she knew that he had never admitted those feelings to another living soul. 'Shortly after she informed me that I was sterile,' he continued in a clipped undertone, 'it became clear that she no longer wished to share my bed. I needed her desperately then. It wasn't until I understood that she was ill that I could forgive her for that.'

So much that she had never understood was now painfully obvious to Polly. Instinctively she stood up and crossed over to him, wrapping her arms round him tightly, thinking how ironic it was that she should want to cry for Berah. Berah had lied to Raschid because she didn't want to lose him. 'She is at peace now,' she muttered against his shirt-front, drowning in the evocative heat and scent of him, the petty bite of her consuming jealousy finally laid to rest.

'But I am not at peace, *aziz*. I cannot live without you by my side,' Raschid confessed harshly. A fear and an aching loneliness that put talon claws into her heart was in his eyes as he looked down at her. 'I love you,' he said fiercely.

'Yes,' Polly mumbled shakily, seeing that so very clearly now.

'How could you have doubted it?' he groaned, enfolding her slender body to the muscular hardness of his taut length. 'I fell in love with you when you had the flu—that is not very romantic, is it? But I couldn't stay away from you, I couldn't pass the door. Just to hear the sound of your voice, to see you. I couldn't help myself. But I didn't know I was in love until I saw you with the children. Then I knew, and I fought it. How could I ask you to spend the rest of your life with me?'

She smiled tremulously. 'You can ask me.'

His dark head bent. 'I am not asking you now, I am telling you that I will never let you leave me.' Lifting her up against him, he found her mouth hungrily, and it was a long time before either of them was in the mood for conversation again.

Sleepily Polly asked about the letters Asif had carried off.

'No doubt we will hear all about them when we go back, but it seems that Louise did forgive my grandfather in the end. However, she wouldn't return to live with the rest of the family. Salim was a very proud man. He did not even want his son to realise that he had accepted her terms,' Raschid clarified, viewing her lazily with unreserved adoration. 'I think it pleased my father greatly, for he was full of it last night when I went to speak with him, but he did not get to tell me very much, for I had more important news.'

'Like what?' Polly enquired.

He grinned. 'That I am to be a father in August. I could not keep it to myself!' His smile dimmed at her sudden tension. 'It just came out, Polly. I wanted to tell everybody.'

'Well, you might have got the month right. It's more likely to be June,' she told him, but she smiled at the awareness that he had accepted the truth without the knowledge of when she had conceived.

'So soon?' he exclaimed.

Polly looked forgivably smug at his astonishment. The baby had been the eighth wonder of the world even before this; it had now added the ninth to its tally. 'And you can go and change that teddy for a blue one,' she tossed in for good measure. 'I'm convinced that I'll have a boy.'

'I don't care,' Raschid confided with a reverent hand resting on the slight curve of her stomach. 'A baby is a baby. A child—our child.'

'What did your father say?' she asked worriedly.

'Initially little. He was overjoyed into unusual silence until I explained about Berah, and then he called me all kinds of a fool for accepting her word without question. I have no doubts that the whole palace knows by now—he was shouting at the top of his voice!'

Polly relaxed until another concern gripped her. 'I suppose it won't be good news for Asif and Chassa.'

He smoothed her furrowed brow with gentle fingertips, that heart-stopping smile of his strongly in evidence. 'Asif was there, and he is jubilant. My father will no longer insist that Chassa and the children must live in Dharein. They will probably move to London or New York. It is what they have always wanted.'

Her last worry banished, she gave a euphoric little sigh. 'I suppose I ought to admit that Ismeni took me to that staircase and I didn't know where I was going.'

'I had already worked that out for myself.' Bright blue eyes skimmed her blushing face mockingly. 'And after lunch you can put on that glorious outfit again and play the scene afresh. The perfect penance, don't you think?'

Helen Bianchin was born in New Zealand and travelled to Australia before marrying her Italian-born husband. After three years they moved, returned to New Zealand with their daughter, had two sons then re-settled in Australia. Encouraged by friends to recount anecdotes of her years as a tobacco sharefarmer's wife living in an Italian community, Helen began setting words on paper and her first novel was published by Mills & Boon® in 1975. An animal lover, she says her terrier and Persian cat regard her study as much theirs as hers.

DESERT MISTRESS
by
HELEN BIANCHIN

CHAPTER ONE

KRISTI put the finishing touches to her make-up, then stood back from the mirror to scrutinise her reflected image. An image she had deliberately orchestrated to attract one man's attention. That it would undoubtedly gain the interest of many men was immaterial.

The dress she'd chosen was fashioned in indigo raw silk; its deceptively simple cut emphasised her generously moulded breasts and narrow waist, and provided a tantalising glimpse of silk-clad thigh. Elegant high-heeled shoes completed the outfit.

Dark auburn hair fell to her shoulders in a cascade of natural curls, and cosmetic artistry highlighted wide-spaced, topaz-flecked hazel eyes, accented a delicate facial bone structure and defined a sensuously curved mouth. Jewellery was kept to a minimum—a slim-line gold watch, bracelet and earstuds.

Satisfied, Kristi caught up her evening coat, collected her purse and exited the hotel suite.

Downstairs the doorman hailed her a taxi with one imperious sweep of his hand, and once seated she gave the driver a Knightsbridge address, then sank back in contemplative silence as the vehicle eased into the flow of traffic.

The decision to travel to London had been her own, despite advice from government officials in both

5

Australia and England that there was little to be gained in the shift of location. '*Wait*,' she'd been cautioned, 'and allow them to do their job.'

Except she'd become tired of waiting, tired of hearing different voices intoning the same words endlessly day after day. She wanted action. Action that Sheikh Shalef bin Youssef Al-Sayed might be able to generate, given that his assistance with delicate negotiations in a similar situation more than a year ago had resulted in the successful release of a hostage.

The slim hope that she might be able to persuade him to use his influence to set her brother free had been sufficient for her to book the next available flight to London and arrange accommodation.

Yet in the two weeks since her arrival Kristi's telephone calls had been politely fielded, her faxes ignored. Even baldly turning up at his suite of offices had met with failure. The man was virtually inaccessible, his privacy guarded from unwanted intrusion.

Kristi's long-standing friendship with Georgina Harrington, the daughter of a foreign diplomat, with whom she'd attended boarding-school, provided the opportunity to meet the Sheikh on a social level. There could be no doubt that without Sir Alexander Harrington's help she would never have gained an invitation to tonight's soirée.

The decision to replace Georgina with Kristi as Sir Alexander's partner had been instigated by a telephone call to the Sheikh's secretary, and had been closely followed by a fax notifying him that Georgina had fallen prey to a virulent virus and would not be able to attend. It had gone on to ask if there would be any objection to Kristi Dalton, aged twenty-seven, a friend of long-standing, taking Georgina's place. Details for security purposes were supplied. Acknowledgement together with an acceptance had been faxed through the following day.

The taxi cruised through the streets, the glisten of recent rain sparkling beneath the headlights. London in winter was vastly different from the Southern hemispheric temperatures of Australia, and for a moment she thought longingly of bright sunshine, blue skies and the sandy beaches gracing Queensland's tropical coast.

It didn't take long to reach Sir Alexander's elegant, three-storeyed apartment, and within minutes of paying off the taxi she was drawn into the lounge and handed a glass containing an innocuous mix of lime, lemonade and bitters.

'Ravishing, darling,' Georgina accorded with genuine admiration for Kristi's appearance—a compliment which was endorsed by Sir Alexander.

'Thank you,' Kristi acknowledged with a slightly abstracted smile.

So much rested on the next few hours. In her mind she had rehearsed precisely how she would act, what she would say, until the imagery almost assumed reality. There could be no room for failure.

'I've instructed Ralph to have the car out front at five-thirty,' Sir Alexander informed her. 'When you have finished your drink, my dear, we will leave.'

Kristi felt the knot of tension tighten in her stomach, and she attempted to disguise her apprehension as Georgina gave her a swift hug.

'Good luck. I'll ring you tomorrow and we'll get together for lunch.'

Sir Alexander's car was an aged Rolls, the man behind the wheel a valued servant who had been with the Harrington family for so many years that employer and employee had given up trying to remember the number.

'The traffic is light, sir,' Ralph intoned as he eased the large vehicle forward. 'I estimate we will reach the Sheikh's Berkshire manor in an hour.'

It took precisely three minutes less, Kristi noted as they slowed to a halt before a massive set of wrought-iron gates flanked by two security guards.

Ralph supplied their invitation and sufficient proof of identity, then, as the gates swung open, he eased the Rolls towards the main entrance where they were greeted by yet another guard.

'Miss Dalton. Sir Harrington. Good evening.'

To the inexperienced eye he appeared to be one of the hired help. Given the evening's occasion, there was a valid reason for the mobile phone held in one hand. Yet the compilation of information that Kristi had accumulated about his employer left her in little doubt that there was a regulation shoulder-holster beneath his suit jacket, his expertise in the field of martial arts and marksmanship a foregone conclusion.

A butler stood inside the heavily panelled front door, and Kristi relinquished her coat to him before being led at Sir Alexander's side by a delegated hostess to join fellow guests in a room that could only have been described as sumptuous.

Gilt-framed mirrors and original works of art graced silk-covered walls, and it would have been sacrilege to suggest that the furniture was other than French antique. Multi-faceted prisms of light were reflected from three exquisite crystal chandeliers.

'I'll have one of the waiters bring you something to drink. If you'll excuse me?'

An elaborate buffet was presented for personal selection, and there were several uniformed waitresses circling the room, carrying trays laden with gourmet hors d'oeuvres.

Muted background music was barely distinguishable beneath the sound of chattering voices, and Kristi's smile was polite as Sir Alexander performed an introduction to the wife of an English earl who had recently presented her husband with a long-awaited son.

Kristi scanned the room idly, observing fellow guests with fleeting interest. Black dinner suit, crisp white cotton shirt and black bow-tie were *de rigueur* for the men, and her experienced eye detected a number of women wearing designer gowns whose hair and make-up bore evidence of professional artistry.

Her gaze slid to a halt, arrested by a man whose imposing height and stature set him apart from everyone else in the room.

Sheikh Shalef bin Youssef Al-Sayed.

Newspaper photographs and coloured prints in the pages of glossy magazines didn't do him justice, for in the flesh he exuded an animal sense of power—a physical magnetism that was riveting.

An assemblage of finely honed muscle accented a broad bone structure, and his facial features bore the sculpted prominence of inherited genes. Dark, well-groomed hair and olive skin proclaimed the stamp of his paternal lineage.

Information regarding his background gleaned from press releases depicted him as the son of an Arabian prince and an English mother—a woman who, it was said, had agreed to an Islamic wedding ceremony which had never been formalised outside Saudi Arabia, and after a brief sojourn in her husband's palace had fled back to England where she'd steadfastly refused, despite giving birth to a much coveted son, to return to a country where women were subservient to men and took second place to an existing wife.

Yet the love affair between the Prince and his English wife had continued to flourish during his many visits to London, until her untimely death, whereupon the ten-year-old Shalef had been removed from England by his father and introduced to his Arabian heritage.

Now in his late thirties, Shalef bin Youssef Al-Sayed had won himself international respect among his peers for his entrepreneurial skills, and in the years since his father's demise his name had become synonymous with immense wealth.

A man no sensible person would want as an enemy, Kristi perceived wryly. Attired in a a superbly cut evening suit, there was an elemental ruthlessness beneath his sophisticated faҫade.

As if some acute sense alerted him to her scrutiny, he lifted his head, and for a few timeless seconds his eyes locked with hers.

The room and its occupants seemed to fade to the periphery of her vision as she suffered his raking appraisal, and she was unable to control the slow heat coursing through her veins. Intense awareness vibrated from every nerve cell, lifting the fine body hairs on the surface of her skin.

No man of her acquaintance had made her feel so acutely vulnerable, and she found the sensation disconcerting. Had it been any other man, she would have displayed no interest and openly challenged his veiled evaluation. With Shalef bin Youssef Al-Sayed she couldn't allow herself the luxury of doing so.

For one split second she glimpsed lurking cynicism in his expression, then his attention was diverted by a man who greeted him with the earnest deference of the emotionally insecure.

The study of body language had been an integral part of her training as a photographer, inasmuch as she'd consciously chosen to emphasise the positive rather than the negative in the posed, still shots that had provided her bread and butter in the early days of her career in her parents' Double Bay photographic studio.

Kristi's gaze lingered, her interest entirely professional. Or so she told herself as she observed the slant of Shalef bin Youssef Al-Sayed's head, the movement

of his sensually moulded mouth as he engaged in polite conversation, the piercing directness of his gaze.
To the unwary he appeared totally relaxed, yet there
was tensile steel apparent in his stance, a silent
strength that was entirely primitive. And infinitely
dangerous.

A feather of fear pricked the base of her neck and
slithered slowly down the length of her spine. As an
enemy he would be lethal.

'Kristi.'

She turned at the sound of her name and gave Sir
Alexander a warm smile.

'Allow me to introduce Annabel and Lance
Shrewsbury.' His voice was so incredibly polite that
Kristi's eyes held momentary mischief before it was
quickly masked. 'Kristi Dalton, a valued friend from
Australia.'

'*Australia!*' Annabel exclaimed in a voice that diminished the country to a position of geographical
obscurity. 'I'm fascinated. Do you live on a farm out
there?'

'Sydney,' Kristi enlightened her politely. 'A city
with a population in excess of five million.' She
shouldn't have resorted to wry humour, she knew, but
she couldn't help adding, 'The large farms are called
stations, each comprising millions of acres.'

The woman's eyes widened slightly. 'Good heavens. *Millions*?'

'Indeed,' Kristi responded solemnly. 'A plane or
helicopter is used to check boundary fences and mon-
itor stock.'

Annabel suppressed a faint shudder. 'All that red dirt, the heat, and the snakes. My dear, I couldn't live there.' Red-tipped fingers fluttered in an aimless gesture, matching in colour the red-glossed mouth, and in perfection the expensive orthodontic work, and the considerable skill of cosmetic surgery.

Thirty, going on forty-five, married to a wealthy member of the aristocracy, and born to shop, Kristi summarised, endeavouring not to be uncharitable.

'Sir Alexander.'

Awareness arrowed through her body at the sound of that smooth, well-educated drawl, and she turned slowly to greet their host.

His shirt was of the finest cotton, his dinner suit immaculately tailored to fit his broad frame, and this close she could sense the clean smell of soap mingling with the exclusive tones of his cologne.

Unbidden, her eyes were drawn to his mouth, and she briefly examined its curve and texture, stifling the involuntary query as to what it would be like to have that mouth possess her own. Heaven and hell, a silent voice taunted, dependent on his mood. There was a hint of cruelty apparent, a ruthlessness that both threatened and enticed. A man who held an undeniable attraction for women, she perceived, yet willing to be tamed by very few.

It was almost as if he was able to read her thoughts, for she glimpsed musing mockery in those slate-grey eyes—a colour that was in direct defiance of nature's genetics, and the only visible feature that gave evidence of his maternal ancestry.

'Miss Dalton.'

'Sheikh bin Al-Sayed,' Kristi acknowledged formally, aware that his gaze rested fractionally long on her hair before lowering to conduct a leisurely appraisal of her features.

It was crazy to feel intensely conscious of every single breath, every beat of her pulse. Silent anger lent her eyes a fiery sparkle, and it took considerable effort to mask it. An effort made all the more difficult as she glimpsed his amusement before he turned his attention to Sir Alexander.

'Georgina is unwell, I understand?'

'She asks me to convey her apologies,' Sir Alexander offered. 'She is most disappointed not to be able to attend this evening.'

Shalef bin Youssef Al-Sayed inclined his head. 'It is to be hoped she recovers soon.' He moved forward to speak to a woman who showed no reticence in greeting him with obvious affection.

'Would you care for another drink?'

Kristi felt as if she'd been running a marathon, and she forced herself to breathe evenly as everything in the room slid into focus. The unobtrusive presence of the waiter was a welcome distraction, and she placed her empty glass on the tray. 'Mineral water, no ice.' She didn't need the complication of a mind dulled by the effects of alcohol.

'Would you like me to get you something to eat, my dear?' Sir Alexander queried. 'Several of the guests seem to be converging on the buffet.'

Kristi summoned a warm smile as she linked her

hand through his arm. 'Shall we join them? I'm feeling quite hungry.' It was a downright lie, but Sir Alexander wasn't to know that.

There was so much to choose from, she decided minutes later: hot and cold dishes, salads, hot vegetables, delicate slices of smoked salmon, seafood, chicken, turkey, roast lamb, slender cuts of beef. The selection of desserts would have put any of the finest London restaurants to shame, and the delicate ice sculptures were a visual confirmation of the chef's artistic skill.

Kristi took two slices of smoked salmon, added a small serving of three different salads, a scoop of caviare, then drifted to one side of the room.

How many guests were present tonight? she pondered idly. Fifty, possibly more? It was impossible to attempt a counting of heads, so she didn't even try.

Sir Alexander appeared to have been trapped by a society matron who seemed intent on discussing something of great importance, given the intensity of her expression.

'All alone, *chérie*? Such a crime.'

The accent was unmistakably French, and she moved slightly to allow her view to encompass the tall frame of a man whose smiling features bore a tinge of practised mockery.

'You will permit me to share a few minutes with you as we eat?'

She effected a faint shrug. 'Why not? We're fellow guests.'

'You are someone I would like to get to know—

very well.' The pause was calculated, the delicate emphasis unmistakable.

Kristi's French was flawless, thanks to a degree in Italian and French, her knowledge and accent honed by a year spent in each country. 'I am selective when it comes to choosing a friend—or a lover, *monsieur.*' Her smile was singularly sweet. 'It is, perhaps, unfortunate that I do not intend to remain in London long enough to devote time to acquiring one or the other.'

'I travel extensively. We could easily meet.'

His persistence amused her. 'I think not.'

'You do not know who I am?'

'That is impossible, as we have yet to be introduced,' she managed lightly. Perhaps she presented a challenge.

'Enchanté, chérie.' His eyes gleamed darkly as he reached for her hand and raised it to his lips. 'Jean-Claude Longchamp d'Elseve.' He paused, head tilted slightly as he waited for an expected reaction. When she failed to comply, his mouth assumed a quizzical slant. 'I cannot believe you lack the knowledge or the intelligence to be aware of the importance my family hold in France.'

'Really?'

He was an amusing diversion, and he was sufficiently astute to appreciate it. 'I am quite serious.'

'So am I, Jean-Claude,' she declared solemnly.

'You make no attempt to acquaint me with your name. Does this mean I am to be rejected?' The musing gleam in his eyes belied the wounded tone.

'Do you not handle rejection well?'

His mouth parted in subdued laughter. 'I am so rarely in such a position, it is something of a novelty.'

'I'm relieved. I would hate to provide you with an emotional scar.'

He still held her hand, and his thumb traced a light pattern over the veins of her wrist. 'Perhaps we could begin again. Will you have dinner with me?'

'The answer is still the same.'

'It will be relatively easy for me to discover where you are staying.'

'Please don't,' Kristi advised seriously.

'Why not?' His shrug was eloquent. 'Am I such objectionable company?'

She pulled her hand free. 'Not at all.' She cast him a slight smile. 'I simply have a tight business schedule and a full social calendar.'

The edge of his mouth curved in pensive humour. 'You mean to leave me to another woman's mercy?'

In different circumstances he might have proved to be an amusing companion. 'I'm sure you can cope.'

His eyes gleamed with hidden warmth. 'Perhaps. Although I may choose not to.'

'Your prerogative,' she accorded lightly. 'If you'll excuse me? I should rejoin Sir Alexander.'

Jean-Claude inclined his head and offered a teasing smile. *'Au revoir, chérie.'*

Her food had remained almost untouched, and she handed the plate to a passing waitress, her appetite gone.

Sir Alexander wasn't difficult to find, although he

appeared deep in conversation with a distinguished-looking guest and she was loath to interrupt them.

'Champagne?'

Kristi cast the waitress and the tray she carried a fleeting glance. Perhaps she *should* have a glass to diffuse her nervous tension. Even as the thought occurred, she dismissed it. Coffee, strong black and sweet was what she needed, and she voiced the request, then made her way to the end of the buffet table where a uniformed maid was offering a variety of hot beverages.

Declining milk, she moved to one side and sipped the potent brew. The blend was probably excellent, but she hardly noticed as she steeled herself to instigate a planned action.

Seconds later her cup lay on the carpet, and the scalding liquid seared her midriff. The pain was intense—far more so than she'd anticipated.

'Oh, my dear, how unfortunate. Are you all right?' The voiced concern brought attention, and within minutes she was being led from the room by the hostess who had greeted them on arrival.

'We keep the first-aid equipment in a bathroom next to the kitchen.' The hostess's voice was calm as she drew Kristi down a wide hallway and into a room that was clinically functional. 'If you'll remove your dress I'll apply a cold compress to cool the skin.'

Kristi complied, adding a sodden half-slip to the heap of ruined silk, then stood silently as the hostess efficiently dealt with the burn, applied salve, then covered the area with a sterile dressing.

'I'll organise a robe and have someone take care of your dress.'

Minutes later Kristi willed the hostess a speedy return, for despite central heating the room was cool, and a lacy bra and matching wispy bikini briefs were hardly adequate covering.

A frown creased her forehead, and she unconsciously gnawed at her lower lip, uneasy now that she had implemented her plan. There was a very slim chance that Sheikh bin Al-Sayed would check on her himself. Yet she was a guest in his home, and courtesy alone should ensure that he enquired as to her welfare—surely?

Her scalded flesh stung abominably, despite the hostess's ministrations. A wide, raised welt of red skin encompassed much of her midriff and tapered off in the region of her stomach. Even she had been surprised that one cup of hot liquid was capable of covering such an area.

A sound alerted Kristi's attention an instant before the door swung inwards. Her eyes widened measurably as Shalef bin Youssef Al-Sayed stood momentarily in its aperture.

He held a white towelling robe, his features schooled into a fathomless mask, and she shivered, unable to control the slither of apprehension as he moved into the room and closed the door.

Its soft clunking sound was somehow significant, and her hands moved instinctively to cover her breasts.

'I suggest you put this on. It would be unfortunate to compound your accident with a chill.'

The room suddenly seemed much smaller, his height and breadth narrowing its confines to a degree where she felt stifled and painfully aware of the scarcity of her attire.

Reaching forward, she took the robe and quickly pushed her arms into the sleeves, then firmly belted the ties, only to wince and ease the knot. 'Thank you.'

'Rochelle assures me the burn, while undoubtedly painful, is not serious enough to warrant professional medical attention. Your gown is silk and may not fare well when cleaned. Replace it and send me the bill.'

'That won't be necessary,' Kristi said stiffly.

'I insist.' His gaze was startlingly direct, and difficult for her to hold.

'It was a simple accident, and the responsibility is entirely mine,' she declared, hating her body's reaction to his presence. It had been bad enough in a room full of people. Alone with him, it was much worse.

His eyes narrowed. 'You decline the replacement of an expensive dress?'

'I don't seek an argument with you.'

With easy economy of movement he slid one hand into a trouser pocket—an action which parted the superbly tailored dinner jacket and displayed an expanse of snowy white cotton shirt, beneath which it was all too easy to imagine a taut midriff and steel-muscled chest liberally sprinkled with dark, springy hair.

'What precisely is it that you do seek, Miss

Dalton?' The words were a quizzical drawl laced with cynicism.

There was an implication, thinly veiled, that succeeded in tightening the muscles supporting her spine. It also lifted her chin and brought a brightness to her eyes.

His smile was totally lacking in humour. 'All evening I have been intrigued by the method you would choose to attract my attention.' His mouth assumed a mocking slant. 'No scenario I envisaged included a self-infliction of injury.'

CHAPTER TWO

KRISTI felt the color drain from her face. 'How dare you suggest—?'

'Save your breath, Miss Dalton. An investigation fell into place immediately after your second phone call to my office,' Shalef bin Youssef Al-Sayed informed her with deadly softness. His gaze never left her features as he listed the schools she'd attended, her educational achievements, her parents' names and the cause of their accidental death, her address, occupation, and a concise compilation of her inherited assets. 'Your visit to London was precipitated by a desire to accelerate the release of your brother, Shane, who is currently being held hostage in a remote mountain area,' he concluded in the same silky tones.

Anger surged through her veins, firing a helpless fury. 'You *knew* why I was trying to contact you, yet you denied me the courtesy of accepting one of my calls?'

'There seemed little point. I cannot help you, Miss Dalton.'

The words held a finality that Kristi refused to accept. 'Shane was unfortunate to be in the wrong place at the wrong time—'

'Your brother is a professional news photographer who ignored advice and flouted legal sanction in order

22

to enter a forbidden area,' Shalef bin Youssef Al-Sayed declared hardly. 'He was kidnapped by an opposing faction and taken beyond reach of local authorities, who would surely have instigated his arrest and incarcerated him in prison.'

'You consider his fate is better with a band of political dissidents?'

His mouth curved into a mere facsimile of a smile. 'That is debatable, Miss Dalton.'

Concern widened her eyes and robbed her features of their colour. The image of her brother being held captive kept her awake nights; then, when she did manage to sleep, her mind was invaded by nightmares. 'I implore you—'

'You beg very prettily,' Shalef bin Youssef Al-Sayed taunted mercilessly, and in that moment she truly hated him. 'However, I suggest you direct all your enquiries through the appropriate channels. Such negotiations take time and require the utmost delicacy. And patience,' he added with slight emphasis. 'On the part of the hostage's family.'

'You could help get him out,' she declared in impassioned entreaty.

His gaze speared through her body and lanced her very soul, freezing her into speechlessness. There was scarcely a sound in the room, only the whisper of her breathing and she couldn't have looked away from him if she'd tried.

'We are close to the twenty-first century, Miss Dalton,' he drawled. 'You did not imagine I would don a *thobe* and *gutra*, mount an Arab steed and ride into the desert on a rescue mission with men following on horseback, taking water and food from conveniently placed oases along the way?'

Kristi ignored his sardonic cynicism, although it cost her considerable effort not to launch a verbal attack. 'I have a sizeable trust fund which is easily accessed,' she assured him with determined resolve, grateful in this instance for inherited wealth. 'Sufficient to cover the cost of hiring Jeeps, men, a helicopter if necessary.'

'No.'

The single negation sparked a feeling of desperation. She held one ace up her sleeve, but this wasn't the moment to play it. 'You refuse to help me?'

'Go home, Miss Dalton.' His expression was harsh, and his voice sounded as cold as if it had come direct from the North Pole. 'Go back to Australia and let the governments sort out the unfortunate incident.'

She wanted to hit him, to lash out physically and berate him for acting like an unfeeling monster.

He knew, and for one fraction of a second his eyes flared, almost as if in anticipation of her action—and the certain knowledge of how he would deal with it. Then the moment was gone, and it had been so swift, so fleeting that she wondered if it hadn't been a figment of her imagination.

'You will have to excuse me. I have a party to host,' he imparted with smooth detachment. 'Rochelle will bring you something suitable to wear. Should you wish to return to your hotel, it will be arranged for a driver to transport you there. Otherwise, I can only suggest that you attempt to enjoy the rest of the evening.'

'Please.' Her voice broke with emotional intensity.

His eyes flayed every layer of protective clothing, burning skin, tissue, seeming to spear through to her very soul. With deliberate slowness he appraised her slender figure, resting over-long on the curve of her breasts, the apex between her thighs, before sweeping up to settle on the soft fullness of her mouth. 'There is nothing you can offer me as a suitable enticement.'

Anger brightened her eyes, and pride kept her head high. 'You insult my intelligence, Shalef bin Youssef Al-Sayed. I was appealing for your compassion. Sex was never a consideration.'

'You are a woman, Miss Dalton. Sex is always a consideration.'

A soft tinge of pink coloured her cheeks as she strove to keep a rein on her temper. She drew a deep, ragged breath, then released it slowly. 'Not even for my brother would I use my body as a bartering tool.'

His eyes narrowed with cynical amusement. 'No?'

She was sorely tempted to yell at him, but that would only have fuelled his amusement. 'No.' The word was quietly voiced and carried far more impact than if she'd resorted to angry vehemence.

He turned towards the door, and the blood seemed to roar in her ears, then she felt it slowly drain, leaving her disoriented and dangerously light-headed for an instant before she managed to gather some measure of control.

'What would it take for you to make a personal

appeal to Mehmet Hassan on my behalf?' The words were singularly distinct, each spoken quietly, but they caused Shalef bin Youssef Al-Sayed to pause, then turn slowly to face her.

His features were assembled into an inscrutable mask, and his eyes held a wariness that was chilling.

'Who precisely is Mehmet Hassan?' The voice was dangerously quiet, the silky tones deceptive, for she sensed a finely honed anger beneath their surface.

She felt trapped by the intentness of those incredible eyes, much like a rabbit caught in the headlights of a car, and she took a deep, shuddering breath, then released it slowly. 'You attended the same school and established a friendship which exists to this day, despite Mehmet Hassan's little-known link with political dissident leaders.'

Dark lashes lowered, successfully hooding his gaze. 'I know a great many people, Miss Dalton,' he drawled, 'some of whom I number as friends.'

She had his attention. She dared not lose it.

'You travel to Riyadh several times a year on business, occasionally extending your stay to venture into the desert with a hunting party to escape from the rigours of the international corporate world. You never go alone, and it has been whispered that Mehmet Hassan has been your guest on a number of occasions.'

He was silent for what seemed to be several minutes but could only have been seconds. 'Whispers, like grains of sand, are swept far by the desert winds and retain no substance.'

'You deny your friendship with Mehmet Hassan?'

His expression hardened, his eyes resembling obsidian. 'What is the purpose of this question?'

Steady, an inner voice cautioned. 'I want you to take me with you to Riyadh.'

'Entry into Saudi Arabia requires a sponsor.'

'Something you could arrange without any effort.'

'If I was so inclined.'

'I suggest you *are* inclined,' Kristi said carefully.

Shalef bin Youssef Al-Sayed's appraisal was all-encompassing as it slowly raked her slim frame. 'You would dare to threaten me?' he queried with dangerous softness, and she shivered inwardly at the ominous, almost lethal quality apparent in his stance.

'I imagine the media would be intensely interested to learn of the link between Sheikh Shalef bin Youssef Al-Sayed and Mehmet Hassan,' she opined quietly. 'Questions would undoubtedly be raised, public opinion swayed, and at the very least it would cause you embarrassment.'

'There is a very high price to pay for attempted blackmail, Miss Dalton.'

She pulled the figurative ace and played it. 'I am applying the rudiments of successful business practice. A favour in exchange for information withheld. My terms, Sheikh bin Al-Sayed, are unrestricted entry into Riyadh under your sponsorship. For my own protection, it is necessary for me to be a guest in your home. By whichever means you choose you will make contact with Mehmet Hassan and request his help in negotiating for my brother's release. In return,

I will meet whatever expenses are incurred.' Her eyes never wavered from his. 'And pledge my silence.'

'I could disavow any knowledge of this man you call Mehmet Hassan.'

'I would know you lie.'

If he could have killed her, he would have done so. It was there in his eyes, the flexing of a taut muscle at the edge of his cheek. 'What you ask is impossible.'

A faint smile lifted the corner of her mouth. 'Difficult, but not impossible.'

The sound of a discreet knock at the door, and seconds later Rochelle entered the room with a swathe of black draped over her arm.

'Perhaps we can arrange to further this discussion at a more opportune time?' Kristi offered with contrived politeness. 'It would be impolite to neglect your guests for much longer.'

Shalef bin Youssef Al-Sayed inclined his head. 'Indeed. Shall we say dinner tomorrow evening? I will send a car to your hotel at six.'

A tiny thrill of exhilaration spiralled through her body. 'Thank you.'

His eyes were hooded and his smile was barely evident. 'I shall leave you with Rochelle,' he declared formally, then, with a dismissing gesture, he moved into the passageway and closed the door behind him.

'I think these should be adequate,' Rochelle indicated as she held out the evening trousers and an elegant beaded top.

They were superb, the style emphasising Kristi's

slender frame and highlighting the delicate fragility of her features.

'Do you feel ready to rejoin the party? Sir Alexander Harrington has expressed anxiety as to your welfare.'

'Thank you.'

It really was a splendid gathering, Kristi acknowledged silently some time later as she sipped an innocuous fruit punch. She had attended many social events in the past ten years in numerous capital cities around the world, with guests almost as impressive as these, in prestigious homes that were equally opulent as this one. Yet none had proved to be quite as nerve-racking.

Shalef bin Youssef Al-Sayed was not a man to suffer fools gladly. And deep inside she couldn't discount the fact that she was indeed being foolish in attempting to best him. Twice in the past hour she had allowed her gaze to scan the room casually, unconsciously seeking the autocratic features of her host among the many guests.

Even when relaxed he had an inherent ruthlessness that she found vaguely disturbing. Yet familial loyalty overrode the need for rational thought, and she dampened down a feeling of apprehension at the prospect of sharing dinner with him the following evening.

A strange prickling sensation began at the back of her neck, and some inner force made her seek its source, her gaze seeming to home in on the man who silently commanded her attention.

Dark eyes seared her own, and the breath caught

in her throat for a few long seconds as she suffered his silent annihilation, then she raised one eyebrow and slanted him a polite smile before deliberately turning towards Sir Alexander.

'Would you like to leave, my dear?'

Kristi offered him a bemused look, and glimpsed his concern. 'It *is* getting late,' she agreed, moving to his side as they began circling the room to where their host stood listening to an earnest-looking couple conducting what appeared to be an in-depth conversation.

'Sir Alexander, Miss Dalton.' The voice was pleasant, the tone polite.

'It has been a most enjoyable evening,' Sir Alexander said cordially, while Kristi opted to remain silent.

'It is to be hoped the effects of your accident will be minimal, Miss Dalton,' Shalef drawled, and she responded with marked civility,

'Thank you, Sheikh bin Al-Sayed, for the borrowed clothes. I shall have them cleaned and returned to you.'

He merely inclined his head in acknowledgement, and Kristi found herself mentally counting each step that led from the lounge.

As they reached the foyer, instruction was given for the Rolls to be brought around. Within minutes they were both seated in the rear and Ralph began easing the vehicle down the long, curving driveway.

'I trust you were successful, my dear?'

Kristi turned towards Sir Alexander with a faint smile. 'To a degree, although he was aware of the deliberate orchestration. We're to dine together to-morrow evening.'

'Be careful,' he bade her seriously. 'Shalef bin Youssef Al-Sayed is not someone with whom I would choose to cross words.'

A chill finger feathered its way down her spine. A warning? 'Shane's welfare is too important for me to back down now.'

A hand covered hers briefly in conciliation. 'I understand. However, as a precaution, I would suggest you keep me abreast of any developments. I feel a certain degree of responsibility.'

'Of course.'

It was after midnight when Ralph slid the Rolls to a halt outside the main entrance to her hotel, and an hour later she lay gazing sightlessly at the darkened ceiling, unable to sleep. There was still a slight rush of adrenalin firing her brain, a feeling of victory mixed with anxiety that prevented the ability to relax. Would Shalef bin Youssef Al-Sayed present a very clever argument in opposition to her bid to have him take her to Riyadh? Call her bluff regarding her threat to inform the media of his friendship with Mehmet Hassan? She had seventeen hours to wait before she found out.

Kristi stepped out of the lift at precisely five minutes to six and made her way to the foyer. It was raining heavily outside, the sky almost black, and the wind howled along the space between tall buildings and up narrow alleyways with a ferocity of sound that found its way inside each time the main entrance doors swung open.

An omen? It wasn't a night one would have chosen to venture out in, not if a modicum of common sense was involved. The occasional blast of cold air penetrated the warmth of the central heating like icy fingers reaching in to pluck out the unwary.

Kristi drew the edges of her coat together, adjusted the long woollen scarf, then plunged her hands into her capacious pockets.

Where would they dine? There was an excellent restaurant in the hotel. She would feel infinitely safer if they remained in familiar surroundings.

She watched as a black Bentley swept in beneath the portico. The driver emerged, spoke briefly to the attendant, then strode indoors to receive the concierge's attention, who, after listening intently, gave an indicative nod in Kristi's direction.

Intrigued, she waited for him to reach her.

'Miss Dalton?' He produced ID and waited patiently while she scrutinised it. 'Sheikh bin Al-Sayed has instructed me to drive you to his home in Berkshire.'

Her stomach performed a backward flip, then settled with an uneasy fluttering of nerves. *His* territory, when she'd hoped for the relative safety of a restaurant in which to conduct negotiations.

The success of her ploy rested on one single fact: information that was known to only a privileged few. Her source had extracted a vow of secrecy—a promise she intended to honour despite any threat Shalef bin Youssef Al-Sayed could throw at her.

The large vehicle escaped the city's outskirts, gathered speed, its passage becoming much too swift for Kristi's peace of mind.

It was stupid to feel so nervous, she rationalised as the Bentley slid between the heavy wrought-iron gates and progressed up the curved drive. Insane to feel afraid when the house was staffed with a complement of servants. Yet she was consumed with a measure of both when the door opened and Rochelle ushered her inside.

'May I take your coat?' With it folded across one arm, she indicated a door to her right. 'Come through to the lounge.'

The room was measurably smaller than the large, formal lounge used for last night's party, Kristi observed as she followed Rochelle's gesture and sank down into one of the several deep-seated sofas.

'Can I get you something to drink? Wine? Orange juice? Tea or coffee?'

Hot, fragrant tea sounded wonderful, and she said as much, accepting the steaming cup minutes later.

'If you'll excuse me?' Rochelle queried. 'Sheikh bin Al-Sayed will join you shortly.'

Was it a deliberate tactic on his part to keep her waiting? In all probability, Kristi conceded as she sipped the excellent brew.

He had a reputation as a powerful strategist, a man who hired and fired without hesitation in his quest for dedication and commitment from his employees. The pursuit of excellence in all things, at any cost. Wasn't that the consensus of everything she'd managed to learn about him? Admires enterprise, respects equals and dismisses fools.

But what of the man behind the image? Had the contrast between two vastly different cultures caused a conflict of interest and generated a resentment that he didn't totally belong to either? Little was known of his personal life as a child, whether his mother favoured a strict British upbringing or willingly allowed him knowledge of his father's religion and customs.

If there had been any problems, it would appear that he'd dealt with and conquered them, Kristi reflected as she replaced the cup down on its saucer.

'Miss Dalton.'

She gave a start of surprise at the sound of his voice. His entry into the room had been as silent as that of a cat.

'Sheikh bin Al-Sayed,' she acknowledged with a calmness that she was far from feeling. If she'd still been holding the cup it would have rattled as it touched the saucer.

'My apologies for keeping you waiting.'

He didn't offer a reason, and she didn't feel impelled to ask for one. Her eyes were cool and distant as they met his, her features assembled into a mask of deliberate politeness.

'You've finished your tea. Would you care for some more?'

The tailored black trousers and white chambray

shirt highlighted his powerful frame—attire that verged on the informal, and a direct contrast to the evening suit of last night.

It made her feel overdressed, her suit too blatant a statement with its dramatic red figure-hugging skirt and fitted jacket. Sheer black hose and black stilettos merely added emphasis.

'No. Thank you,' she added as she sank back against the cushions in a determined bid to match his detachment.

'I trust the burn no longer causes you discomfort?'

The skin was still inflamed and slightly tender, but there was no sign of blistering. 'It's fine.'

He accepted her assurance without comment. 'Dinner will be served in half an hour.'

'You do intend to feed me.' The words emerged with a tinge of mockery, and she saw one of his eyebrows slant in a gesture of cynicism.

'I clearly specified dinner.'

Kristi forced herself to conduct a silent study of his features, observing the broad, powerfully defined cheekbones and the sensual shaping of his mouth. Dark slate-grey eyes possessed an almost predatory alertness, and she couldn't help wondering if they could display any real tenderness.

A woman would have to be very special to penetrate his self-imposed armour. Did he ever let down his guard, or derive enjoyment from the simple pleasures in life? In the boardroom he was regarded as an icon. And in the bedroom? There could be little doubt that he would possess the technique to drive a woman wild, but did he ever care enough to become emotionally involved? Was he, in turn, driven mad with passion? Or did he choose to distance himself?

It was something she would never know, Kristi decided with innate honesty. Something she never *wanted* to know.

'Shall we define what arrangements need to be made?' It was a bold beginning, especially when she felt anything but bold.

One eyebrow rose in a dark curve. 'We have the evening, Miss Dalton. An initial exchange of pleasantries would not be untoward, surely?' It was a statement, politely voiced, but there was steel beneath the silk. A fact she chose to heed—in part.

'Do you usually advocate wasting time during a business meeting?' Kristi proffered civilly.

'I conduct business in my office.'

'And entertain in your home?'

'Our discussion contains a politically delicate element which would be best not overheard by fellow diners, don't you agree?' he drawled, noting the tight clasp of her fingers as she laced her hands together.

She drew a deep breath and deliberately tempered its release. 'We are alone now.'

His smile held no pretension to humour. 'I suggest you contain your impatience until after dinner.'

It took a tremendous effort to contain her anger. 'If you insist.'

He registered the set of her shoulders as she unconsciously squared them, the almost prim placing of one silk-encased ankle over the other. 'Why not enjoy a light wine? Diluted, if you choose, with soda water.'

It might help her relax. She needed to, desperately. 'Thank you. Three-quarters soda.'

Why couldn't he be older, and less masculine? Less forceful, with little evidence of a raw virility that played havoc with her nervous system? Last night he had dominated a room filled with guests and succeeded in diminishing her defences. A fact she'd put down to circumstance and acute anxiety. Yet tonight she was aware that nothing had changed.

His very presence was unnerving, and she consciously fought against his physical magnetism as she accepted the glass from his hand.

'You are a photographer,' Shalef bin Youssef Al-Sayed stated as he took a comfortable chair opposite. His movements were fluid, lithe, akin to those of a large cat. 'Did you chose to follow in your brother's footsteps?'

Conversation. That's all it is, she reminded herself as she took an appreciative sip of the spritzer. It was cool and crisp to the palate, pleasant.

'Not deliberately. Shane was the older brother I adored as a child,' Kristi explained, prey to a host of images, all of them fond. 'Consequently I was intensely interested in everything he did. Photography became his obsession. Soon it was mine,' she concluded simply.

'Initially within Australia, then to various capitals throughout the world.'

'Facts you were able to access from my dossier.'

He lifted his tumbler and took a long draught of his own drink. 'A concise journalistic account.' His eyes speared hers, dark and relentless beneath the slightly hooded lids. 'Words which can't begin to convey several of the offbeat assignments you were contracted to undertake.'

'Photographs, even video coverage, don't adequately express the horror of poverty, illness and famine in some Third World countries. The hopelessness that transcends anger, the acceptance of hunger. The utter helplessness one feels at being able to do so little. The impossibility of distancing yourself from the harsh reality of it all, aware that you're only there for as long as it takes to do your job, before driving a Jeep out to the nearest airstrip and boarding a cargo shuttle that transports you back to civilisation, where you pick up your life again and attempt to pretend that what you saw, what you experienced, was just a bad dream.'

'Until the next time.'

'Until the next time,' Kristi echoed.

He surveyed her thoughtfully for several long seconds. 'You're very good at what you do.'

She inclined her head and ventured, with a touch of mockery, 'But you can't understand why I failed to settle for freelancing and filling the society pages, in a photographic studio, as my parents did.'

'The lack of challenge?'

Oh, yes. But it had been more than that—a great deal more. The photographic studio still operated, as a mark of respect for their parents, run by a competent photographer called Annie who doubled as secretary. It was an arrangement which worked very well, for it allowed Kristi freedom to pursue international assignments.

'And a desire to become your brother's equal.'

She digested his words, momentarily intrigued by a possibility that had never occurred to her until this man had voiced it. 'You make it sound as if I wanted to compete against him,' she said slowly, 'when that was never the case.'

'Yet you have chosen dangerous locations,' he pursued, watching the play of emotions on her expressive features.

Her eyes assumed a depth and dimension that mirrored her inner feelings. 'I don't board a plane and flit off to the other side of the world every second week. Sometimes there are months in between assignments, and I spend that time working out of the studio, attending social events, taking the society shots, sharing the family-portrait circuit with Annie.' She paused momentarily. 'When I undertake an assignment I want my work to matter, to encapsulate on film precisely what is needed to bring the desired result.' The passion was clearly evident in her voice, and there was a soft tinge of pink colouring her cheeks. 'Whether that be preserving a threatened environmental area or revealing the horrors of deprivation.'

'There are restrictions imposed on women photographers?'

It was a fact which irked her unbearably.

'Unfortunately feminism and equality in the work-force haven't acquired universal recognition.'

'Have you not once considered what your fate might have been if it had been you, and not your brother, who had taken a miscalculated risk and landed in the hands of political dissidents?' Shalef bin Youssef Al-Sayed queried with dangerous softness as he finished his drink and placed the glass down on a nearby side-table.

Topaz-gold chips glowed deep in her eyes as she subjected him to the full force of a hateful glare. A hand lifted and smoothed a drifting tendril of hair behind one ear. 'Shane refused to allow me to accompany him.'

'Something for which you should be eternally grateful,' he stated hardly.

Kristi caught the slight tightening of facial muscles that transformed his features into a hard mask. Impenetrable, she observed, together with a hint of autocratic arrogance that was undoubtedly attributable to his paternal forebears, and which added an element of ruthlessness to his demeanour.

'It would appear that, although a fool, your brother is not totally stupid.'

'Don't you dare—'

She halted mid-sentence as Rochelle entered the room unannounced. 'Hilary is ready to serve dinner.'

Shalef bin Youssef Al-Sayed nodded briefly, and Rochelle exited as soundlessly as she had appeared.

'You were saying?'

'You have no reason to insult my brother,' she asserted fiercely.

He smiled, although it didn't reach his eyes. 'Familial loyalty can sometimes appear blind.' He stood and moved towards her. 'Shall we go in to dinner?'

Kristi tried to bank down her resentment as she vacated the chair. 'I seem to have lost my appetite.'

'Perhaps you can attempt to find it.'

CHAPTER THREE

THE dining room was smaller than she'd imagined, although scarcely *small*, with its beautiful antique table and seating for eight, and a long chiffonier. Glassed cabinets housed an enviable collection of china and crystal. Expensive paintings and gilt-framed mirrors adorned the walls, and light from electric candles was reflected in an exquisite crystal chandelier. Several silver-domed covers dominated the table, with its centrepiece of exotic orchids.

Kristi slid into the chair that Shalef bin Youssef Al-Sayed held out for her, then he moved round to take a seat opposite.

A middle-aged woman with pleasant features busied herself removing covers from the heated platters, then indicated a choice of desserts and the cheese-board, laid out atop the chiffonier.

With a cheerful smile, Hilary—it had to be Hilary, Kristi surmised—turned toward her employer. 'Shall I serve the soup?'

'Thank you, Hilary. We'll manage.'

'Ring when you require coffee.'

He removed the lid from a china tureen. 'I trust you enjoy leek and potato soup, Miss Dalton?'

'Yes.'

He took her plate and ladled out a medium portion

before tending to his own. *'Bon appetit,'* he said with a tinge of mockery, and she inclined her head in silent acknowledgement.

The soup was delicious, and followed by superb beef Wellington with an assortment of vegetables.

'Wine?'

'Just a little,' Kristi agreed, motioning for him to stop when the glass was half-filled.

He ate with an economy of movement, his hands broad, with a sprinkling of dark hair, the fingers long, well formed and obviously strong. She could imagine them reining in a horse and manoeuvring the wheel of a rugged four-wheel drive. Gently drifting over the skin of a responsive woman. *Hell,* where did that come from? Her hand paused midway to her mouth, then she carefully returned the fork to rest on her plate. The pressure of the past few weeks, culminating over the last two days, had finally taken its toll. She was going insane. There seemed no other logical explanation for the passage of her thoughts.

'Can I help you to some more vegetables?'

Her vision cleared, and she swallowed in an endeavour to ease the constriction in her throat. 'No. Thank you,' she added in a voice that sounded slightly husky.

He had eaten more quickly than she, consuming twice the amount of food.

'Dessert?'

She settled for some fresh fruit, and followed it with a sliver of brie, observing his choice of apple crumble with cream. The man had a sweet tooth. Somehow it made him seem more human.

'Shall we return to the lounge for coffee?'

'Thank you,' she returned politely, watching as he dispensed with his napkin. Kristi did likewise and then stood.

He moved to the door and opened it, ushering her into the hallway.

A host of butterfly wings began to flutter inside her stomach. The past two hours had been devoted to observing the conventions. Now it was down to business. And somehow she had to convince him that she'd use the information she held against him in order to ensure that he would enlist Mehmet Hassan's help in freeing her brother.

'Make yourself comfortable,' Shalef bin Youssef Al-Sayed bade her as they entered the lounge, and she watched as he pressed an electronic button beside the wall-switch. 'Hilary will bring coffee.'

Kristi sank into the same chair she'd occupied on her arrival. 'Sheikh bin Al-Sayed.' Now that the moment had come, it was costing her more effort than she'd envisaged. 'Dinner was very pleasant,' she began. 'But now—'

'You want to discuss business,' he concluded with a touch of mockery as he took the chair opposite.

'Yes.'

He placed an elbow on each arm of the chair and steepled his fingers, assuming an enigmatic expression that she couldn't begin to fathom. 'The ball is in your court, Miss Dalton. I suggest you play it.'

Her eyes were steady, the tip of her chin tilting at a firm angle as she carefully put the metaphorical ball in motion. 'When do you plan leaving for Riyadh?'

'Next week.'

The butterfly wings increased their tempo inside her stomach. 'With your influence I imagine that allows sufficient time to have the necessary sponsorship papers processed.'

'Indeed.'

So far, so good. 'Perhaps you could let me have flight details, and any relevant information I need.'

He was silent for several seconds, and the silence seemed to grow louder with each one that passed.

'The flight details are simple, Miss Dalton. We board a commercial airline to Bahrain, then take my private jet to Riyadh.' He regarded her with an intensity that had the butterfly wings beating a frantic tattoo. 'Not so simple is the reason for your accompanying me.'

It seemed such a small detail. 'Why?'

'My father's third wife and her two daughters live in the palace, each of whom will be wildly curious as to why I have chosen to bring a woman with me.'

Surprise widened her eyes. 'You're joking. Aren't you?' she queried doubtfully.

'Since I can avail myself of any woman I choose,' he drawled hatefully, 'the fact that I have brought one with me will be viewed as having considerable significance—not only by my late father's family, but by several of my friends.' He smiled—a mere facsimile which held an element of pitiless disregard. 'Tell me,

Miss Dalton, would you prefer to be accepted as the woman in my life, or a—' he paused imperceptibly '—transitory attraction?'

Hilary chose that moment to enter the room, wheeling a trolley bearing a silver coffee-pot, two cups and saucers, milk, cream and sugar, together with a plate of petit fours.

'Thank you, Hilary. The meal was superb, as usual,' Shalef bin Youssef Al-Sayed complimented her while Kristi inwardly seethed with anger. Somehow she managed to dredge up a smile and add to her host's praise. However, the instant that Hilary disappeared out the door she launched into immediate attack.

'What is wrong with presenting me to your family as a guest?' she demanded heatedly.

His eyes hardened measurably, and she felt the beginnings of unease. 'I accord Nashwa and her two daughters the respect they deserve. Whenever I visit Riyadh I observe the customs of my father's country for the duration of my stay. As sponsor, I must vouch for your good behaviour while you are in Saudi Arabia, take responsibility for your welfare, and ensure your departure when it is time for you to leave.'

Kristi lifted a hand, then let it fall in a gesture of helpless anger. Her main consideration was Shane, and the influence that Shalef bin Youssef Al-Sayed could wield with Mehmet Hassan in negotiating her brother's release.

'OK,' she agreed. 'I don't particularly like the idea

of pretending to be your woman but I'll go along with it.'

He made no comment. Instead, he rose to his feet and proceeded to pour dark, aromatic coffee into the two cups. 'Milk, cream, or a liqueur?'

'Black.' She helped herself to sugar, then sipped the strong brew, watching as he did likewise. When she finished she placed her cup and saucer down on a nearby table and stood up. 'If you could arrange a taxi for me, Sheikh bin Al-Sayed, I'd like to return to my hotel.'

'Shalef,' he corrected silkily. 'As we're to be linked together, it will be thought strange if you continue to address me with such formality.' He unfolded his lengthy frame with lithe ease. 'I'll drive you into the city.'

Why did that cause an immediate knot to form in her stomach? 'A taxi would be less inconvenient.'

'To whom?'

She looked at him carefully. 'To you, of course. An hour's drive each way seems unnecessary at this time of night.'

'There are several spare bedrooms, any one of which you would be welcome to use.'

The hint of mockery brought a fiery sparkle to her eyes. 'As long as you're aware it wouldn't be yours.'

One eyebrow slanted. 'I wasn't aware I implied it might be.'

She drew in a deep breath. 'I don't find verbal games in the least amusing.'

It was impossible to detect anything from his expression. 'I'll get your coat.'

Polite civility edged her voice. 'Thank you.'

In the car she sat in silence, grateful when he activated the stereo system and Mozart provided a soothing background that successfully eliminated the need for conversation.

He drove well, with considerably more speed than his chauffeur. Or had it been his bodyguard? The miles between Berkshire and London diminished quickly, although once they reached the inner city any attempt at swift passage was hampered by computer-controlled intersections and traffic.

Kristi sighted the entrance to her hotel and prepared to alight the instant that Shalef bin Youssef Al-Sayed brought the car to a halt.

'Thank you.' Her hand paused on the door-clasp as she turned towards him. It was difficult to fathom his expression. 'I imagine you'll be in touch with the flight time?'

'I have been invited to a formal dinner on Saturday evening. I'd like you to accompany me.'

'Why?' The single query slipped out unbidden, and his eyes hardened slightly.

'In less than a week you will meet members of my late father's family. It would be preferable if we are seen to share a rapport.'

'Does it matter?'

'I consider it does. Be ready at seven.'

She felt the stirrings of resentment. 'I don't like being given an order.'

'Are you usually so argumentative?'

'Only with people who refuse to respect my right to decline an invitation,' she responded coolly.

'Are you dismissing my request?' His voice was dangerously soft, and despite the car's heating system she felt suddenly cold.

'No,' she said quietly, 'merely stating that I prefer to be asked rather than told.' She activated the door clasp and stepped from the car, hearing the refined clunk as she carefully closed the door behind her; then she turned towards the main entrance and made her way into the foyer without a backward glance.

It wasn't until she was inside her suite that she allowed herself the luxury of releasing an angry exclamation.

Sheikh Shalef bin Youssef Al-Sayed was beginning to threaten her equilibrium in more ways than one. She didn't like it, any more than she liked him. Nor did she particularly like the idea of partnering him to a formal dinner party. Except she couldn't afford to anger him.

Not yet, a tiny imp inside her taunted with mischievous intent. Not yet.

'Formal' was particularly apt, Kristi reflected with idle interest as she scanned the room's occupants. Twenty-four people sat at the table, and were served cordon bleu courses by uniformed maids and offered finest vintage wines by impeccably suited waiters. Gold-rimmed bone china vied with gleaming silver and sparkling crystal, and the floral centrepieces were a work of art.

Expensive jewellery adorned the fingers of the female guests, and there was little doubt that their gowns were designer originals.

'Dessert, Miss Dalton? There is a choice of tiramisu, strawberry shortcake, or fresh fruit.'

Although each single course had comprised a small portion, she'd lost count of the courses served and was reluctant to accept yet another. She offered the waitress a faint smile. 'No, thank you.'

'You have no need to watch your figure.'

Kristi turned towards the man seated on her left and felt the distinct pressure of his knee against her own. Without any compunction she carefully angled the tip of her slender-heeled shoe to connect with his ankle. 'I doubt Shalef would appreciate your interest,' she ventured sweetly.

'Point taken,' he acknowledged with sardonic cynicism. 'Literally.'

Her smile held no sincerity. How much longer before they could leave the table and adjourn to the lounge?

'Try some of this cheese,' Shalef suggested smoothly as he speared a small segment onto a wafer then offered it to her. His eyes were dark, their expression enigmatic, and her own widened marginally at the studied intimacy of his action.

Kristi's mouth curved slightly in response as she sampled the wafer. 'Superb,' she acknowledged. She had never doubted that he was dangerous. When he set out to charm, he was positively lethal.

'Would you like some more?'

'No. Thanks,' she added.

'So polite.'

'Don't amuse yourself at my expense,' she warned in a silky undertone.

He considered her thoughtfully. 'Is that what you think I'm doing?'

'You're playing a game for the benefit of fellow guests who are intent on displaying a discreet interest in Sheikh Shalef bin Youssef Al-Sayed's latest companion.'

'What is it you particularly object to?' he queried musingly. 'Being a subject of interest, or labelled as my latest conquest?'

Her gaze was level. 'I have little control over the former, but as the latter doesn't apply I'd prefer it if you would decline from indicating an intimacy which doesn't exist.'

'You have a vivid and distorted imagination.'

'While you, Sheikh bin Al-Sayed,' she re-sponded evenly, 'parry words with the skill of a master chess-player.'

A soft chuckle started at the back of his throat and emerged with a genuine humour that was reflected in the gleaming warmth of his eyes. 'Shalef,' he insisted quietly.

Kristi looked at him carefully. 'I imagine it is much too early to request that you take me back to the hotel?'

His mouth curved with slow indolence. 'Much too early.'

'In which case I shall attempt dazzling conversation with a fellow guest.'

'Alternatively, you could attempt to dazzle me.'

She picked up her glass and sipped the chilled water, then set it down carefully. 'Don't you tire of women who strive to capture your attention?'

'It depends on the woman,' he said mockingly. 'And whether it's more than my attention she attempts to capture.'

The request for guests to adjourn to the lounge was timely, and Kristi rose to her feet with relief, glad of the opportunity to escape the close proximity of Shalef bin Youssef Al-Sayed.

But her freedom was short-lived as he moved to her side, and she didn't pull away when he caught her elbow in a light clasp as they made their way from the dining room.

Her senses seemed more acute, and she was conscious of his clean male smell mingling with the subtle tang of his cologne. His touch brought an awareness of sexual alchemy together with a heightened degree of sensuality that quickened her pulse and had the strangest effect on her breathing.

Such feelings were a complication she couldn't afford, and she deliberately sought to impose a measure of control.

'Shalef, how wonderful to see you again.'

Kristi heard the distinct purr in the light, feminine voice and glimpsed the perfection of scarlet-tipped fingers an instant before a model-slim, dark-haired young woman slid an arm through his.

Beauty enhanced by the skilful application of cosmetics and the clothes of a noted European couturier lent and exclusivity that was unmatched by any of the other female guests, and Kristi couldn't help the uncharitable thought that such a stunning result had probably taken the entire afternoon to achieve.

'Fayza.'

Was it her imagination or did she sense a barrier of reserve fall into place?

'Allow me to introduce Kristi Dalton. Fayza Al-Khaledi.'

The features were exquisitely composed, and her mouth curved into a smile that revealed perfectly even white teeth. But the brilliant dark eyes were as cold as an Arctic floe.

'If you'll excuse me, I'll fetch some coffee.' Kristi took longer than necessary in adding sugar and a touch of cream to the aromatic brew.

She started to show an interest in the mingling guests, assured her hostess that the coffee was fine and indulged in polite small talk. Not once did she glance towards Shalef bin Youssef Al-Sayed or the glamorous woman who had commandeered his attention.

'There was no need for you to desert me.'

She turned slightly as he rejoined her, and met his solemn gaze. 'Just as there was no need for me to compete.'

Shalef chose not to comment, and Kristi finished

her coffee, refused a second cup and managed to contain her relief when he indicated that they would leave.

'You found the evening boring?'

The illuminated clock on the dashboard revealed that it was after midnight, and she sank back against the deep-cushioned seat as the large car gained the motorway and gathered speed.

'Not at all,' Kristi assured him with polite civility. 'The food was superb, and one would have to grant that the company was equally so.'

'Including the guest who indulged in a surreptitious play for your attention during the main course?'

'You noticed.'

'He has a certain reputation,' Shalef informed her drily.

'I don't need a protector.'

'In London you can rely on Sir Alexander Harrington for friendship and support. In Riyadh it will be different.'

She turned to look at him in the semi-darkness of the car, noting the harsh angles and planes of his profile. 'Are you issuing a subtle warning?'

'A suggestion that you accept the political and religious dictates of my father's country,' he corrected.

'I won't attempt to wield any Western influence or encourage the younger members of your family to challenge your will, Sheikh bin Al-Sayed,' Kristi said with a touch of mockery.

'Shalef.' His voice was silky soft, and her stomach

began to knot with nerves as she focused her attention on the scene beyond the windscreen.

It had begun to snow—light flakes that settled with an eerie whiteness on tree branches and hedges.

City lights appeared in the distance, and soon they were traversing inner suburbia at a reduced speed. Streetlights gave out a regimented glow, and most of the houses were shrouded in darkness, their occupants tucked up warmly in bed.

Kristi shivered despite the car's heating. In a few days she would board a plane in the company of a man she hardly knew, forced to place not only herself but the fate of her brother in his hands.

How long would the rescue mission take? It *had* to be successful. She couldn't, *wouldn't* contemplate failure.

The car eased to a halt outside the hotel's main entrance, and she turned towards the man behind the wheel.

'What time shall I meet you at the airport?'

He shifted in his seat and leaned an arm against the wheel. 'My chauffeur will collect you from the hotel. I will have you notified of the time.'

'Thank you.' She reached for the door-clasp and stepped out of the car. 'Goodnight.'

'Goodnight, Kristi.' His voice was a deep drawl that seemed to mock her long after she'd gained her suite and undressed for bed.

It kept her awake, then haunted her dreams as she slept.

CHAPTER FOUR

RIYADH rose from the desert like a high-tech oasis of glass, steel and concrete, with office towers, freeways, hotels, hospitals and, Shalef informed Kristi as his private jet landed and taxied down the runway, the largest airport in the world.

The subdued whine of the engines wound down to an electronic hum as the pilot wheeled the jet round towards an allotted bay. With almost simultaneous precision they slid to a halt as the hostess released the door and activated the steps for disembarkation.

Ten minutes later Kristi followed Shalef into the rear seat of a black stretch Mercedes. A man already occupied the opposite seat and Shalef effected an introduction.

'Fouad is the son of the daughter of my father's first wife,' he informed her quietly. 'He holds a managerial position with one of the family companies here.'

Kristi turned towards the man and inclined her head in silent acknowledgement. 'How many daughters are there?'

'Four. Two from my father's first wife, both of whom are older than me, and two younger, the daughters of my father's third wife.'

'Happy families,' she quipped lightly. 'I imagine there is a variety of distant aunts and cousins?'

'Several. My father's first wife developed cancer and died five years ago.'

The two men lapsed into Arabic as the large vehicle slipped free of the terminal traffic, and Kristi transferred her attention beyond the tinted windows.

This was a land where the muezzin called the faithful to prayer five times a day, where the male was revered while the female remained subservient.

She was intrigued by a culture that viewed women as less important than their male counterparts, their role so defined and protected that it amounted to almost total discrimination.

Did the women silently crave for more freedom, both in speech and action? To dispense with the *abaaya* and the veil, and adopt westernised apparel? And, if they did, would they dare speak of it to a stranger, albeit a stranger presented to them as Shalef bin Youssef Al-Sayed's current companion?

The Mercedes began to slow, and Kristi felt the nerves in her stomach awaken as it paused beside massive gates, cleared security, then swept through to a large courtyard.

The architecture was interesting—solid walls plastered in stark white, surprisingly small windows, given the hot climate, and an impressive set of carved wooden doors overlaid with ornate, metal-pressed panels.

One of the doors swung inwards as the Mercedes

slid to a halt, and a middle-aged couple emerged to extend a greeting.

'Amani and Abdullah manage the house and staff,' Shalef informed her when he'd completed an introduction.

Indoors there was an assemblage of neatly attired staff waiting to greet their sheikh, and, although Shalef made no attempt at individual introductions, he presented her as a close friend from England.

The reception hall was the largest that Kristi had seen, with imposing marble columns and Carrara marble floors covered in part by a matched selection of exquisitely woven rugs. Tapestries adorned the walls, and expensive works of art vied with gilt-edged mirrors.

'At your request I have made ready the east suite for Miss Dalton,' Amani revealed. 'Refreshments are ready to be served in the sitting room.'

'Thank you. Shall we say half an hour?'

'I will take Miss Dalton to her room.'

Shalef inclined his head, then turned towards Kristi. 'I am sure you'll find everything to your satisfaction.'

Dismissal, she determined wryly. Yet she had expected no more. With a faint smile she turned and followed Amani towards a wide, curving staircase leading to an upper floor.

The palace was sufficiently substantial to house several families and still ensure individual privacy, she realised as she traversed a long, marble-tiled hallway.

Ornate side-tables and velvet-upholstered, gilt-framed chairs lined the walls and expensive silk rugs covered the marble floor.

'I'm sure you'll be very comfortable here, Miss Dalton. If there is anything you need, please don't hesitate to ask.'

Kristi preceded the manageress into a magnificent suite comprising sitting room, bedroom and *en suite* bathroom. The furnishings were an exotic blend of deep emerald, gold and white.

'Thank you.'

With twenty-five minutes in which to shower and change, Kristi managed it in less, choosing to use minimum make-up and leave her hair loose. Aware of a preference for women to wear clothes that covered their legs and arms, she'd packed smartly tailored, loose-fitting trousers, a variety of blouses and a few tunic-style tops.

As she added a spray of perfume to her wrists she couldn't help a wry smile, for the trousers and tunic top were a deep emerald...a perfect match for the suite's furnishings.

Would members of his family join them for refreshments? She had an intense curiosity to meet the woman who had been content to take second place to an existing wife. Had a sense of rivalry existed between the two women? And what of Shalef's mother? One could only wonder at her situation—an English rose, unversed in Islamic customs, set among the desert jewels. Yet if the Prince had displayed his son's obvious attraction for the opposite sex it was probable that Shalef's mother had been caught up in a dream that had soon dissipated in the light of reality.

Kristi emerged from her suite to find a Filipino servant waiting to escort her down to the sitting room. It was a courtesy for which she was grateful, as the palace was vast, the rooms many, and she'd begun to wonder if she would need to embark on an adventure of seek and find.

They arrived downstairs and walked along a main corridor from which led three long hallways, linking, the servant informed her, further wings of the palace. No wonder there was such a large complement of staff!

The room Kristi was shown into was large and airy and filled with exquisite gilt-framed furniture, priceless items of gold-painted porcelain and original works of art.

Her eyes flew to the tall man who stood to one side of the window, his breadth of shoulder and stature emphasised by the silk-edged white *thobe* with Western-style collar and French cuffs. A white headscarf secured with an *agal* provided an electrifying effect, and made her all the more aware of the extent of his wealth, and his mantle of power.

'Kristi. Allow me to introduce you to Nashwa.'

She wrenched her eyes away from him and turned towards a slim, attractive woman attired in a royal blue traditional robe, whose dark hair was almost hidden by an exotic royal blue scarf beautifully embroidered in gold thread.

Kristi extended her hand in formal greeting, then

followed Nashwa's action by touching her heart with the palm of her right hand.

The gesture brought forth a warm smile. 'I'm very pleased to meet you, Miss Dalton. May I call you Kristi?'

'Please.'

Nashwa's smile widened as she indicated a comfortable chair. 'Do sit down. Would you prefer coffee or something cool to drink? I can have tea served, if you wish.'

Kristi opted for coffee, then took a seat, all too aware that Shalef followed her action by choosing a chair close to her own.

'I understand you are a photographer. It must be an interesting profession.'

Kristi accepted a delicate cup and saucer from the maid, added sugar, then selected a pastry from an offered plate. 'My father founded a photographic studio, which my brother and I still operate. Shane's speciality is freelance photojournalism.' She smiled, unaware that her eyes held a tinge of warm humour which lent their hazel depths a velvety texture. 'He enjoys the challenge of venturing into far-flung territory in search of the unusual.'

'You have brought your camera with you?' Shalef enquired, his dark gaze steady, daring her to resort to any fabrication.

'It forms part of my luggage wherever I travel,' she managed evenly.

'I suggest you exercise caution whenever you use it, and request permission before you do.'

'Including the palace?'

'I would prefer it if you did not photograph any of the rooms within the palace. I have no objection to external shots, or those of the gardens.'

Security? She had no desire to flout his wishes.

She turned towards Nashwa. 'You have two daughters. I'm looking forward to meeting them.'

Nashwa's expression softened. 'Aisha and Hanan. They are aged twenty-one and nineteen respectively. Aisha is en-joying a sabbatical after lengthy university studies. Soon she will leave for Switzerland to spend a year in finishing school. Hanan is not quite so academically inclined, and after emerging from boarding-school in England at the end of last year she too has opted to join Aisha in Switzerland.' She proffered a warm smile. 'You will meet them both at dinner.'

Kristi sipped the coffee, finding it very pleasant if a little too strong, and declined anything further to eat.

Shalef, she noted, drank Arabic coffee flavoured with cardamom from a tiny handleless cup that was so small it looked ludicrous held between his fingers.

Nashwa was an impeccable hostess, adept at maintaining a flow of conversation, and Kristi found herself agreeing to a conducted tour of the palace itself, while Shalef retired to the study for a few hours in order to apprise himself of business affairs.

The palace was even larger than Kristi had imagined, with innumerable rooms set aside for the sole purpose of formal and informal entertaining. Opulent, she decided silently as she admired the elaborate draping. Each room was large, the colours employed lending a cool, spacious effect that was enhanced by ducted air-conditioning. An indoor swimming pool was Olympian in proportion, the tiled surrounding area sufficiently wide to harbour a variety of casual cushioned loungers and chairs. Beyond that were the Turkish baths and beautiful paved walkways meandering through an exotic garden.

There were three wings attached to the central building, Nashwa explained—one which she and her daughters used, one designated for Shalef's occupation whenever he was in Riyadh, and the remaining one kept for visiting family and guests. Staff were housed separately.

Encompassing two levels, the internal walls enclosed a central courtyard with lush gardens, palm trees and exotic plants. Numerous columns supported wide, covered verandas which could be reached from every room on the upper floor through arched doorways.

Kristi's tour was restricted to the guest wing and the entire ground level. Not offered were Shalef's quarters or those of Nashwa and her daughters. A dual purpose, perhaps...privacy as well as security?

'You have endured a long flight. Perhaps you would like to rest for a while?'

A flight that had been fraught with a degree of apprehension about the destination and its implications. Added to which, she'd been painfully aware

of Shalef's presence and the vibrant energy he'd exuded as he'd relayed information about the history of
his father's country, its rulers, and the positive effects
of an oil-rich nation.

The thought of solitude for an hour or two sounded
ideal. She could write a promised postcard to Annie,
and Sir Alexander and Georgina would also value
word of her safe arrival.

'Thank you.'

Nashwa inclined her head in polite acceptance.
'Dinner will be served at eight. I will send a servant
to your room at seven-thirty, just in case you fall
asleep. She will escort you down to the dining room.'

They were back in the reception hall and, with a
warm smile, Kristi inclined her head before turning
towards the staircase.

Her suite was delightfully cool, and she quickly
discarded her outer clothes, then donned a silk wrap.
An antique escritoire held paper, a variety of post-
cards, envelopes and pens.

Twenty minutes later Kristi placed the completed
cards to one side, then crossed to the bed and lay
down. Half an hour, she told herself as she closed her
eyes.

But she must have dozed longer than she'd meant
to, for she came awake at the sound of a light double
tap against the outer door.

It couldn't be seventy-thirty already! But it was,
and she flew to the door, opening it to discover a
servant waiting outside.

'Could you come back in twenty minutes?'

'As you wish.'

Kristi closed the door and moved quickly into the bathroom, shedding her wrap and her underclothes, as she went. The shower succeeded in removing the last vestiges of tiredness, and she let the water run cold for ten seconds before turning off the taps.

She was ready with one minute to spare, dressed in long black silk evening trousers and matching top, her make-up understated except for her eyes. Jewellery was confined to a gold pendant and matching earrings, and she'd sprayed perfume to several pulse spots. There wasn't time to do anything other than stroke a brush through her hair.

The servant was patiently waiting when she opened the door, and Kristi attempted to dispel a faint fluttering of nerves as they descended the staircase.

'Dining room' was a slight misnomer, she discovered on being directed to a semi-formal lounge with an adjoining dining room.

Shalef was an impressive figure in a royal blue *thobe* edged with silver, and the butterfly wings inside her stomach beat a faint tattoo as he crossed the room to greet her.

'I hope I haven't kept you waiting.' Her voice sounded faintly husky even to her own ears, and her eyes widened fractionally at his indulgent smile.

'Not at all.' He caught hold of her hand and lifted it to his lips, his eyes silently challenging hers as he glimpsed her inner battle to retain a measure of composure.

He was initiating a deliberate strategy, alluding to

a relationship which didn't exist merely to qualify her presence here. Yet Kristi had the distinct feeling that he intended to derive a certain degree of diabolical pleasure from the exercise, and it rankled unbearably that the only time she'd be able to castigate him verbally for his actions would be when they were alone.

Her eyes flashed a silent warning as she offered him a brilliant smile: Don't play games with me.

She saw one eyebrow lift in mocking amusement, and she had to marshal her features not to reflect the burning anger that simmered deep within her.

'Come and meet Nashwa's daughters,' Shalef bade her smoothly as he turned and led her into the centre of the room. 'Aisha.' He indicated a slim girl of average height whose dark gaze was openly friendly, then the younger girl at her side. 'Hanan.'

Both girls were beautiful, with flawless complexions and dark, liquid brown eyes. Each wore traditional dress, Aisha in gold-embroidered aqua silk, while Hanan had opted for a soft blue. Their mother looked resplendent in deep emerald.

At least she provided a contrast in black, Kristi decided as she smiled and offered the girls a greeting. 'I've been looking forward to meeting you both.' She turned slightly and included the young man standing unobtrusively a short distance from Nashwa. 'Nashwa. Fouad.'

'Mother says you're a photographer,' Aisha said politely. 'It must be a fascinating occupation.'

'Most of the time it's routine,' Kristi acknowledged with a touch of wry humour.

'I am to study fashion design when I return from Switzerland,' Hanan declared. 'Shalef has given permission for me to begin in London. If I do well, he will allow me to study in Paris.'

Nashwa stood up. 'Shall we all go in to dinner?'

Shalef took a seat at the head of the table, and indicated that Kristi should occupy a chair close to him. An honour, she assumed, that merely endorsed her place as his latest 'companion'.

The food was excellent—hot, spicy lamb served with rice and beans, followed by a variety of sweets laden with dates and honey. There was a platter of succulent fresh fruit, and Kristi opted for some sliced melon and a few dates.

They were waited on by a number of Filipino servants, who stood inconspicuously in the background as each dish was served, then moved forward to remove plates and replace them with each subsequent course, and no sooner was a water glass empty than it was unobtrusively refilled.

'Is your photographic work confined to studio portraits?' Fouad queried politely.

Kristi set down her glass. 'Frequently, in between assignments.'

'Tell us something about these assignments. Are any of them dangerous?'

'Not really,' she answered lightly, deliberately meeting Shalef's hard gaze. 'The risk is minimal.'

Shalef's fingers toyed with the stem of his crystal goblet. 'Indeed?'

Kristi held his gaze without any difficulty at all.

'You hunt in the desert and attempt to master the falcon. Is that without risk?'

'Attempt' was perhaps not the wisest choice of word. There could be no doubt that Shalef bin Youssef Al-Sayed achieved success in everything he did, and to hint at anything less was almost an insult.

'Your concern for my safety warms my heart.'

'As does yours for me,' she responded, offering him a sweet smile.

His eyes gleamed darkly and one eyebrow slanted in silent amusement. 'When we've had coffee I'll show you the garden.'

She forced her smile to widen slightly, while silently threatening to do mild injury to certain of his male body parts if he dared anything more than a light clasp of her hand.

At the mention of coffee the servants moved forward to clear the dessert plates from the table, and Shalef rose to his feet, indicating the conclusion of the meal.

The partaking of coffee was leisurely, the conversation pleasant, and throughout the ensuing hour Kristi was supremely conscious of the tall man who chose to sit in a chair close to her own.

For a brief moment she almost considered declining when he suggested that they stroll through the illuminated gardens, and she glimpsed the hint of steel in those dark eyes and was aware that he knew the passage of her thoughts. Then she gave him a slow smile and stood up, offering no protest when he clasped her elbow as they left the room.

The warmth of the early evening was evident without the benefit of the palace's air-conditioning, and she surreptitiously lengthened her step in an effort to move further from his side—an action that was immediately thwarted as he captured her hand in a firm clasp that threatened to tighten should she attempt to wrench it from his grasp.

'What in the name of heaven do you think you're doing?' She kept her voice quiet, but he could hardly have failed to detect her anger.

'If we act as polite strangers it will raise questions about our relationship,' Shalef said smoothly.

'We don't have a relationship!'

'For the purposes of this visit we do,' he reminded her.

She turned slightly in the pale evening light and was unable to discern much from his features. 'I'm not in awe of your wealth or of you as a man,' Kristi declared in an undertone. The first was the truth, the latter an outright fabrication.

'No?'

Her eyes acquired a fiery sparkle at the faint mockery evident in his voice. 'If I didn't need your help, I'd leave and be grateful that I never had to see you again.'

'But you do need me,' Shalef pointed out silkily. 'So we shall walk and admire the garden, and appear to be as engrossed in each other as the situation demands.'

A slight breeze riffled the palm fronds and teased the length of her hair. 'Perhaps you'd care to introduce a subject of conversation that we can both pursue?' she said.

'One that won't digress into an argument?'

'You could tell me how you coped when your father first brought you here.'

'Fill in the blanks that have not been written up in the tabloid press?'

'Alternatively, there's Riyadh itself. Islam.'

'Religion and politics are a dangerous mix,' Shalef dismissed.

'They form an important part of life. Especially in the land of the Prophet Mohammed.'

'And if I were to present you with my views what guarantee would I have that they wouldn't be written up and sold to the media?' he said drily.

She looked at him carefully, aware of the caution he felt constrained to exercise with everyone he met. A man in his position would have many social acquaintances, numerous business associates, but few friends in whose company he could totally relax. 'Is that why you retreat here several times a year?'

The gardens were extensive, with carefully tended lawns, shrubs, and an ornamental fountain strategically placed to provide a central focus. Water cascaded over three levels, and at night, beneath illumination, it was nothing less than spectacular.

No doubt for him the palace represented a welcome and familiar sanctuary, whereas she found that it contained an air of Eastern mystery that she wanted to explore. The people, the culture, their beliefs, the vast, definitive division between men and women. To read and be aware of factual reporting was not the same as experiencing it for oneself.

'This is the land of my father,' Shalef began slowly. 'A land where the power of nature can move tonnes of sand for no apparent reason other than to reassemble a shifting terrain. Man has plumbed its depths and channelled the riches, reaping enormous rewards.'

'Yet you choose not to live here.'

He smiled faintly. 'I have homes in many capital cities around the world, and reside for a short time in several.'

'When do you plan on going to the hunting lodge?'

He paused and turned to face her. 'In a few days, when the first of my guests arrive. Meantime, I will ensure that you see some of the sights Riyadh has to offer, such as the museum, Dir'aiyah, the Souk Al-Bathaa. Fouad will continue to see that you are entertained in my absence.'

His features hardened fractionally. 'I must impress on you the fact that as a woman you cannot venture anywhere beyond the palace unless accompanied by Fouad or myself. Is that understood? Women are not permitted anywhere on their own, and cannot use public transport. To do so will result in arrest. Nashwa will provide you with an *abaaya* to wear whenever you leave the palace.'

Kristi made no protest. Despite her personal views on such issues there was nothing to be gained by flouting Saudi Arabian religious dictates. 'Have we been out here sufficiently long, do you think?'

'You have grown tired of my company?'

What could she say? That he unsettled her more than any man she'd ever met? 'I think you're enjoying the pursuit of this particular game,' she ventured, meeting his gaze.

'There are advantages,' Shalef drawled.

'Such as?'

'This.' His hands caught her close as his head lowered and his mouth closed over hers, his tongue a provocative instrument as he explored the delicate interior and wrought havoc with her senses. At her soft intake of breath his mouth hardened, staking a possession with such mastery that it took considerable will-power not to give in to sensation and kiss him back.

When he released her she stood, momentarily bemused, then reality returned, and with it a measure of anger.

'That was unnecessary!'

'But enjoyable, don't you agree?'

She wanted to hit him, and her fist clenched as she summoned a measure of restraint. 'You're despicable.'

'Come,' he bade her easily. 'We'll explore the garden further then return indoors. By that time your anger will have cooled.'

'Don't bet on it,' she returned inelegantly, unsure just how much control she could exert during her sojourn in the desert. Shalef bin Youssef Al-Sayed was a law unto himself, but when it came to a clash of wills she intended to do battle.

*   *   *

Shalef was as good as his word, and during the ensuing few days he assumed the role of perfect host. In the company of Nashwa, with a Filipino chauffeur at the wheel of the Mercedes, he ensured that Kristi saw many of the sights Riyadh had to offer. They visited the museum, the Masmak Fortress and the Murabba Palace, followed by the King Faisal Centre for Research and Islamic Studies. There was also the King Saud University Museum, and Kristi displayed a genuine interest as their assigned guide explained the history attached to each of the finds from the university's archaeological digs at Al-Fao and Rabdhah. The Souk Al-Bathaa, Shalef explained as they explored what remained of it, had become a victim of Riyadh's rush into the twentieth century.

Being in Shalef's company almost constantly had a disturbing effect on Kristi's composure, as he meant it to have. His behaviour was impeccable, although she was acutely aware of the intensity of his gaze as it lingered on her a trifle longer than was necessary, the touch of his hand when he directed her attention to something of interest, the moment he caught hold of her arm when she almost tripped over the hem of her borrowed *abaaya*.

Frequently she found her gaze straying to the firm lines of his mouth…and remembered what it felt like to have it move over her own.

Kristi didn't know whether to feel relieved or dismayed when one evening he suggested that they dine together in town.

'The night-life here is notoriously thin,' Shalef revealed, watching the fleeting play of emotions on her expressive features. 'However, the hotels have excellent restaurants, and the Al-Khozama has one I can recommend.'

With Nashwa and Fouad present, there wasn't much she could do but agree.

The *abaaya* was a necessary addition, but beneath it she wore silk evening trousers and a camisole top, and kept her make-up to a minimum. In some ways it had been amusing to discover that Nashwa, Aisha and Hanan each wore modern Western clothes beneath their *abaayas*. Saudi Arabian women, they assured her, spent a fortune on European couture.

Shalef was accorded due deference at the hotel as the *maître d'* escorted them to a table reserved, Kristi surmised, for the privileged few.

Choosing mineral water, she deliberated over the choice of starter and main course, conferred with Shalef and was guided by his selection.

'When do you leave for the hunting lodge?'

'Tomorrow.'

At last, she breathed silently with a sense of relief. There were questions she wanted to ask, but refrained from putting them into words, choosing to wonder in silence when Mehmet Hassan would arrive, and how soon it would be before negotiations for Shane's release could be initiated.

'How long will you be away?'

Their drinks arrived and it was a few minutes before he answered.

'A week.'

'I can only wish you an enjoyable and successful sojourn with your guests.'

He inclined his head in mocking acknowledgement. 'While you will be glad to be free of my presence.'

'Of course,' she agreed sweetly. 'It will be a relief not to have to pretend to be enamoured of you.'

The starter was served and Kristi found it delectable. The main course, when it arrived, was a visual work of art.

'It seems a shame to disturb such artistic symmetry.' She picked up her fork and carefully speared a segment of lamb, then paused in the action of transferring it to her mouth as a waiter approached the table and spoke to Shalef in a respectful undertone, listened to the response, then bowed his head and moved away.

'Fayza is visiting her family in Riyadh,' Shalef revealed. 'She is here with her brother and suggests we join them for coffee. Do you mind?'

Oh, *joy*. 'Why not?' Her smile was bright, her tone vivacious.

'You're in danger of creating a case of overkill,' he drawled.

'Why, *Shalef*,' she reproved with deliberate mockery, 'would I do such a thing?'

His eyes gleamed with dark humour. 'I suspect you might.'

'We could,' Kristi mused thoughtfully, 'consider it pay-back time for your unwarranted kiss in the garden.'

One eyebrow rose. 'Unwarranted?'

'Finish your dinner,' she bade him solemnly. 'We mustn't keep the lovely Fayza waiting.'

'Remind me to exact due punishment.'

'A threat?'

'More in the nature of a promise.'

She pretended deliberation. 'Is she merely one of many women in your life or is she special?'

'I have known Fayza for a number of years.'

'Ah,' Kristi responded with comprehension, 'the "we're just good friends" spiel. Does she know that?' She looked at him, then shook her head. 'No, don't answer. She lusts after you, and your wealth is a magnificent bonus. Or should it be the other way round?' She savoured another mouthful of food. 'Mmm, this is good.' She summoned a winsome smile. 'Should I play the jealous "companion", do you think? Take your hands off him, he's mine? Or the bored socialite who knows she has you by the... Well, let's just say I'm very sure I have your attention.'

Shalef finished the course and replaced his cutlery. 'One day some man is going to take you severely in hand.'

'Rest assured it won't be you,' Kristi responded, pushing her empty plate to one side. 'Shall we enter the battlefield?'

Fayza greeted Kristi with polite civility, proffered Shalef a stunning smile, and allowed her brother to perform his own introduction.

You just had to admire Fayza's style, Kristi commended her silently almost an hour later. Demure, with a touch of the exotic, the hint of seething passion beneath a chaste exterior. Was Shalef fooled? Somehow she thought not.

'You are a professional photographer?' Fayza made it sound the lowest of lowly occupations, and Kristi had a difficult time remaining calm.

'It's a job,' she dismissed, and glimpsed the young woman's deliberate raising of one eyebrow.

'I have a degree in business management. But, of course, it's unnecessary for me to work.'

'What a shame,' Kristi sympathised. 'All that study and no need to apply it.'

Fayza's eyes darkened. 'Surely a woman's focus should be looking after a man? Ensuring his home is a tranquil haven?'

Oh, dear, what had she begun? Kristi wondered. She was in the wrong country, and probably in the wrong company, to converse on feminist issues. 'One has to allow that it's possible not all men desire tranquillity,' she opined with due cautiousness.

'Shalef,' Fayza appealed with just the right degree of helpless virtue, 'Miss Dalton has little understanding of a woman's role in Saudi Arabia.' She honed her weapons and aimed for the kill. 'However, I imagine such knowledge is of no importance to her.'

It was obvious that she was unsure of the precise depth of Kristi's relationship with Shalef bin Youssef Al-Sayed, despite the inevitable gossip which would have circulated among the cream of Riyadh society.

It allowed Kristi the advantage of responding with an enigmatic smile.

'You're wrong,' she submitted quietly. 'On both counts.'

Fayza managed a creditable attempt at disbelief. 'Really?'

'If you'll excuse us?' Shalef asked Fayza and her brother. 'It's quite late.' He signalled to the *maître d'*, signed the proffered credit slip, then rose to his feet.

The fact that he took hold of Kristi's hand and enfolded it in his didn't escape Fayza's notice.

'One imagines you will fly out to the hunting lodge during your stay in Riyadh?'

Shalef's expression mirrored polite civility. 'It is something I allow time for whenever I am here.'

'Falconry sounds such a fascinating sport,' Kristi offered, and she gave him an adoring glance. 'Perhaps you could take me out to the lodge some time, darling? It would be a fascinating experience to witness your skill with the falcon.'

Shalef's fingers tightened measurably on her own, and there was little she could do to wrench them from his grasp as Fayza and her brother accompanied them to the hotel foyer, then stood briefly while the doorman summoned both cars to the main entrance.

Immediately Shalef and Kristi were seated the chauffeur eased the Mercedes onto the road and headed towards the palace.

'You excelled yourself tonight,' Shalef commented with dangerous smoothness, and she turned to look at him. The dim light inside the car accentuated the strong angles and planes of his facial bone structure.

'I wasn't the only one acting a part.'

'No,' he agreed as the car sped through the quiet city streets.

All too soon they reached the palace gates, and Kristi followed Shalef from the vehicle when it drew to a halt outside the main entrance.

'Thank you for a pleasant evening,' she said politely once they were indoors. 'Will I see you before you leave tomorrow?'

'The helicopter pilot has been instructed to be ready at seven.'

'In that case I'll wish you a pleasant stay and ask that you be in touch with any news.' She turned away only to come to a halt as a detaining hand clasped her shoulder and brought her back to face him.

'Don't,' he warned with threatening intent, 'concoct a scheme to visit the hunting lodge.'

Her eyes were wide and remarkably clear. 'Why would I do that?'

'You've dared many things in your career.' His hands crept up to cradle her head. 'The hunting lodge and the identities of my guests are *my* business. Do you understand?'

'Yes.' She *did* understand. Yet that didn't change her intention to put a carefully devised plan into action. For days she'd surreptitiously observed the servants' routine, and she knew where the keys to the vehicles were kept. She also knew how to disengage the palace alarm system, as well as the system connected to the garages. She had a map, and over the next few days she would encourage Fouad to en-lighten her about the art of falconry and to disclose the precise whereabouts of the hunting lodge.

However, Shalef wasn't to know that.

'Make sure that you do,' he said hardly. His head descended and he took possession of her mouth, plun-dering it in a manner that bordered on the primitive, and when he released her she lifted a shaking hand to her bruised lips.

'I think I hate you.'

His eyes were so dark that they were almost black, and he offered no apology.

Without another word she turned and made her way to the wide, curved stairway that led to the upper floor, and in her room she slowly removed the bor-rowed *abaaya* and the silken evening clothes beneath it before entering the *en suite* bathroom. Minutes later she slid into bed and systematically went over every aspect of the palace security system, then mentally calculated when she would initiate her plan.

CHAPTER FIVE

KRISTI dressed quickly in blue cotton trousers and a matching cotton shirt, dispensed with make-up except for moisturising cream, twisted her hair on top of her head and secured it with pins, pulled on a cap, pushed her feet into trainers, then scrutinised her appearance, satisfied that she could easily pass for a reed-slim young man.

With a swift glance round the elegant suite, she caught up the backpack into which she'd pushed a change of clothes and minimum necessities then moved silently into the hallway.

The palace was quiet. In another hour Amani and Abdullah would begin organising the staff with daily chores.

Part of her deplored the subterfuge of removing the remote control and spare set of keys to the four-wheel drive from Abdullah's desk. It made her feel like a thief.

Kristi gained the ground floor and made her way to a rear side-door, disengaged the security alarm, then slipped outside and moved quickly to the garages.

For the first time she sent a prayer heavenward for expensive equipment as she depressed the remote

control and saw one set of double doors lift upwards
with scarcely more than an electronic whisper.

The four-wheel drive was large, with wide tyres
and attached spotlights, spare petrol and water cans.
There was no time for second thoughts, and she de-
activated the alarm, then unlocked and opened the
door.

She had driven a Jeep and a smaller four-wheel
drive, but this was a monster by comparison. CB radio, car phone…the interior was crammed with every
conceivable extra imaginable.

Kristi checked the low reduction, ran through the
gears, then started up the engine. All she had to do
now was deactivate the security alarm at the gates,
release them, and she was on her way.

There wasn't a hitch, and she gave thanks to
heaven as she gained the road and moved the heavy
vehicle swiftly through its numerous gears.

During the past few days she'd spent considerable
time memorising streets, time and distance. At this
early hour of the morning there was no other traffic
to speak of, and her passage through the city was
uneventful.

In another hour it would be light, and by then she'd
be on the long road snaking into the desert.

She calculated that she had two hours, perhaps
three, before her absence would be noticed. What she
couldn't surmise was how Nashwa would react to her
carefully penned note. Doubtless Abdullah would be
consulted, and Fouad. There was always the possibil-

ity that she would reach the hunting lodge before anyone could notify Shalef.

His anger was something she preferred not to envisage, and a faint shiver feathered her skin at the
prospect of weathering his wrath.

The buildings began to dwindle, the houses became
fewer and far between, then there was nothing except
the sparse expanse of desert, stretching out beneath
the vehicle's powerful headlights.

Kristi seemed to have driven for ages before the
sky began to lighten, dimming the shadows and bathing the land with a soft, ethereal glow. As the sun
rose the colours deepened and the sky changed to the
palest blue.

There was a sense of isolation—the grandeur of the
sand and the gentle undulation of the land, the stark
beauty of the contrasting colour between earth and
sky.

The desert seemed so vast, so…inhibiting, Kristi
mused. Frightening, she added, aware that a sudden
sandstorm could cover the road, obliterating it entirely
from view.

Don't even think about it, she chastised herself silently. It won't happen. And even if it did she would
only be briefly stranded, for she could notify the palace—*anyone*—of her whereabouts via the car phone
or CB.

As the sun rose higher in the sky its warmth began
to penetrate the vehicle and Kristi switched on the
air-conditioning and donned her sunglasses.

With careful manoeuvring she extracted a water

bottle and a packet of sandwiches from her backpack, then ate as she drove, not wanting to stop and waste time.

As the sun rose further the bitumen began to shimmer with a reflective heat haze. It played havoc with her vision and brought the onset of a headache.

There was almost a sense of relief when she glimpsed a vehicle in her rear-view mirror. It gained on her steadily, then pulled out to pass.

There were two men in the front seat and the passenger gave her an intent look then turned to the driver. Instead of passing, they maintained an even pace with her vehicle, then gestured for her to pull over.

It didn't make sense, so she ignored the directive, accelerating to gain speed. Within seconds they were abreast of her once again, and this time there could be no mistaking their intention to have her pull over and stop.

When she didn't comply, the driver positioned the side of his vehicle against hers, and she felt the sickening thud of metal against metal.

She sped ahead, reached for the CB speaker, depressed the switch and spoke into it rapidly, giving her identity, approximate location and indicating the problem.

The men drew level again, and this time the four-wheel drive took a pounding. Kristi held onto the wheel for grim death and managed to get ahead of them.

Risking a quick glance in the rear-view mirror, she

felt fear clutch hold of her stomach as she saw their vehicle in hot pursuit.

She was an experienced driver. With luck, skill and divine assistance, she thought she might manage to outdistance them.

Within a matter of seconds the vehicle was right behind her, then it pulled out and inched forward until it was abreast. The passenger gestured with a rifle for her to pull over.

There was no point in arguing with someone wielding a loaded firearm so she began to brake.

There was the sound of a shot, followed almost simultaneously by the soft thud of a blown-out tyre, then the vehicle slewed horribly to one side.

For what seemed like half a lifetime she battled to maintain some sort of control and bring the four-wheel drive to a halt, then she hit the door-locking mechanism, grabbed the car phone, hit a coded button, and when a heavily accented male voice answered she relayed an identical message, hoping, praying that whoever was on the other end of the line understood English. In desperation she repeated it in French before replacing the receiver.

She watched with mounting apprehension as one man crossed to the passenger side while the other attempted to wrench open the door closest to her.

They yelled instructions in Arabic, and shook their fists at her when she indicated a refusal to comply.

The man with the rifle crossed round to the passenger side, carefully took aim, then shot the lock.

There wasn't a flicker of emotion evident in their

expressions as they gestured for her to move outside, the command enforced as the driver reached in and hauled her unceremoniously across the passenger seat and threw her down onto the ground.

Two hands grabbed her shoulders and dragged her to her feet. She stood still, returning their heated looks with angry intensity.

The driver reached out and pulled the cap from her head, then gaped in amazement and broke into a heated conversation with his fellow assailant.

Kristi lifted a shaky hand and tucked some of her hair behind one ear. The gesture was involuntary, and both men immediately stopped speaking.

Kristi fixed each of them with a scathing look, then pointed at her four-wheel drive. 'Sheikh Shalef bin Youssef Al-Sayed.' Then she touched a hand to her heart. 'Shalef bin Youssef Al-Sayed,' she repeated with soft vehemence.

The men conversed in rapid Arabic, arguing volubly for what seemed an age, then they turned towards her, subjecting her to a long look that encompassed her slim figure from head to toe before settling with stony-faced anger on her expressive features.

One word was uttered with such force that its explicitness couldn't fail to be universally understood.

It took considerable effort to hold their gazes, but she managed it, unwilling to respond in English, knowing that any verbal exchange would be totally useless.

The car phone rang, its insistent summons sounding

loud in the surrounding stillness, and she lifted one eyebrow in silent query.

For several long seconds they seemed undecided as to whether she should answer, then the driver gave a brief nod and she scrambled into the front seat and snatched up the receiver. When she turned round the men were climbing into their vehicle, and, gunning the engine, tyres spinning, they roared at great speed down the road.

'Kristi? Fouad. Shalef is on his way. Are you all right?'

'I'm OK. The four-wheel drive hasn't fared so well.'

'And the two men?'

'They've just left.'

'Did you get the vehicle plate number?'

'It wasn't high on my list of priorities,' Kristi informed him drily. She thought that she detected a faint noise and quickly checked the rear-view mirror, then swung her attention to the road ahead. Nothing. The noise grew louder and her eyes caught a movement to her right. A helicopter. 'I think the cavalry is about to arrive.'

'The CB and car phone automatically access the palace,' Fouad revealed. 'The instant you rang in I notified Shalef on his mobile net.'

'I imagine all hell is about to break loose.'

'For me it already has.'

'None of this is your fault.'

'I am responsible in Shalef's absence. Therefore some of the blame falls on my head.'

The noise was incredibly loud, the rotor-blades whirling up the dust as the machine settled down a short distance away.

'I can't hear a thing. I'll have to hang up,' Kristi shouted into the receiver, then replaced it slowly as the helicopter door swung open and Shalef jumped down to the ground.

With a sense of detached fascination she watched as he strode towards the four-wheel drive. In a black *thobe* and red and white checked *gutra* he presented a formidable figure.

Suppressed rage emanated from his taut frame. She saw it reflected in his harshly set features as she wound down the window and sat waiting for him to say something—anything.

He opened the door and his eyes pierced hers, penetrating their mirrored depths. 'You are unharmed?'

Kristi wanted to laugh. Except that if she did, she'd never stop. Hysterical reaction, she recognised, and banked it down. This wasn't the first tight situation she'd been in, and it probably wouldn't be the last.

'I'm in one piece, as you can see,' she dismissed lightly.

'Then I suggest you get out of the vehicle.'

The four-wheel drive wasn't going anywhere in a hurry until some worthy soul jacked it up and changed the tyre.

With brief economy of movement she slid from the seat and stepped down. He was much too close, his height and breadth much too...intimidating, she decided.

'I'm sorry about this,' Kristi began, indicating the vehicle with a sweep of her hand.

'Shut up,' Shalef directed quietly, and her eyes widened fractionally.

'You're angry,' she said unnecessarily.

'Did you expect me not to be?' Hard words that had the power to flay the skin from her body. His eyes seemed to sear her soul. 'I issued express instructions that you were to stay at the palace.'

'I had a map,' she said.

'And resorted to subterfuge.'

'Fouad had nothing to do—'

'Fouad will answer to me. As you will.' His gaze raked her slim form, noting the graze on one wrist, the light scratch above her temple. 'The helicopter is waiting.'

'I have a backpack in the four-wheel drive.'

He gave her a searching look, then reached in and retrieved it from the floor. 'Let's go.'

Kristi walked at his side, protesting as he placed his hands at her waist and lifted her into the cabin.

'The rear seat. I'll take the front.'

It would have been difficult to do anything but comply, and, once seated, she secured the belt as Shalef swung up behind her.

The pilot set the helicopter in the air, then wheeled it away in a north-westerly direction. The noise precluded conversation, and since she wasn't offered a set of headphones she sat in silence and focused her attention on the swiftly passing ground below.

She saw the road, and three vehicles blocking another. Her assailants, surrounded by a party of men wielding rifles. Were they the police, or guards in Shalef's employ?

Kristi heard Shalef issue instructions in Arabic and the acknowledgement of the pilot as he swung away from the scene.

Were they heading back to the palace? She wanted to ask but dared not, aware that she would see soon enough.

Within minutes she caught sight of a building, and her breathing quickened as the helicopter cruised down to settle on a helipad inside the compound.

The hunting lodge.

The engine cut out and the rotors slowed as Shalef swung out onto the ground. Kristi followed, catching her breath as he lifted her from the cabin.

His eyes clashed with hers for an interminable few seconds, and she almost died when she saw the ruthlessness in their depths.

Retaining hold of her arm, he led her across a large grassed area to the house, and once indoors he traversed a hallway and drew her into a room near its end.

The door closed with a refined clunk, and the sound had an unsettling effect on her nerves.

'Now,' he intoned silkily, 'tell me everything that happened. Not,' he qualified, 'how you evaded the palace security system and commandeered one of my vehicles.' His eyes became faintly hooded, and she had the feeling that he was keeping a tight rein on his temper. 'From the moment you were threatened by those two thugs.'

Her chin lifted and her eyes were faintly clouded. 'What will happen to them?'

A muscle tensed at the edge of his jaw and his expression hardened with controlled anger. 'They will be dealt with, and charges laid against them. Most certainly they face jail.'

She shivered slightly, aware that the scenario could have had a very different ending if she had not been privileged with Shalef's protection.

'They probably wanted to alleviate their boredom by having a bit of fun.'

His hand slid up to cup her chin, lifting it so that she had to look at him. 'Saudi Arabian women are *not* permitted to drive,' he relayed with soft emphasis.

Kristi digested his implication in silence, unwilling to put a connotation she wasn't sure of on the two men's actions.

Her eyes widened as they searched his, and her stomach executed an emotional somersault that sent warning flares to various pulse spots throughout her body, activating a rapid beat that was clearly visible at the base of her throat.

'I'm sorry.'

'At this precise moment I find it difficult not to make you sorry for the day you were born,' he threatened softly.

Apprehension feathered a trail down the length of her spine as she willed herself to hold his gaze. 'Punishing me to appease your own anger will achieve nothing.'

He released her chin and thrust both hands into the pockets of his *thobe*. 'Your story, Kristi,' he reiterated hardly. 'All of it.'

With deliberate detachment she relayed what had happened from the moment the men's four-wheel drive had drawn alongside her.

Shalef listened intently, his eyes never leaving her face, and when she finished he turned and crossed to the window.

It probably wasn't the time to ask, but she had to know. 'Is Mehmet Hassan at the lodge?'

'No.'

Utter dejection dulled her eyes. Her trip to Riyadh had been in vain. 'So he didn't arrive,' she said in a flat voice.

'He flew out yesterday.'

'So he was here,' she breathed in sheer relief. 'Did you speak to him about Shane?'

Shalef turned towards her. 'There can be no guarantees,' he warned. 'None, you understand?'

Elation radiated through her body, turning her expressive features into something quite beautiful. 'It's the best chance Shane has.' Without thinking she crossed to his side and placed her lips against his cheek. 'Thank you.'

Something flickered in the depths of his eyes, then one hand slid to her nape, his fingers spreading beneath her hair to capture her head, while the other settled at the base of her spine.

Vibrant energy emanated from every pore, exuding an erotic power that she consciously fought against in an effort to retain a gram of sanity.

Kristi saw his head descend as if in slow motion, and her lips parted to voice an involuntary protest as his mouth closed over hers.

No man had ever kissed her with quite such a degree of restrained passion, and she shivered at the thought of what force might be unleashed if ever he allowed himself to lose control.

He plundered at will, ignoring the faint protesting groan that rose and died in her throat, and the ineffectual punches she aimed at his shoulders.

Kristi wasn't aware of precisely when the pressure changed, only that it did, and there was a wealth of mastery evident as his tongue explored the softness inside her mouth, then tangled with hers in a swirling dance that took hold of her conflicting emotions and tossed them high.

Almost of its own volition her body swayed into his, and her hands reached for his shoulders, then linked together behind his head.

His hand spread against her lower spine, lifting her in against him, and his mouth hardened in demanding possession.

The kiss frightened her, awakening sensations that tore at her control and ripped it to shreds. She wanted him, badly. So badly that when his hand moved to cup her breast she gave an indistinct groan of despair and closed her eyes, exulting in the moment and the heady emotions that he was able to arouse.

When his mouth left hers she made a slight murmur of protest, then cried out as he teased a trail of evocative kisses down the sensitised cord at the side of her neck. His lips circled the rapidly beating pulse as he savoured it with his tongue, and she went up in flames, uncaring at that precise moment as his fingers loosened the buttons on her blouse.

He dealt with the front fastening of her bra with adept ease, and she arched her throat as his lips sought one taut peak, tasting it gently, then teasing the engorged nipple with the edge of his teeth until she hovered between pleasure and pain.

Just as she thought that she could bear no more, he drew it in with his tongue and began to suckle shamelessly. Extreme ecstasy arrowed through her body, centring at the junction between her thighs, and she gave a low, gratified groan when his hand slid to ease the ache there.

It wasn't enough. It would never be enough. Yet when his fingers sought the zip-fastener of her jeans she stilled, caught between the heaven of discovering what it would be like to share with him the ultimate intimacy and the hell of knowing that if she did she'd never be the same again.

He sensed her indecision and moved his hand back to the base of her spine, trailing it gently up and down the vertebral column in a soothing motion that heightened her emotions even further.

With considerable care he closed the edges of her blouse and re-did the buttons, then he gently pushed her to arm's length.

'I'll instruct the servants to prepare something for you to eat.'

Kristi wanted to close her eyes and dismiss the previous ten minutes. Yet such a feat wasn't possible. Somehow she had to reassemble her emotions into some sort of order and act as if everything was normal. If *he* could, then so could she.

'I'm not hungry.' She had to look at him, and she managed it bravely.

'If you should change your mind, just go into the kitchen and help yourself.'

She didn't want to ask but the words tumbled out before she could halt them. 'When will you be back?'

'Before dark.'

He turned and left the room, and she could hear his footsteps retreating down the hallway.

Kristi stood where she was for a long time, then she stirred and looked round the room, noting the masculine appointments, the king-size bed. She walked to the *en suite* bathroom and examined the spa, deciding on a whim to fill it and take a leisurely bath.

Half an hour later she switched off the jets and climbed out, then towelled herself dry. She crossed into the bedroom and extracted fresh underwear from her bag, donned clean trousers and blouse, then went in search of the kitchen.

The lodge was reasonably large, comfortably furnished, and entirely male. Kristi wondered idly if Shalef ever brought any women here, then dismissed the idea. He had homes in capital cities all over the world. Why bring a woman here, when he could woo her in luxurious surroundings in an exotic location?

She found the kitchen and discovered it occupied by a middle-aged woman and a young girl. From the aroma permeating the air it was apparent that they were preparing a meal. Simultaneously they turned to look at her as she entered their domain.

The older woman beckoned as she crossed to a bank of cupboards, took out a plate and cutlery, then crossed to the stove and ladled a generous portion from each pot onto the plate.

It was more than Kristi could possibly eat, and she used sign language to indicate that she required less than half. Seconds later she was shown into an informal dining room and seated at the table.

The food was good, the meat tender and succulent, the vegetables cooked with herbs, lending a delicate flavour.

The afternoon seemed to drag, and she wished that she had something to read…anything to pass the time. There was a television somewhere, for she'd seen a satellite dish when they'd flown in. Perhaps if she went on a tour of the lodge she'd eventually find it. There might even be stereo equipment and compact discs.

Kristi discovered both in an informal lounge adjoining the games room, and after checking the electronic remote control she switched on the television and went through numerous channel changes before settling on one.

It was after five when she heard the sound of vehicles returning, and she crossed to the window to watch as four men exited one Jeep and three stepped down from the other.

Shalef was easily identifiable, and she wondered which of the men were friends and which were staff. More importantly, did they speak English? If not, conversation over dinner was going to prove difficult.

From the sound of their voices it seemed that they'd had a successful day. There was deep laughter, followed shortly by the closing of doors as the men retired to their rooms to wash and change for the evening meal.

'I thought I might find you here.'

Kristi turned in surprise, for she hadn't heard Shalef enter the room. His black *thobe* had been exchanged for one of dark brown, and he presented an indomitable figure. A man who held sufficient power to shape his own life and change the lives of many of his fellow men. His effect on women didn't need qualification.

'You have a comprehensive audio-visual system,' she complimented lightly as she rose to her feet. His height was intimidating from a seated position, and she felt the need of any advantage she could gain.

He inclined his head in silent acknowledgement. 'Dinner will be served in half an hour.'

She looked at him carefully, noting the fine lines fanning out from the corners of his eyes, the vertical cleft slashing each cheek, and the strong jawline curving down to a determined chin.

Although she felt at ease in the company of men,

she was aware of the segregation of the sexes in this country.

'It won't bother me if you'd prefer to dine alone with your guests.'

His eyes darkened fractionally and he made an impatient gesture. 'They know you are here, and I have no inclination to hide you away in a separate room.'

Kristi effected a slight shrug and cast her clothes a rueful glance. 'I'm not exactly dressed to impress.'

'You are not required to impress,' Shalef returned with mocking amusement. 'Shall we join our guests?'

The four men varied in age from early thirties to mid-fifties, and their status was evident in their distinguished bearing and demeanour. A Western woman in their midst was viewed with polite circumspection, and if they thought Shalef bin Youssef Al-Sayed had temporarily lost a measure of his sanity they were careful by word and action not to give a hint of this.

English was spoken throughout the evening, but although the conversation flowed easily Kristi gained the impression that her presence was an intrusion.

After coffee had been served she excused herself and bade the men goodnight.

In her room she shed her clothes, removed her bra and briefs, handwashed both and draped them over a towel stand in the *en suite* bathroom to dry, then she slid between the crisp, clean sheets of the king-size bed and switched off the lamp.

The darkness was like an enveloping blanket, and she lay staring sightlessly ahead, her mind active as she weighed Mehmet Hassan's influence in negotiating Shane's release.

How long would it take? Days—*weeks*? What if he wasn't successful at all?

Kristi plumped the pillow and turned on her side. She'd been up since an hour before dawn and she was tired.

Overtired, she cursed silently an age later. She should never have had coffee after her meal.

A shaft of light lanced through the darkness then disappeared, and she detected the almost silent click of the bedroom door.

Who—? She reached out and switched on the lamp, then gave a surprised gasp at the sight of Shalef in the process of removing his *thobe*.

CHAPTER SIX

'WHAT the hell are you doing here?' Kristi's voice was filled with outrage.

Shalef directed her a faintly mocking look. 'This happens to be my personal suite.'

She sat up, carrying the sheet with her. 'Either you go to another room or I will,' she vented with thinly veiled fury.

'The lodge has four guest suites,' he enlightened her. 'I have four guests.'

'Couldn't two of your guests share?'

'Each suite is identical to this one,' he revealed. 'To suggest sharing would constitute a grave insult.' His mouth curved into an amused smile. 'You are my...' he paused deliberately '...woman. Where else would you sleep, except with me?'

'Like hell,' Kristi said inelegantly.

'I don't perceive there is a problem. The bed is large.'

It might not be a problem for him, but there was no way she would calmly accept sharing the same room with him, let alone the same bed.

'I'll get dressed and go sleep on the sofa in the entertainment room,' she declared purposefully.

'And risk the possibility of being discovered by any one of my guests who might find it difficult to sleep and seeks the solace of music or television for an hour or two?' One eyebrow slanted. 'At least here you are beneath my protection.'

Anger lent her eyes a fiery sparkle. 'I don't want to be beneath you for *any* reason.'

He began to laugh softly. 'I'm pleased to hear you enjoy variety.'

Colour flooded her cheeks, and, without thinking, she caught up a nearby pillow and threw it at him, uncaring at that precise moment if he should choose some form of retribution.

He fielded it neatly and tossed it back onto the bed, then he continued undressing, and she was unable to look away from the superb musculature of his near-naked body. Sinews stretched and flexed, their fluid movement beneath silk-sheened skin a visual attestation to a man who took care to maintain a physical fitness regime.

When he reached his briefs she averted her gaze. She wasn't sufficiently bold to watch as he stripped off the last vestige of clothing.

Damn him. Didn't he possess a skerrick of modesty?

Determination set her features into an angry mask. 'I'll opt for the chair.'

Shalef walked calmly to the opposite side of the bed and slid in beneath the covers. 'As you please.'

'It doesn't please me at all,' she vented in a furious undertone as she scrambled to her feet. She wrenched the sheet from the bed and wrapped it round her slim form, holding it firmly above her breasts with taut fingers as she scooped up the excess length.

'Be careful you don't trip,' came a lazy drawl, and she turned to shoot him a fulminating glare.

The chair was large and looked reasonably comfortable, and she curled into its cushioned depths, adjusting the sheet so that it covered every visible inch of her, then positioned her head on the armrest and closed her eyes.

The early-morning start coupled with the events of the day gradually overcame her resentment, and she drifted into a light doze, only to stir some hours later as the air temperature dropped several points. The sheet was no longer adequate against the coolness of the air-conditioning, and she carefully attempted to reassemble its folds so that it provided another layer of cover.

Half an hour later any thought of sleep was impossible. There had to be a store of blankets somewhere, but as she had no knowledge of where they might be there was no point in trying to search for them in the dark. That only left the clothes she'd discarded earlier.

With considerable care she sat up and attempted to orientate herself to her surroundings. The *en suite* bathroom had to be directly ahead, the bed to her left, and the door to her right. Therefore all she had to do was creep into the bathroom, reach for her clothes, don them, and creep back to the chair.

She dared not risk putting on a light, even had she been able to remember precisely where any one of several switches were located. And the room was dark. Not inky black, but sufficiently shrouded to make any movement in unfamiliar territory a bit of a hazard.

Kristi knew that she could handle the situation in one of two ways: carefully, so that she didn't make any noise and disturb the man sleeping in the nearby bed, or brazenly, by searching for the light switch and waking Shalef. Somehow *carefully* presented itself as the better option.

The sheet had to go. It would rustle with every move. Seconds later she eased out from the chair and trod slowly across the room. Four, six, eight, ten steps. The *en suite* bathroom's door should be a few more steps ahead to her left.

Except that when she reached for the knob she discovered the wall. It had to be further along. Inch by inch she moved to the left, then clenched her teeth as her toe made contact with a solid piece of furniture.

'Kristi?'

She spun towards the sound of that deep male voice and cried out in anguished despair, 'Don't turn on the light!' Dear God, this had to rank high on her list of embarrassing moments. 'The sheet is on the chair!'

'And you're afraid I might catch a glimpse of you *au naturel*?'

He was amused. Oh, how she'd like to wipe the smile from his face and delete the mockery from his voice! 'I was looking for my clothes.'

'I doubt you'll find them in my wardrobe.'

She drew in a deep breath. 'I left them in the *en suite* bathroom.'

'Your sense of direction leaves something to be desired,' Shalef informed her drily. 'The *en suite* is several feet to your left.'

Kristi wanted to throw something at him and, preferably, have it connect with a vulnerable part of his anatomy. 'Thank you,' she acknowledged with as much civility as she could muster, then gave an anguished cry as the room was illuminated. 'I asked you not to do that!' The fact that he had a view of her back didn't make it any less mortifying.

'I doubt I could forgive himself if you were to add to your list of existing injuries.' She detected the soft sound of bedclothes, sensed rather than heard him move.

She began to shake, partly with anger, partly from sheer reaction. 'At least have the decency to get me a shirt—*anything*.'

He hadn't touched her, but she felt the loss of his immediate presence as much as if she'd been in his embrace.

Seconds later he was back. 'Lift your arms.'

She obeyed, feeling the coolness of fine cotton on her skin as he slid the sleeves in place, then smoothed the shirt over her shoulders. Her fingers clutched the front edges and drew them together.

'You look like a child playing with grown-up clothes,' Shalef commented with a soft laugh. The shirt-tail brushed the backs of her calves and the sleeves were far too long. 'Now,' he ordered quietly, 'get into bed before I put you there.'

She turned round to face him, increasingly aware of his essential maleness, and her heart leapt, then thudded into a quickened beat.

One eyebrow lifted in a gesture of silent mockery. 'Do you really want to suffer a loss of dignity?'

What price defeat? Yet she refused to concede easily. 'Don't close your eyes, Shalef,' she warned. 'I might seek vengeance in the night.'

He reached out and caught hold of her chin between thumb and forefinger. 'Be aware that such an action will have only one ending.'

Something clawed at her innermost being, tightening into a deep, shooting pain that radiated from her feminine core. Sex with this man, simply as an assuagement of anger, would tear her emotions to shreds.

'I don't like being manipulated.' Yet she was helpless in this present situation, and she hated the thought of capitulation.

'You placed your fate in my hands when you left the sanctuary of the palace for the desert,' he reminded her, tilting her chin as he studied the conflict visible in her expressive features.

She opened her mouth to voice a protest, only to have it stilled by the placing of his finger over her lips.

Her eyes mirrored her inner anguish, and the pressure on her mouth eased. 'You could have sent me back. Why didn't you?'

The curve of his mouth deepened as it relaxed into a faint smile. 'Perhaps it pleases me to have you here.' His forefinger brushed over the contour of her lower lip, then travelled a similar path along the upper curve.

A deep shiver feathered its way down her spine at his action, and she consciously stilled the flood of warmth that invaded her veins.

'To share with you the stark beauty and the cruelty of a land that holds such an attraction for the men born to it.' His hand moved to cup her chin, while the other lifted and held fast her nape.

Kristi hated the sudden breathlessness that seemed to have taken control of her lungs. She had to stop this *now*. 'It's late, I'm tired, and I'd like to get some sleep.'

His faint smile was tinged with wry humour. 'So too would I.' He released her, and walked round to the opposite side of the bed. 'Get in, Kristi,' he ordered with dangerous softness as he slid in beneath the covers.

Something leapt inside her—anger, fear, *resentment* at his high-handedness. Yet instinct warned her not to voice it. The consequences of doing so hung like a palpable threat, and she had no intention of providing further provocation.

With extreme care she took the few steps to the bed, then lifted the covers and lay down as close to the edge of the mattress as possible.

Seconds later she felt the slight movement as he

reached for the lamp switch, then the room was plunged into darkness.

Her body was the antithesis of relaxed, with every cell, every nerve acutely tuned to the presence of the man lying within touching distance. It was almost as if every part of her was silently reaching out to him, *aware* to such a degree that she ached with need.

Imagining what it would be like to have him caress each pleasure pulse, touch his lips to every part of her body was an unbearable torture. And that would be only the prelude to a concerto that she instinctively knew would be wildly passionate, its crescendo bringing such tumultuous joy that a woman might feel as if she'd died and gone to heaven.

Or was it simply a fallacy, a fantasy created by emotions so strong, so impossibly vivid that the reality could only be a disappointment by comparison?

Kristi assured herself that she didn't want to find out. You lie, a tiny voice taunted.

Dammit, *sleep*, she commanded herself silently with irritated frustration. In desperation she forced herself to breathe evenly in an attempt to slow the emotional pendulum.

She wasn't successful, and it seemed an age that she lay staring sightlessly at the ceiling, hating, *hating* the ease with which the man slept beside her.

Eventually she must have dozed, for when she woke the darkness of night had been replaced by an early-dawn light that filtered into the room, dispensing with shadows and providing colour where previously there had been none.

Slowly, carefully, she turned her head, only to find the bed empty, and a long, shuddering breath left her body as she stretched each limb in turn before rolling over onto her stomach. One more blissful hour, then she'd rise from the bed, shower and dress, before seeking some food and strong black coffee.

The next thing she knew was a hand on her shoulder and a deep male voice intoning, 'If you want to accompany me into the desert, you have fifteen minutes to dress and eat.'

Kristi lifted her head from the pillow and felt her pulse leap at the sight of Shalef standing at the side of the bed.

'I thought you had already left.' With deft movements she secured the top few buttons of her shirt, tugged its length into respectability, then slid to her feet.

'My guests have. I'll join them later in the day.' He reached out and smoothed back the tousled length of her hair.

The breath caught in her throat, momentarily robbing her of the ability to speak. 'Please don't do that.'

His smile was infinitely lazy. 'You sound almost afraid.'

Because I am, she longed to cry out. 'You said fifteen minutes,' she reminded him, neatly sidestepping him as she moved towards the *en suite* bathroom.

'I'll have one of the servants pour your coffee.'

She would have been willing to swear that she detected a tinge of humour in his voice, and she quickly showered, then pulled on her clothes.

When she entered the dining room there was a dish of fresh fruit salad, toast, and the tantalising aroma of freshly brewed coffee, steaming from a small pot.

When she had finished the meal she joined Shalef in the foyer.

'You'll need to wear a *shayla* and apply sunscreen.'

She stood perfectly still as he fixed the long scarf in position. 'Shall we leave?'

The four-wheel drive was the same model as the one she'd driven from the palace, and she wondered if he'd ordered them by the half-dozen.

An hour later Shalef eased the vehicle off the road and drove along a well-worn track for several kilometres before slowing to a halt close to a large black tent.

He indicated a tall elderly man moving forward to greet them. 'My father sprang from the seed of the Bedouin. I thought it might interest you to meet some of them. We'll be offered coffee, which if we refuse will cause offence. Remember to accept the cup with your right hand. Follow my example.'

He offered her a faintly quizzical smile. 'This man and his family have no command of English. They will accept your dutiful silence as a mark of respect for me.' He leaned forward and caught the edge of her *shayla*, adjusting it to form a partial veil. 'Let the edge fall when we are inside the tent and refreshments are about to be served.'

Kristi was enthralled by their hosts, and she was careful to follow Shalef's brief instructions, all the time aware of their circumspect appraisal.

Her jeans were well washed, their cut generous, and her chambray shirt was buttoned almost to the neck, the sleeves long and cuffed. The *shayla* felt a little strange, but it covered her head and shoulders.

Out here, she could almost sense Shalef's empathy with these people, the link by birth, the inheritance of definitive genes. He was at one with them, yet different.

His education, she knew, had been extensive, and gained in one of the best boarding-schools in England. He was fluent in several languages and held a doctorate. His business acumen and standing in the financial sector were legendary. Yet he spoke Arabic as if it were his first language, mingled with the Bedu, and chose the simplicity and the relative isolation of this desert land for his home for weeks on end at least twice a year.

Was the call of his Bedouin blood so strong? Or was it contrived out of duty to his late father, to Nashwa and her daughters?

The woman in his life would have to understand that, while she could be his hostess in London, New York, Paris, Lucerne or Rome, there would be times when she would need not only to accompany him to Riyadh, but to accept the severe restrictions that extended to women in this land. She would also have to don the *abaaya*, *shayla* and veil—light, gauzy colours in the palace, and black in public. She would have to forgo her independence temporarily, and never in the presence of others would she be able to question his opinions, his direction or his wishes.

Yet there was a dignity, a sense of timelessness, an acceptance that was encapsulated in *inshallah*...if God wills it.

Kristi watched as the coffee was served first to Shalef, then their host. Kristi was careful to accept her cup as Shalef had instructed, then she waited until he drank from his cup before attempting to touch the contents of her own.

She would have liked to know the topic of their conversation, but she sat quietly, instinctively aware that she should not intrude. When she was offered another coffee she didn't refuse.

The encampment was small, and there were a few camels that contrasted sharply with a Japanese-assembled pick-up truck. Even the equipment and utensils were at variance with each other. Water reposed in plastic containers instead of bags made from animal skins, and there was a modern transistor radio close to where their host's wife had prepared the coffee.

At last Shalef rose to his feet, his actions repeated by their host, and Kristi followed suit as it became apparent that they were preparing to leave.

Outside the tent, Shalef was drawn by his host towards the camels, and each was solemnly inspected and commented upon. Then came the formal farewell before Shalef made his way to the four-wheel drive.

As soon as they were on their way he asked, 'You found the encounter interesting?'

The four-wheel drive gathered speed, billowing dust behind it as Shalef headed for the bitumen road.

'Intriguing,' Kristi amended.

'Perhaps you'd care to elaborate?'

'You fit in so well, yet your Arabian persona is totally at variance with the Western image.'

'You find that strange?'

'No,' she said slowly. 'Somehow it suits you. Yet I can't help wondering if you suffer a conflict of interests. Having enjoyed the best of what the West has to offer, doesn't it even bother you that Aisha and Hanan are not free to experience the freedom of their Western sisters?'

He directed her a sharp glance. 'One does not choose the country of one's birth,' Shalef pointed out. 'One simply accepts the dictates of one's heritage until education and personal choice instil the will to change. Aisha and Hanan are fortunate in that their education will be completed abroad, they are free to work in their chosen careers, and they are free to marry—wisely, one hopes—a suitable man of their choosing.'

'Yet, as head of the palace, your opinion is sacrosanct.' It was a statement, not a query.

'Their welfare is very important to me. If they displayed bad judgement, and Nashwa requested me to intervene, I would hope to be able to persuade them to rethink the situation.'

'And if you failed?'

'I would take measures to ensure no mistakes were made.'

'Such as?'

'Refuse to hand over their passports, the restriction of their allowance.'

'Confine them to the palace?'

'The palace is hardly a jail,' Shalef reminded her.

She ventured soberly, 'It could be, if you didn't want to be there.'

'Since this is a purely hypothetical conversation, without any basis of fact, I suggest we change the subject.'

'That's a cop-out,' Kristi protested.

'A tactical sidestep,' Shalef amended.

'Because it's an issue you don't want to discuss?'

'An issue that cannot be addressed without understanding of the Koran in a country which has no constitution. Much of the legal system is based on a straight application of Islamic *sharia* law as interpreted by the Hanbali school of Islamic jurisprudence, the most conservative of Sunni Islam's four main legal schools.'

'I see.' It was a contemplative comment that brought a faint smile to his lips.

'I doubt that you do.'

She studied his features, wanting to dig beneath the surface and determine his personal views, rather than political observations. 'And you, Shalef? Do you consider yourself fortunate to enjoy the best of both worlds? The Western and Islamic? Or are you frequently caught between the two?'

'I accept my Arabian heritage, for that was my father's wish.'

'And when you marry, will you follow the Islamic tradition by taking more than one wife?'

'I would hope to choose a wife whose love for me would be such that there was no need to seek another.'

'But what of your love for her?'

'You doubt I could please a wife?'

He was amused, and it rankled. 'Sex is only one aspect of a marriage. There has to be mutual respect, emotional support,' she ventured. 'And love.'

'Many women would forgo the last three in exchange for wealth and social position.'

'You're a cynic,' Kristi reproved him, and caught the mockery evident in his expression.

'I have reason to be.'

She didn't doubt it. Women flocked to his side like moths dazzled by flame. Yet very few would be interested in the man himself, only what his wealth could provide in terms of jewellery and cash, magnificent homes and social prestige, in exchange for sexual favours.

The hunting lodge was clearly visible, and Kristi evinced surprise.

'Time flies when you're having fun,' Shalef commented, tongue-in-cheek, and she pulled a face at him.

'Lunch,' he announced in response. 'After which you can witness the taming of the falcons.'

'Birds held in captivity, manacled and chained,' she said with veiled mockery.

'Yet when set free they merely circle and eventually return to their master.' He swung the vehicle into the compound. 'They are well housed, well fed, and lead an infinitely better life than they would in the wild.'

'What a shame they can't communicate; they might tell a different story.'

He cut the engine and turned towards her. 'Then again, they may not.'

'You're a superb strategist,' Kristi commended him with intended irony. 'In the business arena you'd be a diabolical adversary.'

'In *any* arena,' Shalef corrected silkily, and she suppressed a faint shiver at the knowledge that there were few men, or women, who could best him.

CHAPTER SEVEN

LUNCH comprised grilled chicken, rice and a fava bean dish. The simple fare was filling, and Kristi accepted a small portion, preferring to complete the meal with fresh fruit.

'You wish to rest for an hour?'

She glanced across the table and met Shalef's steady gaze. 'You suggested showing me the falcons. I don't want to delay your joining your guests.'

'In that case we shall leave.' He rose from the table and Kristi did likewise, following him through the hallway to a rear door.

'The falcons are housed opposite the stables,' he indicated as they moved away from the house.

'You have horses?'

'Is that so surprising?'

Nothing about this man would surprise her. 'I didn't expect to find them here.'

'Do you ride?'

'Yes.' Her eyes glowed with remembered pleasure. 'I was taught as a child.' There was something magical about sharing the power rather than controlling it, the wonderful feeling of speed and the empathy one achieved between man and beast. 'They're beautiful animals.'

'Then you shall ride with me at sunrise tomorrow.'

A singularly sweet smile curved her generous mouth. It was months since she'd last ridden, and there could be little doubt that Shalef owned the finest Arabian stock. 'Thank you.'

'Is it the prospect of the ride or the sharing of it with me that affords you such pleasure?'

'The ride,' Kristi returned without hesitation, and heard his soft laughter.

The compound was large, much larger than it had appeared from the air, and she followed Shalef to the end of a long building some distance from the house.

'Stay there,' he bade her as they drew close to a large enclosure. 'You are a stranger, and the falcons will be wary.'

She watched as he unlocked an outer door and disappeared inside, only to emerge some minutes later wearing a heavy leather glove on one arm upon which rested a blue-grey falcon whose lower body was white with blackish-brown bars; it was leg-bound—attached to a short lead whose ring was firmly secured.

'This is one of my most prized falcons,' Shalef explained. 'It is extremely rare, and the most powerful of all the breeds. Its speed when it swoops on its prey is estimated at two hundred and ninety kilometres per hour.'

It looked fearsome, exuding a tremendous sense of predatory strength, and the claws, the beak were undeniably vicious.

'You enjoy the sport?'

'Falconry is a method of hunting game which was begun about four thousand years ago by the Persians.

The challenge is in the training of the falcon, for it is an art that takes skill, a lot of time, and endless patience. First they must become used to having men around them. Then they are broken to the hood, which is placed over their head while they are carried in the field. The hood is removed only when the game is seen and the falcon is turned loose to pursue it. Finally, the birds must be trained to lure, so that they will not fly off with the game after they have struck it down or pounced on it.'

She looked at him carefully. 'One assumes you own some of the finest falcons in the country. Is that why Mehmet Hassan retreats here as your guest?'

'He is one of a chosen few.' The falcon rose up on its feet and arched its wings. Shalef said something briefly in Arabic and it immediately quietened. 'He's getting restless. I'll return him.'

Minutes later he rejoined her, and they walked slowly back to the house.

'You like being here.' It was a statement, and one he didn't refute.

'It's a place where I can relax and enjoy the company of valued friends without the intrusion of society.'

Kristi gestured towards the house, then widened the gesture to encompass the desert beyond. 'I can understand why. There is a harshness that challenges the survival of man.'

'Very profound, Kristi Dalton,' he lightly mocked as they entered the house.

Without thinking, she placed a hand on his arm. 'Thank you,' she said quietly.

'For what, precisely? Giving you a few hours of my time?'

'Yes. My being here must be a source of irritation.'

'Are you suggesting I deny it?'

She felt stung, the hurt incredibly strong for one brief second before she was able to mask it. She turned away, wanting only to be free of his disturbing presence, but a hand closed over her shoulder and forced her back to face him.

Kristi met his gaze and held it, hating him at that precise moment for being able to render her vulnerable.

When his head began to descend she averted her own, then she cried out as he cradled her nape so that she couldn't escape the pressure of his mouth.

She had no defence against a kiss that was hard and possessively demanding. He seemed to fill her mouth, exploring, coaxing a capitulation that she was loath to give.

Just as she thought she'd won, the pressure eased, and in its place was a soft, open-mouthed kiss that swamped her emotions and left her weak-willed and malleable.

The desire to kiss him back was impossible to deny, and her body swayed into his as she lifted her arms and linked her hands behind his head.

He permitted her to initiate a kiss, then he subjected her mouth to the explorative sweep of his tongue, teasing, tantalising in a manner that sent an electrifying awareness tingling through her veins, heightening her senses to a frightening degree as she began to melt beneath the magnetic thrill of his sensual onslaught.

Slowly, with infinite care, he eased the flare of passion, tempering it with one lingering kiss after the other on the soft fullness of her lower lip, the edge of her mouth, before trailing his lips up to rest against her temple. Then he gently pushed her to arm's length.

'I must leave.'

Kristi didn't feel capable of uttering so much as a word, yet she managed a sigh before turning away from him to seek the sanctuary and solitude of his bedroom.

A shower would rinse off the desert sand, and she'd shampoo her hair. Then she'd find pen and paper and compose a letter to Georgina Harrington. She'd also write a short note to Annie.

Thoughts of the studio brought forth an image of home. For a moment she almost wished that she were back in Australia. If it hadn't been for Shane, she wouldn't be in a desert a few hundred kilometres from Riyadh. Nor, she vowed silently as she stepped beneath the pulsing jet of warm water, would she be in a constant state of emotional turmoil over a man who could never be a part of her life. Or she a part of his.

It was late when the men returned, and after eight before dinner was served. Conversation was convivial, and it was clear that the falcons had performed well, the kill excellent. Kristi's vivid imagination conjured up their prey, the deadly power of the falcon, and she endeavoured to mask her distaste for a sport that centred on the death of the victim.

The last of the meal was cleared from the table and the men began to move into the lounge for coffee. Two of the guests displayed a penchant for strong cigars, and after an hour Kristi was conscious of a persistent headache as a result of passive smoking.

'If you don't mind, I'll retire for the night.' She stood, smiled at each of the men in turn, then moved towards the door.

Once clear of the room she contemplated taking a walk, but the evening air would not have cooled sufficiently for it to be more pleasant outdoors than in the air-conditioned interior of the house.

The bedroom was blissfully cool, and after brushing her teeth she undressed, donned the shirt that Shalef had provided the night before, then slipped beneath the covers of the large bed.

An hour later she was still awake and the pain in her head had intensified into a full, throbbing ache that showed no sign of dissipating.

Maybe there was some medication in the *en suite* bathroom that might alleviate the pain, she thought, and got up to see.

Switching on the light, she opened a drawer, and was in the process of searching the second when she heard Shalef's unmistakable drawl from the doorway.

'What are you looking for?'

'Paracetamol,' Kristi responded without preamble.

'Try the last cupboard above the vanity to your right.'

She moved towards the designated cupboard, extracted a slim packet, removed two tablets from the blister pack, found a glass and half filled it with water, then swallowed both tablets.

'You are unwell?'

She turned towards him. 'The cigar smoke gave me a headache.' Her fingers shook slightly as she closed the pack, and as she reached for the cupboard the pack slipped from her grasp.

She bent quickly to pick it up, then winced as the downward movement magnified the pain. In her hurry she neglected to foresee that the loosely buttoned shirt would gape, given its voluminous size, and she clutched the edges and held them tightly against her midriff. Her defensive action came too late, and there was little she could do to avoid the firm fingers which extricated her own from the cotton shirt.

'You are bruised.' He undid one button, then the one beneath it, drawing the edge down over her shoulder.

There were more bruises on various parts of her body, and he seemed intent on inspecting them all.

'You assured me you were uninjured,' Shalef said grimly, ignoring her efforts to remove his hands.

'I don't class a few bruises as *injuries*.' Her voice rose as his fingers probed a large, purpling patch close to her hip. *'Don't.'*

'You didn't suffer these from being held at bay, locked in the four-wheel drive,' he observed with deadly softness. 'Did the men undo the door and drag you out?'

His voice was like the finest silk being abraded by steel, and for some inexplicable reason her nerves felt as if they were stretched close to breaking-point.

'They didn't appear to understand English or French,' she related starkly, and the muscles of his jaw tensed with chilling hardness.

'Did they beat you? Touch you in any way?'

'They stopped when I said your name.' The words sounded stilted even to her own ears, and his eyes narrowed at the fleeting changes in her expression.

She watched in mesmerised fascination as he lifted a hand and brushed his fingers across her cheek then trailed them down to the corner of her mouth. Gently he outlined the contour of her lower lip, then slid down the column of her throat to trace a path over the stitched edge of the shirt to the valley between her breasts.

Then his head lowered to hers, and his lips followed an identical route as he pushed the shirt aside and brushed his mouth back and forth against each bruise in turn.

Something wild and untamed unfurled deep within her, flooding her being with a slow, sweet heat as his lips closed over hers in a kiss that was so erotically evocative that she never wanted it to end.

No man had ever wreaked such havoc with her emotions, nor made her feel so wickedly wanton as she returned his kiss and silently begged for more.

She needed to feel the touch of his skin, the silky

external layer sheathing the finely honed muscles and sinews that bound his broad bone structure into a frame that was solely, uniquely *his*.

His clothes followed the path of her shirt, and she gave a silent gasp as he swept an arm beneath her knees and lifted her high against his chest to carry her into the bedroom.

The sheets felt deliciously cool as he laid her down on the bed; then he lowered his body beside her, bracing his weight with his hands as he began an erotic tasting path that slowly traversed every hollow, every intimate crevice until each separate nerve-end screamed for the release she craved.

Not content, he rolled onto his back and carried her with him so that she sat nestled in the cradle of his thighs.

Kristi stilled as he extracted prophylactic protection, broke the seal, then extended it in silent query. She accepted it with fingers that trembled slightly, unsure whether to feel relieved or dismayed. A bubble of silent hysteria threatened to escape her lips as she contemplated whether she could complete the task with any degree of finesse. Perhaps she could opt out and hand it back to him…

His fingers closed over hers, guiding them, and her discomfiture was no longer an issue as his hands slid to her shoulders and captured her head, forcing her mouth down to his as he initiated a long, slow kiss that heated her veins and heightened her emotions to fever-pitch.

The juncture of her thighs ached, and she almost

cried out as he gently exposed the aperture then lowered her against the length of his shaft.

She gained some relief, but not enough, not nearly enough, and a low, guttural moan rose in her throat as he drew her forward and brushed his lips against the soft, aching curve of her breast.

His tongue sought one hardened, highly sensitised peak and outlined the dusky aureole, drawing it carefully into his mouth as he gently traced the delicate ridges, before teasing the peak with the edge of his teeth.

'Please…Shalef.' She wasn't aware of uttering the plea, or that she said his name, and she gave a low groan of encouragement as he began to suckle. The pleasure was so intense that it became almost pain, and just as she thought that she could stand no more he diverted his attention to its twin.

His hands spanned her hips, encouraging a delicate sliding movement that almost drove her crazy, and she began to plead with him to ease the torturous ache deep within her.

He did, with such exquisite slowness that the alien invasion merely stretched silken tissues rather than tore them, and, when she gave a slight gasp and momentarily stilled, he stopped, sliding one hand up to cup her jaw as he forced her to look at him.

For long, timeless seconds his gaze raked her flushed features, searing through the moisture shimmering in those heavily dilated hazel eyes, disbelieving, yet having to believe, infinitely curious and filled with a white-hot rage that tightened the fingers at her jaw and sent his hand raking through the tousled length of her hair.

'You would set yourself up to experience the pain of vertical penetration,' he condemned in a dangerously silky voice moving fractionally so that she felt an edge of it, 'unsure whether or not you could accommodate me?'

She wanted to cry, but she was damned if she'd give in to a loss of control. A mixture of anger and despair began to replace passion, and with it came shame and a degree of embarrassment.

It was unnecessary to demand cessation, for he simply removed her, and she was unable to prevent an involuntary gasp at the acute sense of loss.

With an economy of movement he replaced the discarded covers, then settled back against the pillows.

She was incapable of saying so much as a word, although many chased incoherently through her brain. How could she tell him that no other man had made her feel the way he did? Or that there had been no one else because she'd never met a man with whom she'd wanted to share her body? Until now.

She lay quite still, consciously marshalling her breathing into a slow, measured pattern as she silently willed the tears to remain at bay.

They didn't, slowly welling and overflowing from the outer corners of her eyes, rolling down to disappear in her hair.

She wanted to slip out from the bed and dress, then leave the house and drive one of the vehicles through the night to the palace, where at first light she'd pack and have a taxi take her to the airport so that she could catch the first plane back to London. Except that she had no idea where the keys were, or how to neutralise the hunting lodge's security system.

'Why didn't you warn me?'

Kristi wasn't sure if her voice would emerge intact through the constriction in her throat, so she didn't even put it to the test.

The light from the bathroom cast a wide shaft of illumination across the bedroom, highlighting a strip of carpet, a large rosewood cabinet and a valet frame.

He shifted slightly, turning towards her, and even in the shadows he could determine a measure of her distress.

'If I had declared I'd never been this intimate with a man, you probably wouldn't have believed me,' she managed huskily. She'd led an active life, enjoyed numerous sporting pursuits. How could she have known her hymen was still intact?

'No,' Shalef admitted drily. 'Women usually choose to play the coquette, or pretend an innocence which doesn't exist.'

She didn't want to look at him, for she couldn't bear to see the mockery that she was sure must be evident, or glimpse the frustrated anger of a man who had pulled himself back from the brink of achieving sexual satisfaction.

She felt rather than saw his hand move, and she was unable to prevent the faint flinching of her facial muscles as he touched light fingers to her temple and discovered the damp trail of her drying tears.

She closed her eyes tightly as he followed their path, then slowly roamed her cheek with tactile gentleness, pausing at the edge of her mouth as he felt the trembling of her lips.

An arm curved over her waist and slipped beneath her shoulders as he drew her close, ignoring the stiffness of her body as he tucked her head beneath his chin.

Kristi felt his lips against her hair, and the light caress of his hand as he soothed the taut muscles in her back.

A rawness crawled deep inside her, an aching loss so intense that it was all she could do not to weep silently. She had come so close to an emotional catharsis that not attaining it generated a feeling of deprivation. And deep inside she experienced a measure of anger—with herself for being so blind in believing that her innocence didn't matter, and with him for calling a halt when, at that finite moment, she would have welcomed the pain in order to experience the pleasure she'd believed must surely follow.

She lay very still, lulled by the solid beat of his heart beneath her breast, and she closed her eyes, wishing desperately for sleep to descend and blank out the events of the past hour.

Part of her wanted a separate space, wanted to turn away from him and move to the side of the bed, yet the delicate tentacles of need were too strong, the comfort he offered too pleasurable, so she remained where she was, gradually relaxing until the shadows deepened and she descended into a dreamless state.

CHAPTER EIGHT

NOT quite dreamless, Kristi acknowledged from the depths of her subconscious as she ascended through the mists of sleep. She felt deliciously warm, and all her senses seemed to be finely tuned to the faint, musky smell of male skin beneath her lips. She could feel the soft brush of a hand as it trailed along her lower spine, while the other teased the softness of her breast.

Sensation unfurled as her body slowly wakened in response to his feather-light touch, and she murmured indistinctly as her breast burgeoned, its peak hardening in anticipation of the havoc his mouth could create.

She stirred, unable to remain still as the hand at the lower edge of her spine began to explore the contours of her hip, slipping down over her thigh to seek the core of her femininity. Her hastily indrawn breath was followed by a purr of pleasure, and her body arched against his as he began to tantalise her with leisurely expertise.

Every nerve-end began to pulsate until her whole body was consumed with a slow-burning fire that heated her veins and sent the blood pumping at an accelerated rate.

Slowly, with infinite care, he continued an evocative exploration of her body, heightening each sensual pleasure-spot to its ultimate pitch until she became suffused with an aching warmth. Not content with that, he repeated the exploration with the touch of his lips, creating such unbearable sensations that she clung to him unashamedly, silently begging for release from the tumultuous tide of emotion threatening to consume her.

Gently he eased himself between her legs, adjusting her hips as he coaxed her aroused flesh to accept his masculinity.

Kristi felt a sense of total enclosure as silken tissues expanded and stretched, and her faint gasp was caught as his mouth closed in possession over her own, the kiss so erotic that she didn't notice the sting of pain.

He began a gentle pacing, so that she felt every movement, every inch of the journey as the music of passion built deep within her, its tempo increasing as she urged him further and faster in a crashing crescendo that culminated in shock waves shuddering through her body as she reached breathtaking ecstasy.

A total loss of control, she mused as she began the slow descent back to reality. Although reality would never be quite the same again.

Instinct relayed to her the fact that his response had been too controlled, almost as if he had kept a tight rein in order to ensure that she experienced the ultimate pleasure without threat of it being overshadowed by his own.

Awareness defined new dimensions, and she savoured the musky scent secreted by their skin, the warm heat generated by their bodies, their still rapidly beating hearts, his, her own, and felt them slow as languor replaced passion in the sweet aftermath of satisfactory sex.

Lovemaking, Kristi corrected silently. What they'd shared was more than just *sex*.

Slowly she turned her head, marvelling as the first light of the new day's dawn slowly crept up over the horizon, shifting shadows and bathing all before it in a soft, hazy glow.

'Do you want to ride out into the desert?'

The promise of a new day enthralled her, and she couldn't suppress the delight in her voice as she answered him. 'Yes.'

He buried his fingers deep in her hair, then bent his head and bestowed a brief, hard kiss on her mouth before moving to the side of the bed. 'How quickly can you dress?'

Kristi slid out to stand beside him. 'As quickly as you.'

Ten minutes later they were cantering out of the compound, the horses whickering slightly in anticipation of the exercise.

Her mount was a beautiful thoroughbred, with an arrogant head and a fine, pacing step that promised speed once she gave him the rein.

Shalef moved beside her, looking magnificent in traditional *thobe* and *gutra*.

The steed he'd chosen was large and powerful, and as soon as they cleared the compound he urged it into a steady canter.

It felt wonderful to ride again, to enjoy the exhilaration and the power. The terrain of the desert was stark, the sense of isolation intense, yet she could understand the fascination it held, for there was a sense of timelessness apparent, almost a feeling of awe for early civilisation. With a little imagination, one could almost picture the camel train of an ancient era traversing the distant sand-dunes highlighted against the early-morning sky, a caravan of wandering Bedouin seeking food and a temporary camp. And the marauding plunder of tribal bands who sought to gain and mark territory in a land which had known violence since the beginning of time.

A faint shiver ran down Kristi's spine, and in an attempt to dispel such introspection she leaned forward in the saddle and urged her mount to increase his speed. Faster, until every muscle in her body strained and the air rushed through her clothes, tearing at her headscarf and loosening her hair.

Shalef drew abreast and maintained an identical pace as they raced together across the wide plain without any sense of competition, until Kristi eased back slightly, allowing her mount to slow to a canter.

A hand reached out and caught hold of her reins, and she straightened in the saddle, her features alive as she turned towards the man whose thigh was almost brushing her own.

He wasn't even breathing heavily, while she needed precious seconds to gain control of her voice.

'That was incredible!' Her eyes were deep brown velvet specked with glowing topaz, and her cheeks held a blush-pink glow from exertion. The scarf had come adrift, and her hair was in a state of tousled disarray.

'So are you,' Shalef offered softly, and her eyes widened as he leaned close and took her mouth in a long, hard kiss.

It was after seven when they entered the compound, and as they drew close to the stables two Filipino servants emerged to take care of the horses.

'Would you prefer a cold drink or coffee?' Shalef enquired as they entered the house.

'Cold,' Kristi responded without hesitation, following him through to the kitchen.

'Water or orange juice?'

'Juice.' She ran a hand over the taut muscles of one arm. 'Then I'm going to have a long, hot shower.'

The cook looked up as they entered, moving quickly to the refrigerator to extract a carafe of orange juice and chilled water before she tended to the coffee.

Kristi was supremely conscious of the man at her side, and all her fine body hairs seemed to extend like tiny antennae in recognition of his proximity. All her senses appeared to be in a state of heightened anticipation, for she was conscious of every breath she took, every beat of her heart, and it bothered her more than she cared to admit.

The hand that held her glass felt slightly unsteady, and she drank quickly in the need to escape his disturbing presence.

In the bedroom she gathered her spare set of

clothes, which seemed to disappear and reappear freshly laundered in a short space of time each morning, and went through to the bathroom.

It took only seconds to discard her jeans and blouse, briefs and bra, and for a moment she looked wistfully at the spa-bath, then decided on the shower.

Kristi moved the dial to 'WARM', stepped beneath the flow of water and picked up the bar of soap. 'Bliss,' she breathed minutes later as she applied shampoo to her hair, only to freeze at the sound of the shower door sliding open.

Shalef stood framed in the aperture, and her eyes flew to his in consternation.

'You can't,' she protested as he stepped in beside her and closed the door.

'I can.' Irrefutable, the words merely confirmed his action, and she gave a startled gasp when he removed the shampoo bottle from her hand and completed her task, massaging her scalp with tactile expertise as the water rinsed the suds from her hair.

The soap came next, and she swept his hand aside as it glided over one breast then moved towards the other. 'Don't.'

The remonstration brought forth a husky laugh. 'You are embarrassed? After what we shared together in the early hours of this morning?'

His hand moved to her abdomen, then traced across to her hip and slid to the base of her spine, soothing in a manner which tugged alive a fierce ache in the pit of her stomach.

'Shalef—'

Whatever else she might have uttered was lost as his mouth covered hers in a kiss that became flagrantly seductive as it gently coaxed, seeking a response that she was afraid to give. Her hands reached out, touching hard muscle and sinew as her fingers conducted a slow tracing of his ribcage, the indentation of his hard waist, and down over the flat musculature of his stomach.

A deep groan sounded low in his throat as he caught hold of her hands and held them, then his mouth eased away from hers and he rested his chin on the top of her head.

'Enough,' he said heavily. 'Otherwise we'll never get beyond the bedroom and there are guests who expect to sit down to breakfast with me in fifteen minutes.' He moved fractionally, letting his hand slide to cover her breast. 'Go.'

Kristi went, pausing only long enough to collect a towel, basic toiletries and her clothes.

By the time he entered the bedroom she was dressed and doing the best she could to persuade her damp hair into a semblance of order.

She was aware of his every move as he extracted briefs, trousers, shirt, and donned each of them before reaching for a clean *thobe*.

'Ready?'

Physically, although her emotions were in a questionable state!

The meal seemed to last for ever, the men inclined to linger over several cups of coffee, and it was almost ten when Shalef accompanied them out to the waiting helicopter.

The sound of the rotor-blades intensified, then the craft lifted off, paused, then wheeled away to the east.

Kristi listened till the sound disappeared, and she turned as Shalef re-entered the house. Her eyes locked with his as she tried to disguise her uncertainty. 'When do we leave for the palace?'

His expression was impossible to read. 'There is no immediate need to return for a few days.'

Kristi couldn't think of a thing to say.

'Unless, of course, you object,' Shalef added quietly.

She knew she should. Knew that to remain here with him was akin to divine madness. Yet the rational part of her brain was motivated by the dictates of her heart, urging her to embark on an emotional experience that would almost certainly end in heartbreak...although the journey itself would be unforgettable.

'I'll stay.'

Without a word he closed the distance between them and swept her into his arms.

'What do you think you're doing?' she asked in a faintly scandalised voice.

'Taking you to bed.' He carried her down the wide hallway to the room at its very end, then, once inside, he closed the door and allowed her to slide down to her feet.

Her eyes widened slightly at the vital vibrancy evident in those strong facial features, and she was unable to hide her own haunting vulnerability as his head began a slow descent.

The touch of his lips tantalised as they traced the outline of her mouth with evocative persuasion, then slid to the sensitive cord at the edge of her neck, grazing the sweet hollows before trailing up to take possession of her mouth.

Firm fingers dispensed with her clothes, then his own, and before she had time for coherent thought he urged her towards the bed and drew her onto its wide expanse.

Kristi lay still, mesmerised by her heightened senses and enraptured by the dark passion evident in his eyes. This close, she could sense the clean body smell emanating from his skin, and awareness coursed through her body like an igniting flame.

Her lips parted as he sought an erotic exploration of the sweet depths of her mouth, teasing the delicate ridges of her tongue with the tip of his own in an oral dance that matched the rhapsody created by his hands as they drifted with sensual sensitivity over her aroused skin.

She lost track of time, of place, as he submitted her to an erotic tasting of such exquisite proportion that her entire body began to ache with the need for fulfilment, and she began to move, silently enticing his possession.

His lips settled in the vulnerable hollow at the base of her throat, then trailed slowly down to the gentle swell of her breast, and she cried out as he took the engorged peak into his mouth and began a tender suckling that slowly intensified until it became a physical torment.

Kristi was unaware of the soft groan emerging from her throat as she reached for him, instinctively begging him in a voice she didn't recognise as her own.

Wild, pagan need consumed her as he began an intimate exploration, his touch attacking the fragile tenure of her control until she began to sob in helpless despair.

Then with one slow movement he entered her, his hard length enclosed by a tight sweetness that took his breath away.

She clung to him, unashamedly caught in the deep, undulating rhythm as she instinctively matched him stroke for stroke, exulting in the sensation that radiated through her body with such exquisite exhilaration.

Pagan, she acknowledged seconds later as he tipped her over the edge, then joined her there in a shuddering climax of his own.

Kristi was supremely conscious of every nerve-end, every cell in her body as she became filled with a languorous warmth, and she cradled his large frame close, loving the feel of his weight, the heat of his skin, slick with the sweat of his passion.

His heart beat strong and fast close to her own, and she sought his mouth, initiating a kiss which soon became *his* as he deepened her soft foray, changing it to something that staked his possession and branded her his own.

Afterwards he rolled onto his back, carrying her

with him, and she arched her body, laughing softly as she felt his immediate response.

His hands slid up her ribcage and cradled her breasts, testing their weight as he began to caress each peak with the pad of his thumb, delighting in her reaction as she threw back her head.

Erotic abandon, she admitted a long time later, unsure whether to be pleased or dismayed that she'd become a begging wanton in his arms as he'd led her down a path to sensual conflagration.

'Should we get up, do you think?' Kristi queried as she lay in his embrace.

'I can't think of one good reason why right at this moment,' Shalef drawled, moving his head to brush his lips against her shoulder.

'Lunch?' she offered hopefully.

He bit her gently, then inched his way to the edge of her neck, nuzzling in a manner that sent a renewed surge of sensation arrowing through her body. 'We could have an early dinner.'

'Alternatively, I could go into the kitchen and bring us back a snack.'

'You're hungry for food?' he asked, and she responded teasingly,

'I need to keep up my strength.'

He levered himself easily off the bed and reached for his clothes. 'Stay here,' he commanded gently.

A slow, witching smile curved her lips, and her eyes sparkled with amusement. 'I wasn't planning on going anywhere.'

Shalef returned with a tray of chicken, salad and

fresh fruit. After they'd eaten they talked, discussing anything and everything from early childhood memories to world politics, books, movies, art. Then they made leisurely love, and she became an avid pupil beneath his tutorage, taking pleasure from the depth of passion that she was able to arouse.

When the sun began to descend in the sky they rose from the bed, shared the spa-bath, then dressed and went to the dining room for dinner. And later, when the stars shone bright in an inky night sky, they made passionate love until sleep overcame desire.

It became the pattern for the next three days. Days that were filled with lovemaking and laughter, and with the passing of each night Kristi became more aware that to walk away from this man would bring unimaginable heartache.

Seize each moment, a tiny voice bade her. Treasure it and hold it close.

Yet such time-honoured axioms did nothing to help her sense of approaching despair. They couldn't stay here for ever. Sooner or later a phone call or a fax would summon Shalef back to the palace.

It happened on the morning of the fourth day. They arrived back from their early-morning ride to find a servant waiting for them with a cryptic fax which had come through in their absence. Shalef scanned it, then folded the sheet in three and thrust it into the side-pocket of his *thobe*.

'We have to return to Riyadh. Negotiations for your brother's release have been successful.'

Kristi couldn't believe it. 'Shane is to be freed?'

Her face mirrored the immense surge of joy that tore through her body. 'How? When? *Where*?'

'Later today. He'll be transported out of the country and receive debriefing before being put on a plane to London.'

'When will I be able to see him?'

'The media circus will begin within hours of his arrival in England, I imagine,' Shalef declared as they crossed the compound. He cast her a dark, probing look. 'It would be advisable for you to be there before he arrives.'

Kristi felt her heart sink. Within a very short time the helicopter would deposit them at the palace. In less than twenty-four hours she would be on a plane to London.

Mission accomplished.

'I agreed to pay any expenses.'

His eyes darkened with anger. 'You insult me.'

'*Why*?' she demanded.

'I requested a favour from a friend,' he said silkily, 'without any pressure that it be granted.' He looked as if he wanted to shake her. 'There was no cost that you have not repaid me.'

Kristi absorbed his words, and felt part of her slowly die. It took tremendous effort to summon a smile, but she managed a passable facsimile. 'Thank you.'

Shalef inclined his head in silent acknowledgement, his eyes hooded, his features assuming a harsh mask.

It was over. The words echoed inside her brain like

a death-knell. Without a word she turned and followed him indoors, showered, collected her spare set
of clothes, and was ready to board the helicopter
when it arrived less than an hour later.

CHAPTER NINE

THE wheels of the large Boeing hit the tarmac, accompanied by the shrill scream of brakes as the passenger jet decelerated down the runway, then cruised into its designated bay at Heathrow airport.

Kristi moved through the terminal, showed her passport, then made her way to the revolving carousel, waited for her luggage to come through, collected it and completed Customs.

Securing a taxi was achieved without delay, and Kristi sank into the rear seat as the driver stowed her bags in the boot. Minutes later the vehicle eased forward into the queue of traffic seeking exit from the busy terminal.

The weather was dull and overcast, cool after the heat of Riyadh, and she fixed her attention beyond the windscreen as the taxi moved smoothly along the bitumen.

A complexity of emotions racked her body, not the least of which was relief that Shane was safe.

Saying goodbye to Shalef as she'd transferred from his Lear jet onto a commercial flight in Bahrain had been the most difficult part of all. Despite her resolve to keep their parting low-key, his brief, hard kiss had stung her lips, and his words of farewell had held the courteous tones of a business associate rather than the emotional intensity of a lover.

What did you expect? she demanded silently. You were attracted to the man, succumbed to his magnetic sex appeal, and shared a few days and nights of passion. Don't fool yourself it was anything other than that.

A week from now you'll be back in Australia, and a romantic interlude in the desert with a Saudi Arabian sheikh of English birth will gradually fade into obscurity.

But she knew that she'd never be able to forget him, and that no man could take his place.

Love, desire, passion. Were the three interdependent, or could they be separated and judged alone? The cold, hard fact was that women were far more prey to emotions than men.

Kristi viewed the streets of London, the traffic, and watched dispassionately as the taxi slid into the wide parking bay adjacent to her centrally placed hotel.

Within a matter of minutes a porter had taken charge of her bag and she was traversing the wide carpeted foyer to Reception.

On being shown to her room she unpacked only what was necessary, discarded her clothes, took a long, hot shower, then opted for a few hours' sleep, for despite it being mid-morning her body-clock was attuned to a different time-zone and she hadn't closed her eyes during the long flight.

When she woke it was early evening, and she donned a robe, made herself a cup of tea, then perused the room-service menu. After dinner she'd ring Sir Alexander Harrington and apprise him of Shane's release.

At nine she switched on the television and alternated channels until way past midnight, slept briefly, then rose and showered ready for an early breakfast.

Loath to venture far from the hotel in case a message came in regarding Shane's expected arrival, she met Georgina in one of the hotel's restaurants for an extended lunch.

'*Tell* me,' Georgina cajoled when they had eaten the entrée, done justice to the main course, and were partway through a delicious concoction of fresh fruit and ice cream.

Kristi lifted her head and met her friend's teasing smile. 'Tell you what?'

'Shane's release is wonderful. It made the initial subterfuge worthwhile.' Georgina's eyes sparkled with intense interest as she leaned forward. 'But give me the details on Shalef bin Youssef Al-Sayed.'

'What details?'

'I refuse to believe you weren't attracted to the man.'

It would have been so easy to confide in a trusted friend, but to do so would only have caused Kristi pain and, perhaps, a feeling of regret. 'He was a very gracious host,' she said carefully.

'Kristi,' Georgina admonished her, 'you're being evasive.'

'OK, what do you want me to say? That he's a wildly sensual man who has women falling at his feet with practically every step he takes?' As you did, a silent voice taunted. She'd been gone two days. Had he contacted any one of his many women friends in Riyadh—*Fayza*?—dined with her, perhaps sated his sexual appetite in her bed? Dear God, even the thought made her feel physically ill.

'Aren't you going to finish dessert?'

Kristi collected herself together. 'No. Shall we order coffee?'

That evening she dined with Sir Alexander and Georgina, and when she returned to the hotel there was a coded message indicating that Shane was due to arrive the following morning.

Sleep was almost impossible and caught in intermittent snatches. With no knowledge of what flight he'd be on, or where it was coming from, she could only wait.

The telephone call came through shortly before midday, and at the sound of her brother's voice all the pent-up emotion culminated in a rush of tears.

'You're in the same hotel?' She couldn't believe it, wouldn't believe it until she saw him. 'What floor, what room number?'

'Order a meal from Room Service, a magnum of champagne, and give me twenty minutes to shower and shave,' Shane instructed, adding gently, 'Then I'll join you.'

He made it in fifteen, and once inside her room he swooped her up in a bear hug and swung her round in a circle before depositing her on her feet. 'Hi there.' His smile was the same, his laughter as bright as ever, but he looked tired and he'd lost weight. He was tall, his hair darker than hers—a deep brown with a hint auburn—and he had strong features and a skin texture that bore exposure to the sun.

'Hi, yourself,' Kristi said softly, leading him to the table set at one end of the room. The food had arrived only minutes before, and she watched as he took a seat, uncorked the champagne, then filled two flutes.

'Here's to being back in one piece.'

'Unharmed?'

'As you see.'

'I think,' Kristi ventured unsteadily, 'you'd better consider assignments in less politically volatile countries. I don't want to go through this again in a hurry.'

His eyes—deep brown flecked with topaz like her own—speared hers. 'Point taken. Off the record, whose influence did you employ to gain my release?'

'Shalef bin Youssef Al-Sayed's.'

An expressive, soft whistle escaped his lips. 'Should I ask how you made contact with him?'

'Initially through Sir Alexander Harrington.'

'And?'

She effected a faint shrug. 'I gave my word.' There was no need to say why, or to whom. Shane possessed the same degree of integrity with *his* sources.

'Do I get to meet Al-Sayed?'

'Possibly. Maybe.' She lifted a hand and smoothed back her hair. 'I'm not sure.'

He noted the nervous gesture, the faint tenseness at the edge of her mouth, and clenched his teeth. If she'd been hurt, by *anyone*, there would be hell to pay.

'So, tell me what happened,' Kristi encouraged, and Shane took up the story from the time of his capture. She recognised the holes he failed to fill, and accepted them.

'This afternoon a statement will be issued to the media,' he concluded with weary resignation. 'I'll be caught up with interviews, television. Then I fly back to Sydney tomorrow afternoon.'

'So soon?'

'The Australian media will want their piece of the action,' he said wryly. 'Then I'm going to lie low for a while.'

'Maybe I can get the same flight,' she said pensively. It seemed an age since she'd left home, and she wanted to resume her life from where she'd left off…how long ago? Five weeks? It felt like half a lifetime.

'No. That wouldn't be advisable. Give it a few days, then follow me.'

She looked at him carefully, seeing the visible signs of strain and tiredness, and expressed her concern. 'You should get some sleep.'

'I will. I'll ring through when I can, but it may not be until tomorrow morning,' he warned as he stood up.

Kristi saw him out, then closed the door behind him.

Within hours of Shane's departure Kristi secured a flight for Sydney for a few days ahead. Once the booking had been made and she had her ticket, her leaving seemed more of a reality.

Filling those days required little effort as Georgina took charge, first of all dragging her into Harrods, then following it with dinner and a show. The following morning was devoted to attending a beauty parlour for a massage, facial, pedicure, manicure, followed by lunch and a movie.

'Tonight is *mine*,' Kristi declared as they emerged from the cinema in the late afternoon. 'I'm going back to the hotel, ordering room service, followed by an early night.' She gave her friend a stern look. 'And no arguments. I have a long flight ahead of me tomorrow afternoon.'

'So what? You sleep on the plane.' Georgina was carried away with enthusiasm. 'We could go to a nightclub.'

'And get home at three in the morning? No, thanks.'

'It's your last night in town,' Georgina protested. 'You can't spend it alone.'

'Watch me.'

'You leave me no choice but to ring Jeremy and have him take me out.'

'Enjoy,' Kristi bade her, offering a wicked grin, and Georgina laughed.

'I will, believe me.' She leaned forward and pecked Kristi's cheek. 'You only have a block to walk to the hotel. I'll catch a taxi. See you at the airport tomorrow.'

It was almost six when Kristi entered the hotel foyer and took the lift to her floor. There were no messages, and she ordered room service, then stripped off her clothes and pulled on a robe.

Her meal arrived, and she picked at it, then pushed the plate aside. Television failed to hold her interest, and at ten she cleansed her face of make-up, brushed her teeth then slid into bed, only to lie awake staring at the ceiling, fervently wishing that she had agreed to go out with Georgina. At least the bright lights and loud music would have done something to alleviate this dreadful sense of despondency.

She must have fallen asleep, and when she woke the next morning it was late. A shower did much to restore her equanimity, and she ordered breakfast, then made a start with her packing.

A double knock at her door heralded the arrival of Room Service, and she moved across the room to unlock it and allow the waiter access.

But no waiter resembled the tall, dark-haired, immaculately suited man standing in the aperture.

CHAPTER TEN

'SHALEF.' Kristi hadn't realised that it would hurt so much to say his name.

Cool grey eyes raked her slender form, lingered briefly on the soft curve of her mouth, then slid to meet her own. 'Aren't you going to ask me in?'

She dug deep into her resources and managed to display a measure of ease, all too aware of the rapid pulse beat at the base of her throat. 'Would there be any point if I refused?'

'None at all.'

He moved into the room as she stood to one side, and his expression hardened as he saw the open suitcase on the bed.

'You're leaving?'

She looked at him carefully, seeing the inherent strength, the indomitable power that allowed him to shape life in the manner he chose. 'Yes.'

The silence in the room was such that it almost seemed a palpable entity, and her nerves stretched until they felt as taut as a finely strung bow. The sensation angered her unbearably, and she silently damned him for being able to generate such havoc.

He looked at her for what seemed an age, his eyes dark, their inscrutable depths successfully shielding him from any possibility of her gauging his emotions.

When at last he spoke, he appeared to select his words with care. 'We need to talk.'

There wasn't a thing she could say that wouldn't sound inane, so she remained silent, waiting for him to continue.

'I'll be in London for a month, then I fly to Paris,' he revealed. 'I want you with me.'

The breath caught in her throat and threatened to choke her.

'No comment, Kristi?' he queried with a degree of mocking cynicism.

'As what?' Was that her voice? Even to her own ears it sounded impossibly husky. 'Your mistress?'

He didn't answer for several long seconds. 'There are many advantages.'

The tissues around her heart began to tear. Her eyes met his and held them without any effort at all. 'I won't be content with second best, waiting for a stolen night or two whenever you could slip away.' She was breaking in two, and the pain was so intense that she was sure it must be clearly visible to him. Her throat began to ache with the constriction of severe control. 'I would rather not have you at all.'

'Then marry me.'

For a moment she was robbed of the ability to speak. 'Why?' she demanded at last. Her eyes clung to his, searching for some hint of passion, any intensity of emotion by way of reassurance.

'You're a rarity among women of my acquaintance,' Shalef said with quiet emphasis. 'Intelligent, courageous. Equally at ease among the social glitterati as you are with my Bedu friends in the desert.'

She closed her eyes in an effort to veil the pain. 'That's hardly a reason for marriage,' she managed slowly.

'You refuse?'

She looked at him carefully, wanting, needing so desperately to accept, yet knowing that if she did she could never be content with good sex and affection as a substitute for love.

It would be so easy to say yes. To accept what he offered and make do with it. Yet she wanted it all, and he wasn't ready to give it.

'I'm flying back to Australia on the early-afternoon flight. Shane is already in Sydney, and it is more than time we both attempted to attend to business.'

'You know I will follow you.'

She looked at him with clear eyes, the pain hidden deep beneath those liquid brown depths. 'Please don't.' Not unless you love me, she added silently.

'You are prepared to discard what we have together?'

It will kill me, she thought. 'Without love there is very little to discard.'

She was mad, *insane* to consider turning him down. A faint bubble of hysteria rose in her throat with the knowledge that she had to be the only woman on any continent in the world who would consider rejecting Shalef bin Youssef Al-Sayed.

Yet, if she accepted him *now*, it would be akin to accepting a half-measure. Most—dear heaven, *all* women of her acquaintance would be content with less. To have him in their bed, access to his immense wealth and the rewards it would bring would be enough.

'You offer me everything,' Kristi said slowly, and was unable to prevent the faint, husky catch in her voice. Deep inside she felt incredibly sad. She'd hoped for so much, *prayed* that he would say the words she desperately wanted to hear. 'Everything except your love.' Her eyes searched his, hoping to pierce the inscrutable barrier and discover a depth of emotion that was based on more than just desire for her body.

'I want, *need* to be more to you than just a woman gracing your arm, a hostess in your home.' She paused, then added quietly, 'A mistress in your bed.'

There wasn't so much as a flicker in his expression to give any visible indication of his feelings. It angered her unbearably, making her want to rage, *shout*, hit him in order to get some kind of reaction.

'I asked you to be my wife.' The words were softly spoken, yet deadly, and she shivered inwardly as a sliver of ice slid down the length of her spine.

She lifted her head, tilting her head fractionally in silent challenge. 'To bear your sons?' Inside she was slowly dying. 'If you plant only the seeds of daughters in my womb, will you cast me aside for another wife who might sire the son you desire—you *need* to uphold the coveted name of Al-Sayed?'

Icy rage flared briefly in his eyes before it was quickly masked. 'You would lead an envied lifestyle.'

She thought of Nashwa and her daughters, and knew she could never be meekly accepting of such subjugation.

'It isn't enough,' Kristi offered with incredible sadness, aware that life without him would be like dying a very slow and painful death. 'When I marry, I want to believe it will be for ever. That *I* am as important to the man I accept as my husband as he is to me.' Her eyes felt as if they were drowning in unshed tears. 'Above all others. Beyond material possessions.' The ache in her throat was a palpable lump she dared not attempt to swallow. 'I need to know I am everything you need. All you ever want.' She felt boneless, and in danger of falling in an ignominious heap at his feet.

'You ask for guarantees, when with human emotions there can be none? Assurances are only words, given at a time when the head is ruled by the heart.'

'I feel sorry for you, Shalef. True love is a gift. Priceless.'

'I do not require your sympathy,' he declared with an infinite degree of cynicism.

'No,' she agreed bravely. 'You do not even require me.' It almost killed her to voice the words. 'My position in your life, your bed will be easily filled.'

His eyes narrowed fractionally, their depths so darkly unfathomable that it made her feel immeasurably afraid. 'You play for high stakes.'

Her chin lifted, and it took every ounce of strength she possessed to keep her voice level. 'The highest.'

'And if you lose?'

Kristi was aware of her fragile hold on her emotions. Afterwards, she could cry. But not yet. *'In-shallah,'* she said with quiet simplicity.

A tiny flame leapt in his eyes, flaring briefly before being extinguished beneath the measure of his control.

For one infinitesimal second she thought that he might strike her, so intense was his anger, then she silently damned a vivid imagination. He could employ a far more effective method of retribution if he so chose, without resorting to physical violence.

'You try my patience.'

There were words she could have uttered, but they were meaningless phrases, and not worth uttering. 'Please.' She lifted a hand, then let it fall helplessly down to her side. 'I have to finish packing.'

His eyes resembled dark shards of slate as he thrust one hand into his trouser pocket in a tightly controlled gesture.

'You want me to leave?'

'Yes.'

His facial muscles tensed over sculptured bone. 'As you please. But first—'

He reached for her, and she froze, her eyes widening with an apprehension that had little to do with fear as he lowered his head to hers.

The touch of his mouth was soft against her own, and she was unaware of the tiny, inarticulate sound that emerged from her throat as the edge of his tongue made an exploratory sweep over the full curve of her lower lip.

She wanted to cry out, Don't do this to me. A treacherous warmth invaded her veins, firing her body with a passion that she knew she'd never experience with any other man.

It was like drowning, descending with exquisite slowness into a nirvana-like state where reality faded into obscurity. There was only *now*, and the wealth of sensation that he was able to evoke.

Her body shook slightly as she fought against giving a response, and she felt the ache of unshed tears as he alternately teased and cajoled, pressing home with each small advantage gained, until her mouth aligned with his in involuntary capitulation.

A despairing groan rose and died in her throat as he deepened the kiss, possessing, demanding, *invading* in a manner that made her body tremble, and she clutched at his shoulders in a desperate bid to cling onto something tangible as he swept her into an emotional void from which she doubted she could emerge intact.

His passionate intensity was almost a violation, and when he released her she stood perfectly still, afraid that the slightest movement would rend every crack in her crumbling composure.

Part of her wanted to scream, *Go*; get out of my life before I break into a thousand pieces; the other part wanted to beg him to utter the necessary words that would bind her to him for ever.

His eyes were dark and partly hooded, making it impossible to read anything in his expression.

Lifting a hand to her face, he trailed a forefinger

lightly over the swollen curves of her mouth, then traced a path along the edge of her jaw and back again.

For what seemed an age he simply looked at her, imprinting on his mind her delicate features, the flawless skin, waxen-pale from the intensity of her emotions, the wide-spaced, fathomless deep brown and topaz eyes, and the bruised softness of her mouth.

Then his hand dropped to his side, and he turned towards the door, walking to it, through it without so much as a backward glance.

The sound of the lock clicking into place proved the catalyst for the release of her tears, and she stood exactly where he'd left her as their flow trickled to each corner of her mouth, then slowly slid to her chin.

Kristi stayed locked into immobility for a very long time, then something stirred within her, providing her with sufficient strength to turn and walk back into the bedroom, where she methodically completed her packing.

She even managed to bathe her face and apply fresh make-up before crossing to the in-house phone and alerting Reception that her bags were ready to be taken down.

'Thank you, Miss Dalton. A car is waiting.'

One last check round the suite, then she caught up her shoulder bag and moved out into the hallway. The lift transported her down to Reception, where she was informed that her account had already been settled.

Her fingers shook as she put away her credit card then handed over the key. Shalef. Like the sleek

Bentley parked by the kerb outside the main entrance, with its boot open ready to receive her luggage, it represented a final gesture. A silent, mocking attestation to what she had given up.

Kristi stepped through the revolving door and out into the cool air, and the chauffeur opened the rear passenger door.

She didn't hesitate as she crossed to his side. 'Please thank Sheikh bin Youssef Al-Sayed for his kindness,' she said firmly, 'and tell him that I chose to hire a taxi.'

The chauffeur paled with concern. 'Miss Dalton, I have strict instructions to drive you to the airport and assist you through Customs.'

She offered a faint smile of dismissal. 'That won't be necessary.'

'The Sheikh will be annoyed.'

'With me,' she clarified. One eyebrow rose in wry amusement. 'I don't imagine his instructions included bundling me into the car against my will?'

'No, Miss Dalton.'

'Then you are exonerated from any blame.' Turning away, she spoke to the porter and had him beckon a hovering taxi.

Within minutes it pulled out into the flow of traffic and Kristi leaned back against the seat and stared blindly out of the window. There were people briskly walking on the pavements, coats caught tightly closed against the cold. And it began to rain, settling into a heavy deluge that diminished visibility and set the wipers swishing vigorously back and forth against the windscreen.

In less than twenty-four hours she would touch down to warm summer temperatures, soft balmy breezes, and *home*. The prospect of seeing Shane again, and a few very close friends, should have evoked anticipatory pleasure. Instead, she was filled with a desolation so acute that it became a tangible pain, tearing at her insides and leeching the colour from her face.

CHAPTER ELEVEN

'ANYTHING of interest in next week's bookings?' Kristi queried as she deposited her camera-case on a nearby chair.

'Nothing outstanding,' Shane relayed as he scanned the appointment book spread out on the desk.

It was late, Annie had left for the day, commuters were on their way home, and outside a traffic lull had emptied the streets.

Soon it would be dark, bright neon signs would vie for attention, and the restaurants and theatres would fill with people seeking food, fun and laughter.

Kristi had been back in Sydney for more than a month. Six weeks, three days and counting, she mused idly as she crossed the floor and stood gazing idly out over the city's skyscape.

The inner harbour waters were a brilliant, sparkling blue beneath the sun's rays, their surface dotted with a mix of pleasure craft, two ferries sailing in opposite directions and a huge freighter led by a pilot tug *en route* to a harbour dock.

Two days after her return from London she'd thrown herself into work, taking every assignment that was logged into her appointment book in an effort to keep busy during the daylight hours so that she wouldn't have time to *think*.

She had even let it be known that she was prepared to cover the social circuit, and as a consequence she'd been out most nights at one function or another, photographing some of the city's glitterati. Two weddings, two christenings…the list was far too lengthy, the pace too frenetic for one person alone.

The sun's warmth had coloured her skin a light honey-gold, but her eyes held shadows of sadness, her seldom offered smile lacked any real warmth, and her soft curves had become redefined into almost waif-like slenderness.

She could cope, she assured herself silently. She *had* to cope. The nights were the worst—hours when she lay awake staring into the darkness, *remembering*, caught up with visions so graphic, so explicit that it became an agony of the mind as well as of the flesh.

'I've had an offer which I'm tempted to accept,' Shane offered slowly, hating the shadows beneath her eyes, the carefully contrived smile, and the hint of sadness apparent whenever she thought no one was looking.

'Hopefully not in the wilds of Africa, or Bosnia?' Despite her lightly voiced query, there was an underlying concern. Neither location was an impossibility.

'New Zealand. A geographic spread for the tourism industry. It'll provide a contrast to my last assignment,' he noted with wry humour. 'As a bonus I get to go skiing and trek the Milford Sound.'

She turned back to face him. 'When do you leave?'

'How well you know me,' came the slightly wry observation. 'Tomorrow. Is that a problem?'

'When will you be back?'

'The end of next week, providing the weather holds and there are no delays.' His expression softened. 'Why don't you cancel a few appointments and take some time off? You look ragged.'

'Thanks.' She managed a smile that didn't fool him in the slightest. 'Just what I needed to hear.'

'Hey,' Shane chided her gently. Lifting a hand, he brushed his knuckles along the edge of her jaw. 'I care.'

A smile trembled at the edge of her lips. 'I know.'

'Shalef bin Youssef Al-Sayed may have been instrumental in saving my hide,' he said quietly, 'but if I could get my hands on him now I'd kill him for whatever it is that he's done to you.'

Her eyes were remarkably steady as she met his. 'He wanted marriage,' she said evenly. 'For all the wrong reasons.'

'You love him.'

It was a statement she didn't bother to deny. For as long as she could remember they'd shared an affinity, an extra perception that transcended the norm. It generated an indestructible bond—two minds so attuned to each other's thoughts that there had rarely been the need to explain an action.

'It isn't enough.' Her eyes felt large and ached with suppressed emotion.

'The man is a fool,' Shane said gently.

There had been no phone call, no fax. But then, she hadn't expected any. You lie, a tiny voice taunted. Admit you hoped he would initiate some form of contact. Shalef bin Youssef Al-Sayed was a master player, and she hadn't played the game according to his plan. There were a hundred other women who could fill his bed. Ten times that many who would leap at the chance.

Kristi switched on the answering machine and caught up her camera-bag. 'Let's lock up and get out of here.'

'Dinner. Somewhere that serves good food,' Shane suggested as he followed her to the door.

'I'd rather go home.'

He tended the lock, checked that it was firmly in place, then moved ahead of her down the single flight of stairs. 'A restaurant. I'm buying. And don't argue,' he added softly as they reached the pavement.

French cuisine at its best, Kristi mused almost two hours later. Despite her professed lack of appetite, she'd managed to do justice to chicken consommé followed by a delectable portion of steamed fish with a delicate lemon sauce, accompanied by an assortment of vegetables. To finish, she'd selected a compote of fresh fruit doused in brandy, then flambéed and served with cream.

'Coffee?'

'Please,' she said gratefully. 'Black, very strong.'

A few months ago she would have requested a de-caffeinated variety and added milk. How some things change, she mused idly as she pushed down the plunger of the cafetière and poured the dark, aromatic brew into two cups. Adding a liberal amount of sugar, she sank back in her chair, then lifted the cup to her lips and took an appreciative mouthful.

The glass of Cabernet Shiraz she'd sipped throughout the meal had had a mellowing effect. 'Thanks.'

'For dinner?'

Kristi smiled. 'For insisting on bringing me here.'

'My pleasure.'

It was late, she was tired, and she knew that she really should go home, but she was loath to return to her empty apartment. So she finished her coffee and poured another for herself and for Shane.

'Want to talk about it?' he queried lightly, and she shook her head.

'Then let's do the business thing. What do you think about allowing Annie to buy a small share of the studio?'

'You're serious?'

'You have reservations?'

'It's been Dalton Photographics for years,' she protested. 'Why change?'

'It will still be Dalton Photographics.'

Comprehension dawned as she remembered the faintly wistful expression on a certain young woman's face whenever Shane was in town. '*Annie*?'

'Is it so obvious?'

'Not to anyone else.' A slow, sweet smile lit her features. 'I can't think of anyone I'd rather have as a sister-in-law.'

'I proposed last night. When I get back from New Zealand we'll make it official. More coffee?'

She shook her head, and he beckoned for the account, then checked off each item, signed, and handed over a tip as he got to his feet.

He took her key as they reached their parked vehicles, unlocked her door, then saw her safely seated behind the wheel with her belt in place.

'Drive carefully.'

She cast him a teasing glance. 'Always,' she assured him. 'Don't fall off the side of a mountain.'

'No chance.' He reached out a hand and brushed his fingers against her cheek. 'I'll phone.'

'Make sure of it.' She turned the key in the ignition and fired the engine, then put the car into gear. *'Ciao.'*

It took fifteen minutes to reach her apartment, another fifteen for her to shower and slip into bed.

Perhaps it was the wine or the numerous sleepless nights but the next thing she heard was the sound of her alarm the following morning.

Annie was on the phone when Kristi walked into the studio shortly after eight, and in comical sign language she indicated that there was hot coffee in the percolator and could Kristi pour one for her too.

Annie should have opted for a career on the stage, Kristi mused as she extracted two mugs, added sugar, filled each with the hot, deliciously aromatic brew and deposited a mug on Annie's desk. The girl was a nat-ural-born satirist who could mimic anyone you cared to name.

'Miss Dalton,' Annie reiterated in a low, devilishly husky voice as soon as she replaced the receiver, her eyes sparkling with impish humour, 'is summoned to undertake a photographic session at one of *the* most fabulous homes Point Piper has to offer. An interior decorator is being flown in from London *after* she's sighted photographs of each room, the existing land-scaping, and the exterior shot from every imaginable angle.'

'When?'

'One gets the feeling it should have been yesterday. I said that you couldn't possibly fit him in until this afternoon.'

Kristi took an appreciative sip of coffee. 'And?'

'He negotiated for this morning.'

'What did you say?'

'I almost considered rescheduling. But he sounded…' She paused, then continued with dramatic intonation, 'frightfully autocratic. I decided he de-served to be taught a little humility.'

'You're incorrigible.'

'I know. I need taking in hand,' she declared with humour, and Kristi gave a subdued laugh.

'Shane assures me he is in line to do just that.' Her features softened with genuine affection. 'I'm de-lighted for both of you.'

Annie's eyes acquired an extra sparkle. 'Thanks. It'll be a small wedding, just immediate family. Shane wants it to happen three days after he returns from New Zealand.' Her smile widened into a mischievous grin. 'I'm plumping for the end of the month.'

'It will be interesting to see who wins.'

'I'll have fun enjoying Shane's method of persuasion.'

Kristi experienced a shaft of pain at Annie's obvious happiness, and endeavoured to bury it deep beneath the surface. 'I don't imagine he'll find cause for complaint.'

The strident sound of the phone interrupted their conversation and Annie snatched up the receiver, spoke into it at length, scanned the appointment book, made a booking, then concluded the call.

'Now, where were we?'

'Our so-named autocratic client,' Kristi reminded her. 'What if he wants shots of the pool reflecting the early-morning sun?'

'You develop this afternoon's film then shoot tomorrow,' Annie rationalised, raising her hands in an expressive gesture. 'As long as the courier picks up before five they'll be on a flight out of here tomorrow night.'

'You were able to convince him of that?'

'He didn't threaten to use one of the competition.'

'What time am I supposed to be there?'

'One-thirty. He didn't even query the fee.'

Kristi shot her a sharp look. 'Tell me you didn't load it.'

'*Moi*?' Annie queried with mock humour. 'I simply informed him there was an extra charge for a rush job.'

'What would I do without you?'

'Survive,' the vivacious brunette responded with a sunny smile.

Kristi finished the last of her coffee, then rinsed and put away the mug before checking the appointment book. 'Bickersby, studio, eight-thirty, followed by a ten-thirty session at a client's home in Clontarf. Children's photographs.' She would have enough time to finish, return to the studio, grab some lunch, then be at Point Piper by one-thirty.

Annie was right—the house was fabulous, Kristi decided a few hours later as she parked her car in a street lined with prestigious homes. Some had been there a long time, while there were a few huge modern structures which had obviously replaced the original houses, comprising three and sometimes four levels against the sloping cliff-face. The view out over the harbour was spectacular, and the price-tag for each home would run into several millions of dollars.

She ran a quick check of the house number, then alighted from the car, collected her gear, and approached the security intercom attached to an ornate steel gate.

At the front door a housekeeper greeted her and led

the way through a spacious foyer to an informal lounge.

The interior was a little too ascetic for Kristi's taste. There should have been artwork on the walls, bowls filled with freshly cut flowers, and the primrose-painted walls needed be repainted in cool off-white or pale calico to emphasise the light, airy design.

'My employer requested that I convey his apologies. He's been delayed by a business call which may take up to ten minutes. Would you like a cool drink or a cup of coffee or tea while you wait?'

'Tea would be lovely, thanks.' Lunch had been an apple eaten *en route* from her previous booking. Photographing children was a hazardous occupation, for they tended to be unpredictable when faced with a stranger wielding a camera. This morning's session had run badly over time, with a harried young mother professing that it would be *years* before she could contemplate assembling her normally angelic little darlings for another professional sitting. Despite Kristi's efforts to capture their amusement with a hand puppet, the children, aged eighteen months, three and four years, had collectively gone from shy to awkward to uncooperative, resorted to tears, then finally succumbed to blatant bribery.

There was a sense of relief, Kristi mused wryly, in that this afternoon's booking involved an inanimate house. Crossing to the wide glass window, she turned back and checked the light, mentally choosing the best angles.

The housekeeper appeared with a tray which she set down on a low table. 'I'll leave you to pour.' She indicated a plate of delicately prepared sandwiches. 'Just in case you're hungry.'

Kristi gave an appreciative smile. 'Thanks. I missed lunch.'

The tea was Earl Grey, the sandwiches smoked salmon and cream cheese. Divine, she described them silently as she bit into another and replaced her cup on the tray.

She would have liked to wander through the house while she waited, observing and conducting a professional assessment. It would save time.

With ideal contemplation she wondered at the identity of the new owner. The house was only a few years old, and its design held the stamp of one of Sydney's finest architects whose brilliance commanded an exorbitant fee. Despite the colours not being her personal preference, the workmanship was superb. The fact that he was employing an international interior decorator indicated that no expense would be spared in establishing the owner's individual taste.

'Miss Dalton?'

Kristi turned at the sound of the housekeeper's voice.

'I'll take you down to the office now.'

They descended to the next level via a wide, curved staircase which led to a spacious marble-tiled area complete with an ornate fountain centrally positioned beneath a crystal chandelier. The housekeeper indicated a hallway to her left.

'The office is situated at the end, the last door on the right.'

There was no logical reason for the faint unfurling of nerves inside Kristi's stomach or the prickle of apprehension that settled between her shoulderblades as she drew closer.

Crazy, she dismissed as the housekeeper paused beside the closed door and knocked before standing to one side.

'Please go in, Miss Dalton.'

A faint shiver shook her slim frame, yet her hand was steady as she turned the handle and pushed open the door.

It was a large room, she saw at once, complete with an assortment of high-tech electronic business equipment. Bookcases lined one wall, and the desk was an expensive antique.

Behind it the high-backed swivel-chair was empty, and her eyes slid to a tall figure silhouetted against the floor-to-ceiling plate-glass window.

The man's height and breadth looked achingly familiar, and the breath caught in her throat as she willed him to turn and face her.

Almost as if he sensed her apprehension, he shifted, his movements deliberately slow as he swung away from the window.

Shalef.

There was something primitive in his expression,

and every instinct she possessed warned of the need for caution. It vied with a slow-burning anger that made her want to demand a reason for his presence in Sydney—more particularly, *why* he had summoned her to this house.

Innate dignity put a temporary rein on her temper as she studied his features, noting the fine lines fanning out from the corners of his eyes, the chiselled perfection of his mouth, the slashes down each cheek that seemed more deeply etched than she remembered.

Superbly tailored black trousers accentuated the muscular length of his legs, while the white silk shirt lent emphasis to his height and breadth of shoulder. He had loosened the top three buttons of his neck and folded back both cuffs, lending a casual, relaxed look that was belied by the most electric energy projected with effortless ease.

It was an energy that both thrilled and frightened, for she'd witnessed it unfurled and at its most dangerous.

Now she was unsure of its measure, and of his precise reason for requesting her presence.

It took considerable effort to inject her voice with polite civility. 'There are any number of competent photographers listed in the telephone directory capable of providing the services you require.' She drew in a deep breath, then released it slowly. 'It would better if you contacted one of them.'

One dark eyebrow lifted slightly and his smile was faintly cynical. 'Better for whom?'

If he was going to play games, she'd turn around and walk out *now*. 'Shalef—'

'I was assured by your secretary that the photographs would be ready early this evening,' he declared with dangerous silkiness. 'Are you now implying that you intend to renege on a verbal business agreement?'

Professionalism and sheer inner strength brought a lift to her chin and lent her eyes an angry sparkle. She'd complete the session and provide him with his wretched photographs, if only to prove that he no longer possessed the power to affect her. 'Perhaps you could tell me precisely what you want, then I can get started.'

He didn't move, but she sensed his body muscles tense with restrained anger.

'I return to London tomorrow. I'd prefer to take the prints with me.'

Her eyes flashed with brilliant fire. 'Why a London interior decorator? What's wrong with employing an Australian firm?'

'I have utilised this firm's services for a number of years.' He paused, then continued quietly, 'I trust their judgement and have no qualms about leaving them to complete everything to my satisfaction in my absence.'

Pain knotted in the region of her stomach, and she

had to consciously stop herself from gasping out loud. After tonight she'd never see him again.

'Very well.'

He shifted away from the desk and walked to the door. 'We'll begin outside while the light is still good.'

Instead of choosing the staircase, he led the way to a cleverly concealed lift, and in the cubicle's close confines she could feel the fast hammering of her heart. A tell-tale pulse beat in unison at the base of her throat, and she had to fight the temptation to cover it with a protective hand.

There were five buttons on the indicator panel, and she almost cried out in relief when the lift slid to a smooth halt on the lowest level.

Focus, *concentrate*, she commanded herself silently as she walked at his side through a large, informal area to wide, sliding glass doors opening out onto a terracotta-tiled patio and a free-form swimming pool.

For the next ten minutes Kristi reeled off numerous shots of the pool, external frontage from several angles and the view out over the harbour, before moving inside.

Shalef was never far from her side, suggesting, directing, asking her opinion on occasion as she steadily filled one roll of film, then paused to remove it and insert another.

It was a game, she decided in desperation. Deliberately orchestrated by a man who had no concern for the emotional storm that tore at her insides and ripped her nerves to shreds.

Twice his arm brushed against one of hers, and the faint muskiness of his cologne combined with his masculine scent almost succeeded in driving her insane.

It seemed for ever before the interior shooting was completed, and she welcomed the fresh, cooling breeze as she moved outdoors and shot the house from the street, the gardens, the driveway.

'That's it,' Kristi announced finally, aware that she had far more than she could possibly need. With care she capped the lens and removed the strap from her neck. Her shoulders felt slightly stiff and she had the beginnings of a headache. Tension, from being in Shalef bin Youssef Al-Sayed's company for the past few hours—three, she noted with surprise as she spared her watch a quick glance.

'I'll collect my bag from the foyer then get back to the studio.' The sooner she made a start on the developing process, the sooner she'd be finished.

Several minutes later, bag in hand, she moved towards the front door. The knot of tension inside her stomach tightened into a painful ball, and her smile was a mere facsimile of one as she turned towards him. 'I can't give you a definite time. Somewhere between seven and eight o'clock?'

He inclined his head and accompanied her to her car, waiting as she unlocked it; then, when she was seated, he shut the door.

The engine fired immediately and she paused only long enough to secure her seat belt before sending the BMW down the road.

It wasn't until she had gained the main New South Head road that she was able to relax, and even then it was strictly temporary.

'Well? What is he like?' Annie demanded the instant Kristi entered the studio. 'Make my day and tell me he's tall, dark and gorgeous.'

'Any messages?' Kristi crossed to the desk and checked the message pad. 'I'll be in the lab for the next hour. Maybe longer.'

Annie wrinkled her nose in silent admonition, and her eyes sharpened fractionally. 'You look tired. Why don't you go home and come in early in the morning?'

'Because, Annie, darling,' she revealed, 'the client requires the prints tonight.'

'Tell him you can't do it.'

'Too late. I already told him I can.'

'Then I'll make some fresh coffee.'

Kristi gave a smile in thanks. 'You're an angel.'

It was after seven when she examined the last print. With professional dedication she collated them according to floor level, noting each room and its aspect, before pushing them into a large envelope.

Moving her shoulders, she eased the crick in her neck, then massaged each temple in an effort to diminish the dull, aching sensation which had settled there more than an hour ago.

She felt tired, hungry, and would have given almost anything to go home, sink into a spa-bath and have the tiny, pulsing jets work their magic on her tense muscles.

Fifteen minutes later she wound down the window of her car and pressed the security intercom outside the set of high iron gates guarding the entrance to Shalef's harbourfront home. Within seconds they slid open and she eased the car towards the front of the house, parking it right outside the main door...for an easy getaway, she told herself as she retrieved the thick envelope from the passenger seat.

The housekeeper answered the door and Kristi wondered why she should be surprised. Shalef lived in a world where one employed staff to maintain residences. However, this was Sydney, not London or Riyadh.

'Would you please give this to Sheikh bin Al-Sayed?' Kristi requested, holding out the package. 'I've enclosed the account.'

'Sheikh bin Al-Sayed wishes to pay you now. If you'd care to wait in the lounge?'

No, I wouldn't care to wait, Kristi felt like screaming, and I don't want to see Shalef bin Youssef Al-Sayed.

'Thank you, Emily. I'll take care of Miss Dalton.'

She should have known that he wouldn't allow her to get away so easily, she decided in despair. 'I've delivered the prints as you requested,' she ventured quietly.

'Emily has prepared dinner,' Shalef declared smoothly. 'We'll eat, then I'll go through the prints.'

'*No*.' The single negation took the place of a silent, primal scream that sprang from the depths of her soul. 'I can't. I'm expecting a phone call.' She was babbling—short, stark sentences that sounded desperate even to her own ears.

His eyes hardened measurably. 'I imagine whoever it is will leave a message on your answer-ing machine.'

'Damn you, Shalef,' she flung at him, shaky with anger as he took hold of her arm and led her through to an informal dining room where the table was set for two.

Covered dishes had been placed in the centre, and her stomach clenched in hungry anticipation at the delicious aroma permeating the room.

'Sit down.'

It was easier to capitulate, and she made no protest as he uncorked a bottle of Cabernet Shiraz and poured a generous measure into her glass.

'Emily is an exceptional cook,' Shalef informed her as he uncovered a dish and served her a generous portion, adding rice from the second dish. He served himself, then took the seat opposite. 'Eat, Kristi,' he commanded silkily. He filled his own glass, then raised it in a silent toast.

Kristi picked up her fork and speared a delectable

piece of chicken. Sautéed in wine and mushrooms, it tasted out of this world.

She thought of a dozen things to say, and discarded every one of them. The wine was superb, and gradually it began to dissipate the knot of tension inside her stomach.

'Why did you buy this house?' Surely the house was a safe subject?

His eyes lingered on her mouth, then slowly traversed the slope of her nose before locking with her own. 'I wanted an Australian base.'

'Extending your global interests?'

'You could say that.'

She was breaking up inside, fragmenting into a hundred pieces. If she didn't gather her shattered nerves together, she'd never be able to get up and walk out of here with any semblance of dignity.

She put down her fork, then carefully replaced her glass. Not carefully enough, for the rim caught the side of her plate and slipped from her fingers. With horrified fascination she watched the wine spill into an ever widening dark pool on the white damask. 'I'm so sorry.' The apology fell from her lips as a whisper. Moisture welled from behind her eyes, distorting her vision as she plucked up her napkin and dabbed it over the spillage. 'The tablecloth should be rinsed or it will stain,' she said shakily.

'Leave it,' he commanded. 'It isn't important.'

'I'll replace it.'

'Don't be ridiculous.'

She closed her eyes, then slowly opened them again. Hell couldn't be any worse than this. 'If you'll excuse me, I'd prefer to leave.' She rose to her feet and sidestepped the chair. 'Thank you for dinner.' It was amazing. Even at a time like this she could still remember good manners.

She turned blindly away from the table, only to be brought to a halt mid-stride by a hand closing over her arm.

His eyes were dark, their expression so deeply inscrutable that it was impossible to discern his mood.

For what seemed an age he just looked at her, his silence unnerving in the stillness of the room.

She was damned if she'd cry. Tears were for the weak and she had to be strong. Her eyes ached as she strove to keep the moisture at bay, and she almost succeeded. Almost—the exception being a solitary tear which overflowed and spilled slowly down one cheek. It came to rest at the corner of her mouth, and after a few long seconds she edged the tip of her tongue out to dispense with it.

A husky, self-deprecating oath fell from his lips, and she stood in mesmerised silence as he caught hold of her hand and carried it to his mouth.

'Dear God,' Shalef groaned. '*Don't.*' His hand moved to capture her shoulders, then slid upwards to stroke her hair. His eyes were dark—so dark that they mirrored her own emotional pain as he held her head.

'For years I have enjoyed feminine company and never had to work at a relationship. *You,*' he enlightened her with gentle emphasis, 'mentally stripped me of all my material possessions and judged me for the man that I am without them. For the first time I had nothing to rely on except myself. It wasn't an enviable situation,' he said with a touch of self-mockery.

Kristi stood perfectly still, almost afraid to move.

'You didn't conform and I was intrigued. I thought I knew every facet of a woman, but you proved me wrong.' He paused, tilting her face slightly so that she had to look at him. 'You opposed me at every turn, and argued without hesitation. Yet you were an-gelic with Nashwa, sympathetic with Aisha and Hanan. I knew without doubt that I wanted you as my wife.' His expression became faintly wry. 'I imag-ined all I had to do was ask and you'd agree.'

He smiled, and the first flutter of hope began to stir inside her stomach.

'Instead you refused and walked out on me. My initial instinct was to follow you. Yet if I had then, even if I'd said the words you so wanted to hear, you would have been disinclined to believe them. So I decided to give you time. Not too much, but enough. Enough for me to set up this house and invent a rea-son to get you here.'

Her lips parted to protest, and he stilled her flow of words very effectively by taking possession of her mouth.

When he finally lifted his head, her own was reeling with the degree of passion he'd managed to evoke.

'This afternoon I wanted to declare my love the instant you walked in the door, but I had to allow for your outrage,' he qualified with genuine regret, 'and crack the protective barrier you'd erected around your heart.' His lips settled against her temple, then trailed a gentle path down to the edge of her mouth.

She felt shaky, and almost afraid to believe his words.

'I have something for you,' Shalef said gently. He withdrew a ring from his trouser pocket and placed it in the palm of her hand. 'It belonged to my mother, gifted to her by my father.'

Kristi looked at the wide gold ring embedded with diamonds.

'She never wore it, preferring a plain gold band, but she accepted it for what it represented…a symbol of my father's love.'

She raised her eyes to meet his, saw the depth of passion evident, and was unable to tear her gaze away.

'It was held in safe-keeping and handed to me on my twenty-fifth birthday, with the relayed request that I gift it to the woman I chose to be my wife.'

'It's beautiful,' Kristi said simply.

He brushed his fingers down her cheek, and warmth radiated through her body, bringing with it the need for the sweet sorcery of his touch.

'Marriage was something I viewed as a convenient

necessity with a woman of whom I could become fond...someone who could be my social hostess, the mother of my children, and pleasure me in bed.' He smiled—a slightly wry gesture that was belied by the warm humour evident in the depths of his eyes. 'Then I met you. And every woman of my acquaintance paled in comparison.' He traced the curves of her mouth with a forefinger, and followed its path with his tongue before seeking the soft inner tissues, to create an emotional demand which she didn't hesitate to answer.

When at last he lifted his head she could only look at him in bemusement as she saw the raw need, the hunger and the passion in his eyes.

'I love you. *Love,*' Shalef declared as he slid trembling hands to frame her face.

His eyes were dark, almost black, and Kristi sensed the faint uncertainty in his touch—a vulnerability she'd thought she would never see. It moved her more than she could bear.

'I know the only worthy gift I can bestow on you is my heart,' he said deeply. 'It's yours. For as long as it beats within me.'

Joy unfurled from deep within her and soared to an unbelievable height. Without hesitation she lifted her hands and wound them round his neck.

'I'll take great care of it,' she promised softly.

His features assumed a gentleness that almost made her want to cry. 'And you'll marry me?'

Kristi smiled—a wonderfully warm smile that was

meant to banish any doubts. The desire to tease him a little was irresistible. 'Are you asking?'

His faint laugh was low and husky as he gathered her close in against him. 'You want me to go down on bended knee?'

'I may never see you so humbled again,' she ventured solemnly, and he slowly shook his head.

'You're wrong. Each day I'll give thanks that I have the good fortune to share your life.'

She felt the prick of tears, and was unable to still the twin rivulets that ran slowly down each cheek.

'You haven't answered.'

Her mouth trembled. 'Yes.'

His mouth closed over hers, possessing it with such incredible passion that she felt dizzy when he finally lifted his head.

'Will you mind if the civil ceremony in London is followed by another in Riyadh?'

It was somehow fitting, and something that would have pleased his father. She thought of sharing the arrangements with Nashwa, Aisha and Hanan, and knew the enjoyment it would give them.

'Not at all.'

'We'll spend the first week of our honeymoon in Taif, then cruise the Greek islands for a month.'

'June is a nice month for brides,' Kristi offered wistfully.

'Next week,' Shalef commanded. 'You fly out to London with me tomorrow. Don't object,' he ordered as she opened her mouth.

'I could follow in a few days. No?' Her eyes sparkled mischievously. 'The day after?'

'Tomorrow,' he reaffirmed, giving her a gentle shake.

'In that case I'd better go home and pack.'

'All you need is your passport and a change of clothes, which we'll collect from your apartment *en route* to the airport in the morning.' His mouth fastened over hers in a kiss that left her weak-kneed and malleable. 'I have plans for what remains of the night.' He revealed precisely what those plans were, none of which involved any sleep. 'You can rest on the plane,' he added gently as he placed an arm beneath her knees and swung her into his arms.

In the bedroom he lowered her to her feet, and she reached for the buttons on his shirt, slipping them free before tackling the belt at his waist.

Kristi uttered a small gasp as his fingers brushed against her breast, then she groaned out loud as he began teasing each burgeoning peak, intensifying an awareness that radiated from the centre of her being until it encompassed every vein, every sensitised nerve-ending.

She was *his*, wholly, completely, to do precisely whatever he wanted with, and she helped him shed what remained of her clothes while he gave assistance in discarding his own before drawing her down onto the bed.

'My darling,' Shalef whispered with due reverence as he studied the silky sheen of her smooth-textured skin, and his gaze lingered on the soft curves of her breasts, the delicately shaped waist, before settling on the deep auburn curls protecting her womanhood.

He lifted a hand and brushed his fingers back and forth over the soft concavity of her stomach before trailing to trace the bones at one hip.

Her whole body ached with the promise of passion too long denied, and she reached for him.

'I want you *now*,' she whispered fiercely. 'All of you, inside me, without any preliminaries.' She cried out as his fingers slipped beneath the soft curls to initiate a sweet sorcery that quickly tipped her over the edge into a secret place where passion flared into an all-consuming fire, sweeping aside inhibition as it imbued her with an abandon that completely took his breath away as he carefully prepared her to accept his swollen length.

Silken tissues stretched to accommodate him, warm and wonderfully sleek as she met that initial thrust, encouraging his total possession by rising up against him in a rhythm that increased in pace until there was no master, no mistress, only two people in perfect accord, intent on gifting the other with the ultimate pleasure.

Afterwards she rested her cheek against the curve of his shoulder, too satiated to move so much as a muscle as he lightly trailed his fingers up and down the length of her spine.

This time their lovemaking was slow and erotic, ascending to new heights of intoxicating sensuality, and it was almost dawn before they drifted into a deep sleep from which they woke in time to shower, dress and depart for the airport via her apartment.

Once aboard the plane, Kristi slept most of the way to Hawaii, waking to meet the indulgent eyes of the man who would soon be her husband.

'Hello,' she greeted him softly, giving him a smile so warm and so incredibly sweet that it almost robbed him of breath.

Careless of the other passengers travelling in the first-class section of the aircraft, he leaned over and bestowed a lingering kiss on her lips.

'I've booked us into a hotel for a fourteen-hour stopover.'

Her eyes filled with wicked humour. 'Only fourteen hours?'

His mouth softened into a sensual curve. 'You require more than fourteen?'

She reached out a hand and traced the strong sweep of his jawline before covering his cheek with her palm. 'I love you.'

'Now you tell me,' Shalef groaned softly. '*Here*, where I can do very little about it.'

She cast him an angelic smile that was totally at variance with the witching sparkle lighting her eyes. 'Patience, they tell me, is good for the soul.'

His answering gaze was filled with musing self-mockery. 'Patience,' he stressed lightly, 'will doubtless stretch the limit of my control.'

Kristi laughed softly. 'I promise I'll allow you to make up for it.'

One eyebrow rose in a gesture of wry humour. 'That's supposed to get me through dinner, landing, Customs and a three-quarter-hour drive to the hotel?'

Her eyes teased him unmercifully. 'But think of the reward…for each of us.'

His expression darkened with the promise of re-newed passion. 'Indeed,' he agreed gently. 'A life-time.'

Childhood in Portsmouth meant grubby knees, flying pigtails and happiness for **Sara Wood**. Poverty drove her from typist and seaside landlady to teacher till writing finally gave her the freedom her Romany blood craved. Happily married, she has two handsome sons; Richard is married, calm, dependable, drives tankers, Simon is a roamer—silversmith, roofer, welder, always with beautiful girls. Sara lives in the Cornish countryside. Her glamorous writing life alternates with her passion for gardening, which allows her to be carefree and grubby again!

DESERT HOSTAGE
by
Sara Wood

CHAPTER ONE

TIFFANY almost dropped the armful of watered silk she had been carrying. Instead, she recovered her wits and placed it carefully on a table before turning slowly to face her partner.

'Cancelled?' Her voice sounded shaky. 'Palm Sands? Charlie, that's terrible! It's the second contract to be withdrawn! What's happening? Has the mafia invaded Oman?'

Charles was about to answer when their secretary buzzed on the intercom. The distracted Tiffany picked up the phone.

'There's a Sheikh Hassan here,' said an unusually breathless Leonie. 'Says he wants to discuss an important project.'

Tiffany and Charles exchanged glances. The man didn't have an appointment, but that wasn't unusual. And if he was a prospective customer…

'Please show the sheikh some of our portfolios,' said Tiffany. 'And say we'd be delighted to see him in five minutes.'

She replaced the receiver with a frown, staring through an arched window at the lapping waters of the Arabian Gulf below.

'Looks as if we have another paranoid sheikh who won't give his full name,' she sighed. 'More bulky bodyguards, shouldering into our office with lumpy muscles and itchy trigger fingers.'

'Last one to spot the sheikh's bullet-proof vest and gun

5

holster gets to pay for a round of drinks at the club,' Charles said with a grin.

'If the man has a palace here in Seeb which needs decorating, he can pack ten pistols and ride through that door on an Arab stallion for all I care,' said Tiffany drily. 'With the Palm Sands project a dead duck, we need a nice fat commission.'

Charles shook his head, bewildered. 'It's incredible how abruptly the contract was cancelled. Almost as if someone had heard we were crooks. You haven't anything in your past you're ashamed of, have you?'

'In twenty-six years? Plenty,' she sighed. 'Haven't we all? But nothing to explain why we've lost two juicy projects.'

'We'll find out the reason,' reassured Charles. 'In the meantime, let's roll out the red carpet, flash the teeth and gums nicely and impress the man like hell.'

'And for me, the cool, efficient look?' she grinned.

'Allow me.'

Laughing, Charles passed her the powder-blue jacket of her neatly waisted suit. As she slipped into it, there was a glint of silver out to sea. Her eyes focused on the glistening fish piled in a rope boat, hand-rolled from coconut husks. It was homeward bound for Muscat after an early morning fishing trip.

Home. For her it was anywhere she could get work. Maybe this time she and her eight-year-old son Josef could settle down. *If* Oriental Interiors could get enough contracts.

Hastily, she improved on her almost impeccable appearance, loosing her honey-blonde hair and deftly twisting it back with graceful movements into a severely pinned knot.

The situation was worrying. After six months, she and

Charlie had almost finished their work on the hotel where they had temporary offices. And there was nothing else on the horizon, now the two major contracts for the year had been cancelled. The financial compensation wouldn't be enough to cover their expenses. And if there was some kind of vendetta against them, they were in trouble. Reputation out here was everything.

'Ready?'

She composed herself. A perfect English rose, reserved, controlled, and very unapproachable. A lady. Prim and proper.

She nodded, just as Leonie knocked and slipped into the office, looking very agitated.

'He's getting impatient,' she said, upset. 'He's walking up and down and looking angrier and angrier. His eyes are lethal. Can I tell him you're almost ready?'

'Show him in, Leonie,' said Charles. He raised an eyebrow at Tiffany. 'We have an arrogant man on our hands, it seems.'

'I'll try to remember we're on the breadline and the creditors are knocking on the door,' she said grimly. She didn't like bombastic, self-important men. They reminded her of her late husband, Nazim.

The nervous Leonie showed the Arab into the exotic, mirrored room, rich in oriental golds and reds, in gilt and marble.

Tiffany's grey eyes widened. Sheikh Hassan stood out, even in his ostentatious surroundings. Running a designer's expert eyes over him, she assessed the cost of the handmade Italian suit. It had been built on him, and an excellent construction job it was too. He must have had dozens of fittings for the suit to have fitted so smoothly over that hard, fit body.

Her lips curved into a faint smile. The lines were so

clean and sharp that no weaponry—other than his un-
doubtable male virility—could possibly be hidden beneath
the soft grey cloth.

He had paused, blocking the doorway, an effective and
commanding entrance. Charles was walking towards him,
his hand outstretched, but the sheikh stood solid and im-
movable, only his dark lustrous eyes scanning the room,
no smile on his harsh face.

Then he came forward, startling Tiffany with the swift-
ness of his sudden, energetic stride and directness of his
gaze on Charles.

'Sheikh Hassan. How do you do?' said Charles warmly.
'I am Charles Porter, the head designer of Oriental Interiors.'

'How do you do?' murmured the sheikh. The bright
sun, filtering through the stone tracery of the windows,
gleamed richly on his glossy blue-black hair.

He left Charles and swung around to Tiffany, moving
with that sudden, unharnessed speed which betrayed a
fierce vitality. She had an impression of a man who was
more used to vigorous gallops across the desert than moving within the confines of a room.

'I am Tiffany Sharif,' she offered, with a cool smile.
'Mr Porter's partner and assistant designer.'

He caught her elegant, artistic hand in a grip of hard
iron which drew her off balance and made her stumble
closer to him. An angry light flashed briefly in her eyes.
Astonishingly, she had recognised that he had fully intended to make her do that. A nasty piece of one-
upmanship.

She stared down at the long, tanned fingers impassively.

He didn't let her go. He was crowding her space, his
chest rising and falling in a powerful and daunting swell,
only a short distance from the plush fullness of her jutting

breasts, and she didn't like being that close to any man, let alone this one.

He disconcerted her with his vibrant energy, a lust for living, which made him immediately overbearing.

Keep your distance, her expression said boldly.

He ignored the message. 'I am Sheikh Hassan. Delighted. Absolutely delighted,' he said tightly.

Tiffany's eyes narrowed. There was something oddly sinister about the way he said that. A veiled threat. A sense of unease settled over her.

'What a strong handshake,' she remarked pointedly, injecting a little frost into her voice and expecting he would release her. He didn't.

'I tame horses,' he said cynically. 'High-spirited ones. You need strength to overcome wayward animals and show them who is their master.'

She reeled inwardly from the meaning behind his words. He was trying to dominate her and, dammit, she wasn't in any position to give him any backchat!

'How thrilling!' she fluttered, taking the only way out.

He wasn't fooled. He was too smart.

'Even more thrilling when the training is over and a mere movement of my body brings instant obedience,' he said with soft menace.

Secretly fuming, Tiffany nodded, apparently wide-eyed with admiration. She'd jerk him out of his complacency. Far too many men played macho games with her. She fixed a fascinated smile to her cold face. 'You're the second jockey I've met. The last one was banned for using his whip.'

The Arab's chest inflated dangerously and his hand slid from hers. Tiffany was forced to drop her lashes, intimidated by his anger, for a wave of cold, remembered fear had washed through her, bringing a terrible memory of violence to the surface. And she hated the sheikh for re-minding her of that.

'Please, do sit down,' said Charles hastily. 'Have you had a long journey?'

The sheikh moved to the gold damask ottoman. 'New York. This morning.'

Tiffany looked at him with grudging respect. He ap-peared to be as fresh as a daisy. Into the hothouse atmo-sphere of the office, his clear, desert-hawk eyes and healthily glowing face had brought an air of the out-doors—a harsh, arid and merciless landscape, set under a cruel sun.

'May we offer you some refreshment?' she asked pol-itely. 'Perhaps coffee? Or a soft drink?'

'A large neat whisky, if you have it.'

Tiffany blinked, but went to the cupboard where alco-hol was kept discreetly for European visitors. Ten o'clock in the morning and he was on the bottle!

'Jet lag,' explained the sheikh, his mocking eyes watch-ing Tiffany walk smoothly back across the room towards him. 'My body tells me it's late evening and is making its usual demands.'

She was holding the glass out to him and trying to keep her face blank, but from the way his voice caressed the words, and his roving glance had crawled up her long, long dancer's legs, he was obviously making a point about more than his drinking habits.

What an unpleasant man.

'Where would you like your drink?' she asked with a nearly sweet smile, as if contemplating a few interesting places.

He grinned, the flash of his white teeth dazzling in his tanned face. Smoke-grey eyes met ebony and locked. The grin faded. Something utterly unexpected in his expression caught her attention and held it, preventing her from looking away.

It was dislike! No, more than that, she corrected; it was a scathing contempt, which spoiled his handsome face, curling his smooth upper lip and tightening the muscles of his beautifully carved jaw!

'On the table.'

Her mouth pursed at the arrogant order, but she controlled her temper and flashed him a beaming smile.

Charles began to make conversation. Tiffany walked to her chair and sat down, every movement graceful, every gesture harmonious. Her poise was as natural as breathing.

Adoring ballet as a child, she'd been pushed too hard by an ambitious mother and at the age of sixteen had struggled on in pain, her ankles weakened by overwork. Her promising career was finished and she had a feeling of guilt that her mother's financial sacrifices had been in vain.

Her subsequent oriental-design course, however brief it had been before her marriage to Nazim, had proved useful. When he had died in London, she and little Josef had faced poverty until she'd applied for a job with Charles. He didn't mind that she'd never finished her design course because he liked her ideas, her flair and the polished presentation—evidence of hard work. They'd hit it off immediately, and Tiffany had happily followed him when he'd decided to look for work in Oman. She and Josef had travelled enough in their lives not to mind a move to the Middle East.

She listened to the two men chatting and wisely kept her mouth shut. The sheikh seemed happy now he was talking to Charles. It was plain that he was a raving chauvinist and she'd better keep in the background for the sake of the project.

'...a leisure complex, for weary businessmen,' the sheikh was saying. 'On the Batinah coast, here in Oman. I've financed it. As well as the usual facilities, it houses an ice rink, golf course, clubhouse, swimming-pools, health club, fishing wharfs...'

Tiffany's head reeled as he rattled through the list. What with the public rooms, secretarial areas, offices and restaurants, their work would be cut out to mastermind a coherent design. It was the chance of a lifetime. Her eyes became brilliant with hope and her face lit up with excitement.

'Sharif, you said?'

She started at the venom in his tone, directed at her. He glanced at her left hand, which bore no wedding-ring. She'd removed it the day Nazim had died and never wanted to wear one again. And then his glittering, diamond-hard eyes flicked up to hers again and stayed there.

Didn't he have eyelashes, and blink, like the rest of humanity? she wondered, a little shaken. It was like being hypnotised by a bird of prey! His open scorn reminded her of Nazim. The translucent skin over her cheekbones stretched taut with strain.

'Correct,' she said stiffly.

'Not an English name. And yet I can't believe that you have hot Arab blood racing beneath that pale, soft skin.'

He sat there in a very self-contained way, one long leg crossed elegantly over the other, his pure white shirt cutting a sharply defined line against his dark throat. One tanned hand rested on his silver-grey-clad thigh, the other on the rich damask seat. Everywhere on his person there was the glint of gold; on his wrist, in the deep-shot cuffs, on his little finger, and making a neat bar across his grey tie.

And oh, yes, he had eyelashes—long, curling and thick,

briefly hooding his eyes as he watched her absorbing all this detail, an imperceptible quirk now shaping the masculine, and disturbingly sensual lines of his mouth. Apart from these slight movements, only the gentle swell of his chest betrayed the pulsing life within him.

'How right you are, Sheikh Hassan. I'm pure English, through and through. Pure as the driven snow,' she said coolly. That should tell him where he stood!

'Then I assume you married an Omani.' An unpleasant smile briefly touched his lips. 'The cold, fair beauty has fallen in love with the darkness of the sultry night.'

Darkness was right, she thought with a wince. The darkness of hell. How romantic he made her ghastly marriage sound.

Her hand had involuntarily touched her breast, unwittingly drawing the sheikh's attention to her swelling curves. She saw that his dark, penetrating eyes had become as warm and inviting as hot caramel. Inwardly recoiling, Tiffany recognised the signs of danger in his regard. If he was to see her as anything other than a woman designed for man's pleasure, she'd need to freeze him down. She iced her eyes over till they were as dark as gun-metal.

'I married an Arab,' she said in a low voice.

'Do you have a family, Sheikh Hassan?' asked Charles awkwardly, seeing that Tiffany was becoming distressed.

'No one close. Though soon there will be,' he answered. 'Your husband—'

'Sir...' Charles bit his lip, but was emboldened by Tiffany's white, strained face. 'Forgive me for interrupting, but Mrs Sharif prefers not to speak of her late husband. Nazim died tragically in a car crash, two years ago.'

The effect on Sheikh Hassan was extraordinary. It was

as if he had drawn back into himself, despite the fact that not one muscle of his body had visibly moved.

'How very sad. I trust you are not entirely alone. Your parents must have been a great comfort to you.'

Tiffany frowned at his silky intrusion into her private life.

'I never knew my father. Mother died last year,' she said shortly.

'You have sons, Mrs Sharif?' he asked softly.

For some inexplicable reason, she sensed danger in his question. Yet it was a polite query, one which might well be asked in such circumstances. She knew that in the Arab world a son would grow up to provide for his widowed mother, whereas a daughter would be a financial burden until her bride price had been paid.

'One son. He is all the family I have.'

Sweet Josef. Without her knowing, her face grew tender, its beauty breathtaking as she mentally contemplated her handsome, beloved son.

'And yet you work,' murmured the sheikh.

'For his sake, I must,' she answered, with a tilt of her chin at the implied criticism. 'Josef is a day boy at Gulf International, the boarding school in Muscat. My hours are arranged so that I am home when he returns.'

The sheikh's disapproval had deepened, now he knew she was a working mother. Tiffany felt her stomach twist. The chance of winning this marvellous contract was slipping away. All because she was a woman, and she wasn't at home washing clothes and doing the ironing.

'Mrs Sharif doesn't allow her domestic life to interfere with her work. You can be sure that we both devote ourselves to our assignments,' said Charles, misinterpreting the reason for the sheikh's stony face. 'You only have to look around you to see that we must have put in some considerable thought and time to working on this hotel. The style…' he flicked open a folder and handed it to the sheikh '…is traditional, using the best of Oman's historical designs.'

They waited in silence while Sheikh Hassan examined the portfolio carefully, his face brooding.

'I'll have a contract drawn up this afternoon. That is, if you want the work,' he said abruptly.

'Oh! We would prefer to offer you some preliminary designs first—' began Charles, astonished at the speed of the sheikh's decision. Out here, even the smallest decisions normally took weeks, even months.

'I can see the quality of your work. I already knew of it, anyway. I was involved in the Palm Sands project.' Hassan's eyes flicked to and from Charles and Tiffany, gauging their reactions. He smiled to himself at their evident surprise. 'I know a great deal about you both. We'll get down to details later.' He stood up in a beautifully flowing movement. Harmony, thought Tiffany in surprise. The man moved with grace. 'How fortunate I am that you are free to concentrate on my leisure centre.'

He looked at Tiffany. And so sudden was the turning on of his sexuality that it poured unhindered into her senses, blocking everything else, like a powerful electric shock. A harsh, uncompromising desire flickered in his face, arching the strong mouth into sultry curves, parting his lips over the white teeth.

'And how fortunate I am to have met you, Mrs Sharif. I will be…' he considered carefully, his eyes hotly inciting '…as you say…*in touch*.'

With those softly growled words, he nodded, and strode out before either Charles or Tiffany could respond.

She was trying to cope with the unsettling fact that his deep, rich voice still seemed to be vibrating through her whole body. She'd never known a man so steeped in sex-uality that it had the power to hit her in a forceful wave. He'd deliberately let her glimpse the blatant, raw carnality behind his temporary mask of a sophisticated business-man. A flash of intuition told her that beneath the western dress lay a man in tune with a far more primitive life than she could imagine—one which was stripped of everything but the bare essentials for survival: water, food, sex.

The perfectly tailored clothes and cultured voice had vividly contrasted with the almost indecent passion for life in that tautly honed body. Everything about him added up to the enviable, self-confident air of a man who had mas-tered the art of living in a hard and remorseless environ-ment. And the fact that he was able to successfully step from the harshness of a barren desert straight into an ur-ban jungle was an even more unnerving achievement.

'Whew!' Charles drew a stubby-fingered hand over his forehead. 'Some dynamite!'

'One of the most unpleasantly pushy men I've ever met,' muttered Tiffany. 'Oh, don't worry, Charlie. I can work for swine like him if I have to. That work will keep us in coffee-beans and doughnuts for years. We have to sign. And somehow, I get the feeling that he's tied up with those cancellations. He knew too much about Palm Sands for my liking.'

'We'll push on and finish our work here, then,' said Charles. 'And see what Sheikh Hassan has to offer. I think,' he said, his face blissfully happy, 'that we've just met the goose who goes about laying golden eggs!'

Tiffany smiled faintly. She wasn't so sure. There was something underhand and sinister about the sheikh. And he was no goose. More a savage and hungry wolf.

At the end of the day, she walked through the crowded souk to her tiny flat, situated above a tailor's shop. It was all she'd been able to afford. Nazim's creditors had taken everything and she was still paying off a massive over-draft.

Then there were Josef's school fees. For him, she'd make any sacrifice. He'd have the best education she could buy. Turning down a narrow alley, only as wide as a camel's haunches, she stared up at the flaking old build-ing where she lived. A grimace crossed her face. It was shabby, but they had no choice for the moment, and at least their neighbours were decent people.

Greeting the friendly tailor, she went slowly up the worn steps to her flat. Half an hour later, Josef was dropped off by the school bus and came bursting in, full of news about his day.

By eight o'clock they had eaten. Josef had changed into some old clothes and gone to his room to do some home-work. Tiffany had showered, and washed her hair, leaving it to hang down her back to dry naturally. Slipping on a silk kimono, she sat in her bedroom doing her nails by the fading light from the window. There was a knock on the sitting-room door, and her hand holding the nail-polish brush wobbled a little.

'Who is it?' she called loudly, concentrating on smoothly lacquering her nails. Appearance was very im-portant in her job.

'It's me.'

'Come in, Mike. Come through to the bedroom.' She looked up and smiled at her friend, the serious young newly-wed from the room below. 'Hello. How's Mandy?'

Mike's homely face softened and Tiffany felt a pang to see the love he felt for Mandy. She envied the couple.

'Lovely, as always,' he said happily. 'How can you do that in the dark?'

'I hadn't noticed it was,' she said. 'Can you put the light on for me, Mike? My nails are wet.'

'Sure. I came to ask if you need anything in Muscat. I'm going there tomorrow.'

Tiffany flicked back a lock of hair from her eyes and blinked when an eyelash entered her eye.

'Damn.' She tried to remove it with her knuckle, not wanting to spoil her nails.

'Shall I help?' offered Mike tentatively, after watching her struggle for a few seconds.

'Please. It's really painful.'

She tipped up her face to his and he knelt in front of her, his face screwed up in concentration as he brushed at her lid with his clean handkerchief.

'Thanks,' she said gratefully. 'Um…Muscat. No, I don't think we want anything—but it was nice of you to ask.'

'OK. Call in or leave a note if you change your mind,' he said.

They talked for a few moments about Jo, then he said goodbye, shutting her bedroom door as he went.

Soon after, she heard another rap on the outer door, loud enough to be heard in the bedroom. She hoped Jo would answer it this time. It was bound to be one of his friends. They called often, not seeming to mind what the place looked like. He was very popular. Soon he'd want to board at the school as they did; in fact, he'd pestered her for ages, till she'd had to tell him she couldn't yet afford the extra fees. But she knew she would have to be prepared to watch her son become more and more independent.

Jo needed the balance of a male world, as well as a female one. She'd noticed how much he loved hearing from his friends about the activities they enjoyed with their fathers. It hurt her a little that she couldn't be everything to him. She grinned to herself. Her skills as a footballer left much to be desired!

From the sitting-room came a man's voice, and Josef's delighted laughter. It must be Mike again.

As she approached the connecting door, with a gentle smile on her face, she could hear Josef speaking, his voice high with excitement.

'...and I'm in the rugby team, too. Shall I get Mum? She'll be knocked sideways when she knows who you are! Isn't it brilliant?'

She stopped in surprise. That wasn't like her reserved, thoughtful son! A deep, warm chuckle echoed through the small lounge. Tiffany didn't recognise that as Mike's. But she did recognise the voice which spoke afterwards. Only one man could project pagan sensuality through solid chipboard.

Sheikh Hassan. A chill spread down Tiffany's spine. How on earth had he discovered her address? And why? Her lips firmed into a straight and determined line. She'd known there was more to the arrogant sheikh than met the eye. What tale was he spinning to her son?

Pushing open the door quietly, she saw him sitting on her dilapidated sofa, dressed for an expensive night out in an immaculate dinner-jacket and looking out of place in the down-at-heel room. His arm lay affectionately around Josef. Neither of them looked up.

To her horrified eyes, the two of them were totally wrapped up in each other, beaming stupidly, their eyes shining as if they'd won a lottery. Tiffany was more shocked than she could have imagined.

'Sheikh Hassan! What, *precisely*, are you doing with my son?' she rapped out, her face hot with fury.

Hassan was caught off guard. His eyes momentarily

showed the traces of warmth he had been sharing with Josef, and then a brief flash of fierce, sexual approval as his glance flashed over Tiffany's flowing hair and the revealing robe which rose and fell with every angry breath she took. Then the shutters came down over his face again, and by that time she was coping with Josef, who had flung himself into her arms.

'It's all right, Mum!' he cried, hugging her with all his might.

He looked at her as if he was dizzy with happiness, and her heart lurched. She reached out a tender hand and stroked his dark wavy hair, a feeling of foreboding in every one of her bones.

'Darling,' she reproved sternly, 'this…person is—'

'You don't know, you don't know who he is *really*!' crowed Josef, laughing.

He ran to Hassan, who had risen, and in a swift eager movement the sheikh caught him up, bubbling with suppressed laughter, and held him close as if they'd known each other for a loving lifetime. Tiffany's heart did another little somersault to see the sheikh's tenderness and she clutched at the door-frame in confusion. This was extraordinary behaviour for Josef! He was deeply loving, but like her he saved his affection for those he knew well. A terrible chill sent icicles into her stomach.

'Who are you?' she snapped, intensely irritated at the bond which seemed to have been so easily cemented between the uninvited sheikh and her son.

'My uncle! My very own uncle!' said Josef with a blissful smile, patently unable to tear his eyes away from the sheikh. 'Father's brother! Isn't it wonderful?'

Stunned, Tiffany was unable to speak. The breath had left her body in a sharp gasp. Her eyes and mouth shaped

into circles. It was impossible! Nazim had sworn he was
alone in the world. Why on earth would he lie?

She flicked back her long curtain of golden hair which
had swung around her face, and tried to compose herself.

'Mum, it's true, it's true!' cried Josef, seeing her disbelief. 'And we're invited to Riyam! I can't wait to go!
Uncle has told me all about my ancestors and the desert
and the stables and the fortress and—'

'Just a minute, Josef,' Tiffany said weakly, her mind in
turmoil.

'Sit down,' ordered Hassan, watching her like a hawk.

Too flabbergasted to demur, she obeyed, sinking limply
into a chair, her long slender legs shaking. She didn't
understand. He must have known who she was when he
met her at the office. And then, his hatred of her had
poured from his body in a never-ending stream.

Tiffany flushed. He'd deliberately given her the once-
over. The leisure centre was a ruse, after all. Her future
was still uncertain. A lead weight descended on her shoulders.

But…wasn't it a little suspicious that suddenly he'd
come up with this story that they were related? It was all
too far-fetched. He would have mentioned it before,
surely?

'How can you possibly be my brother-in-law?' she said
coldly.

'Oh, the usual way,' he drawled, arching a wicked eyebrow.

She flushed and he gave a mocking smile, reaching inside his dinner-jacket. He handed her his passport, which
she took with trembling hands and an ominous feeling. If
she did have a brother-in-law, she thought bleakly, she
didn't want him to be this sardonic man whose every

thought seemed to be laced with sexual violence. She shuddered. That alone linked him to Nazim.

With trembling fingers, she opened up the leather folder and flicked over the pages. Hassan bin Hamud al Sharif. Age thirty-two. Born in Riyam, in the city of Shirbat. The same place as her late husband Nazim. She raised her head and met Hassan's dangerous, black-ice eyes. What she saw there made the muscles in her stomach clench. Whatever he was up to, it was more sinister than she knew.

'He never mentioned you,' she breathed. 'He said he was alone in the world.'

'He was, in a way. There'd been a family row. Nazim left Riyam fifteen years ago, when he was twenty,' said Hassan quietly, keeping his arm tightly around Josef, who was gazing at him adoringly.

'Do you play football?' asked Jo hopefully.

'Do I?' grinned the sheikh. 'You try me!'

'Rugby? Cricket?'

'Yes. You like sport?'

Jo hugged himself in delight. 'You bet! But I don't ride.'

'You will,' promised Sheikh Hassan, testing Josef's muscles, and lifting one eyebrow. 'I think you're even stronger than I was at your age,' he said in surprise.

Josef fell for that flattery, to Tiffany's tight-lipped annoyance.

'Wow! Does that mean I'll grow up to be as big as you?' he asked, betraying his hero-worship by his expression.

Oh, God! thought Tiffany, a chill in her spine. Josef has found the father he's always longed for!

'Sheikh Hassan,' she said sharply, 'I went through Nazim's papers. There was nothing about any family— no photographs, no letters—'

'My father disowned him. I suppose he destroyed everything to do with us. In fact, we heard nothing from him till he contacted us a few years ago, shortly before my father died. Nazim was in Turkey...' Hassan hesitated, flicking a glance at Josef as if quickly altering what he had intended to say. 'He wrote to tell me there were some difficulties with the authorities,' he finished tactfully. 'He knew Father would never assist him, so I helped him out.'

Tiffany's grey eyes darkened in pain. Difficulties! That was putting it mildly. Until this day, she'd never known how Nazim had escaped a prison sentence for smuggling Persian carpets, nor how they'd all managed to slip out of the country and find the means to return to England.

'You sent money,' she said flatly.

'Yes. And pulled strings.' His eyes bore remorselessly into hers. 'And started him up in business again.'

'*You?* Oh, my God! I see!'

She frowned. So she was in Hassan's debt! The thought was too ghastly to imagine. Perhaps he'd come to demand payment, and the interest. A small groan escaped her lips.

'That doesn't prove you're Nazim's brother.' she said, putting off the evil moment when she might have to accept that fact. 'Just because you lent him money and your name is Sharif. It's not an uncommon name, is it?'

'I have documentary proof which will confirm that I am. I will show you it. We will have dinner together. There is a great deal to discuss,' said Hassan in a low tone.

Josef's face fell and he sullenly fiddled with his threadbare cuff, his mouth pouting his disappointment.

'You can't go out without me! We've only just met! I want to ask you—'

A brief gesture of Hassan's firm hand stopped Josef's

protest immediately. Tiffany was rather surprised. Her son could be very strong-willed when he wanted to be.

'Josef,' said Hassan, in a voice of infinite gentleness, 'I understand what you feel. I, too, am loath to leave you. But I must talk to your mother urgently. Be patient. We'll have years together. I told you I must return to Riyam late tonight. You can see I have to quickly convince your mother that I am your uncle.'

Hassan accepted Josef's bright-eyed nod. Tiffany was utterly astonished that her son seemed on the edge of tears. What had Hassan told him when they were alone? He must have played on her son's need for a father, as she'd thought. And what dreams of luxury had he coaxed Josef with?

'Why didn't you say anything when we first met?' she asked, in an accusing tone.

'I wasn't absolutely sure you were the right woman. Then, when you confirmed it with one or two remarks, I thought you'd rather hear the news in the privacy of your own home.'

His disdainful glance swept around the tiny room, leaving her in no doubt as to his opinion of it.

'I can't have dinner with you,' she said coldly. 'Josef—'

'Wouldn't Mike and Mandy keep an ear open for me?' begged Josef. 'I do want you to go, Mum! I do want you to believe Uncle Hassan! Besides,' he added craftily, 'you haven't been out since that man—'

'Jo,' she said hurriedly, not wanting to remember one of her less successful dates, a year ago. She'd come home feeling as if she'd been fending off a monster with eight pairs of hands.

'Why not go and ask these friends of yours?' suggested Hassan to Josef.

He leapt up. 'All right, Mum?'

'I have the contract here,' said Hassan quietly, patting his pocket. 'You could look at the terms over dinner and then we can talk about one or two things.'

'You're serious about the Batinah project?' she frowned, wavering.

She needed it so badly! Perhaps she could forget how much she disliked this man, and look on him as a bag of gold. She remembered Charlie's remark and smiled, correcting that to a golden egg.

'Go, Josef,' said Hassan. 'It'll do your mother good to go out.'

With Jo gone eagerly to do Hassan's bidding, the room seemed to shrink. She felt quite unnerved being alone with Hassan—and that was strange, since he was supposed to be her brother-in-law. The silence grew, and with it the atmosphere became oppressively heavy.

'You've dropped something of a bombshell on us,' she said eventually, desperate to break the tension.

'Josef seems thrilled. But not you,' drawled Hassan, lifting one dark eyebrow at an angle.

'You can hardly blame me for being cautious.'

He undid the button on his jacket and treated her to a broad expanse of dazzling white-shirted chest.

'Your son is puzzled and a little unhappy that you don't want him to have an uncle. It's almost as if you're jealous,' he murmured.

She flushed. 'I don't like strangers being familiar with my son,' she said stiffly. 'He knows that.'

'But…when you know for sure that I am your brother-in-law. Will I then be permitted to love Josef?'

Tiffany's face became troubled. As she contemplated the sheikh, her mouth parted, and she became aware of his eyes riveted to it. A small, sharp stab slid unwanted through her breast and her hand fluttered there, as if to keep it from troubling her again.

'You must understand,' she said, struggling with her wayward body and trying to keep her head. The sheikh had a remarkable ability to disconcert her—especially by using her own unfulfilled passions. He was drawing them out of her, like a master. 'The past is painful for me. Links with my late husband are naturally going to affect my equilibrium. You will have to be patient.'

'I have patience when I can see the result is worth waiting for,' he murmured, scalding her with an avid glance. 'I'll wait while you put some clothes on.'

To her amazement, she felt the heat of a sensual flame lick treacherously within her in response to his hot admiration. Confused by it, she wrapped her kimono securely around her body, then realised with a flush of embarrassment that she had pulled it taut over her breasts. Under the liquid darkness of his eyes, she folded her arms defiantly across her body, determined to resist him in every way.

'I don't think I want to go—'

'You have no choice,' he interrupted grimly, all gentleness gone. 'Oriental Interiors is in financial trouble. I can alleviate that pressure. People are beginning to talk about the mysterious cancelling of agreements. You know how important word of mouth is out here. Your good name is in my hands. I could make or break you and Charles Porter.'

She glared at his blatant blackmail.

'You wouldn't!'

'I would,' he said with soft menace.

'You threaten me—!'

'I have little time and I need to talk to you tonight,' he said impatiently. 'I'll use any means I have to. Do you really wish to disappoint your son? Can you dare to leave this matter unsettled? It's his future you're playing with, as well as your own, by disregarding my wishes.'

She stifled a sharp reply at his high-handed behaviour. Whether she liked it or not, he was right; she had to clear all this up, and not within Josef's earshot. But only if the stakes were high enough. If she was going to spend a couple of hours in his company, there might as well be something worthwhile coming from this ridiculous situation.

'Are you serious about the leisure complex?' she asked with a tilt of her firm chin as Jo hurtled back into the room.

Hassan smiled at the boy's excited face and embraced him fondly. Jo clung to him as if he never wanted him to go.

'Oh, yes,' he said, his eyes meeting Tiffany's over Josef's head. 'More than ever. I would like to keep my business in the family, and so I see no reason why we shouldn't sign the preliminary contract tonight if you are willing. The work is yours for the taking.'

Tiffany felt stunned. Josef bounced up and down on the sofa in glee.

'You see,' he grinned. 'You don't have to worry about money any more and working all hours! Uncle Hassan will take care of us! You needn't keep going to sales for clothes and walk miles for cheap vegetables. We can have meat a bit more often. You needn't worry about the rent and my school fees and my uniform. You—'

'Josef!' she breathed. 'Please!'

Hassan's face had turned to stone, his high cheekbones jutting aggressively beneath his glittering eyes. Tiffany could see that his anger was only barely held in check.

And the hatred had returned, blazing its destructive path

through the air, slicing the atmosphere like a knife as they both matched each other, stare for stare.

So. That was the reason for his dislike of working mothers. In fact, it made his claim to kinship more probable; her brother-in-law thought that the women of his family should stay at home and be domesticated, devoting themselves entirely to their children. Everything began to fall into place: Hassan's anger when he arrived—he would have had an inkling that she was a career woman—and his searching questions.

Yet…there was a number of loose ends still. She frowned.

'Mother,' cried Josef, torn between the two of them, his face crumpled in anguish.

'Oh, Jo! It's all right,' she said quietly, holding out her arms and giving him a hug. 'Sheikh Hassan is right. Try to contain your excitement till the morning, and I'll get you up early so we can talk before school. You do want me to go, don't you?' she asked.

'Oh, yes, Mum!' he said earnestly.

'I'll get ready.' She hesitated, not wanting to leave them together.

'I won't harm him,' said Hassan with a cynical glance. 'These walls are so thin, I'm sure you'll be able to hear everything we say.'

She flushed. 'I won't be long,' she muttered. 'Jo, perhaps you'd like to get Sheikh Hassan a coffee. We don't have any whisky,' she said sharply.

'*Uncle* Hassan; he's my uncle,' corrected Josef.

'Your mother must make sure, for your sake,' said Hassan gently. 'She's a little reluctant to believe it. We have to win her round.'

Tiffany pursed her lips at this clever move to make it seem as if he and Josef were on the same side and she was the enemy. Unable to say what she wanted to, she whirled out. To her ears came the sound of much laughter. Uncle Hassan was turning out to be a stand-up comedian, she thought sourly.

Feeling very reluctant, Tiffany dragged on the only smart dress she had which wouldn't let the side down: a bright red, and rather gorgeous hip-hugging, scoop-necked sheath which Nazim had bought for her in one of his extravagant moods. She smoothed on a little eye make-up and lipstick and gave her hair a quick brush, wishing she dared take time to put it up. That would take too long, and she didn't like the cosy intimacy into which her son and the imperious stranger had fallen. The silence and low murmuring behind the door were even worse than the laughter.

She slipped on her high-heeled sandals and dragged on a light cotton jacket before taking a few deep breaths to compose herself.

Only outwardly, though. Her mind was still racing, still going over and over the claims the sheikh had made, and what their implications might be. It was no use wondering. She'd soon know. And the sooner she entered that room and actually got the man alone, the sooner she'd be able to speak frankly and find out what he was up to.

In trepidation, knowing this evening could make or break her and her son, Tiffany pushed open the door.

CHAPTER TWO

JOSEF was curled up with Hassan, looking sleepy, and it seemed that the sheikh was telling him a story.

A fairy-story, thought Tiffany uncharitably, listening to the soothing, hypnotic voice. Hassan was oblivious to everything but Josef.

'They call it Tawi Atair,' he was saying, almost dreamily.

'Tawi Atair,' repeated Josef drowsily. 'What does that mean, Uncle?'

'The well of birds. There are so many. Some you may never have seen before, and a few familiar friends. But you'll see for yourself. Soon. I can hardly wait for that day, Josef.'

'We must make sure there's no mistake, first,' said Tiffany sharply, feeling like a wet blanket when she saw her son's look of alarm and misery at the thought that she might prevent him from acquiring this adored uncle.

As for Hassan, he'd glanced up at her and his rogue's eyes were all but stripping her naked. She gave him a scathing glance.

'There's no mistake,' said Hassan, unperturbed, turning from her to smile at Josef with affection. 'Don't worry. Rely on me.'

Tiffany felt a stab within her chest at the love he seemed to be offering her son. Hassan seemed charged with a greater passion than most men built up in a lifetime. In fact, she had the impression that he was a bigger man in all ways than any male she'd ever known. A natural born leader. Someone who'd stand out in any crowd.

She admired that. It had been her misfortune that Nazim had turned out to be weak-willed beneath his bluster, and had needed to enforce his male domination over her by crushing her spirit. She found the sheikh's inner strength rather refreshing, after that. Odd, if they were brothers.

'You look nice, Mum,' said Jo, his eyes pleading with her to like Hassan.

'Thank you, darling. Are you going downstairs to watch television with Mike?' she asked softly. For his sake, she'd sort this out. Josef nodded, beaming with pleasure.

Hassan stood up and reached out for Jo, picking him up in his strong arms. Tiffany was annoyed. It had been ages since she'd treated Jo like a baby; this man had no right to do so. It irked her even more that Jo seemed to be enjoying the temporary reversion to childhood, rather than being the sensible young boy, longing to be grown up.

By the time they left, she was very irritable. The sheikh had charmed everyone effortlessly, though he'd eyed Mike up and down a bit, as if he was a challenge.

The evening out started badly. They walked through the bustling streets to the square, which appeared to be filled with the biggest car she'd ever seen: a stretch limo, customised to please the most jaded of customers. She held on tight to her familiar portfolio, which Hassan had insisted she brought, and made her way through a small crowd which had collected around the gleaming car in awe.

Flushing with embarrassment at the ostentatious car, she stayed silent while Hassan ordered everyone out of the way and handed her in. It even smelt of money, she thought sourly—a strong aroma of soft leather. Inside, it was pretending to be a nuclear power station, with flashing lights, rows of dials and video screens.

The chauffeur drove off to a chorus of acclaim, as the car raised itself on its hydraulics and smoothly cruised away, like a huge vulture launching itself from a tree.

'It's not mine,' said Hassan tightly, seeing her disapproval. 'It belongs to a friend.'

'Amazing what bad taste some influential men have,' she said coldly, throwing caution to the winds and abandoning any idea of politeness.

'He's certainly influential,' murmured Hassan meaningfully.

'And he's certainly undiscerning,' she snapped.

'No, practical,' muttered Hassan. 'He needs a travelling office.'

He gestured to the computer and fax machine, and the two telephones.

'I'm surprised he can bear to lend the car to you,' she observed tartly. 'He'll get withdrawal symptoms, trying to manage without it tonight.'

'He's dining with the Sultan,' said Hassan in a flat voice.

'I'm staggered you weren't asked too,' she retorted.

'I was.'

He gave her a mocking smile. He was lying, of course. She half turned her back on him. It was an invidious situation, being in this man's debt, and thus in his power. Since the years with Nazim, when she'd been helplessly trapped by his threats, she'd set out determinedly to stand on her own feet. Now Nazim's own brother—if that was who he really was—seemed destined to force her to dance to his tune in the same way. History was repeating itself, she thought, her face cold and wintry.

She slanted a glance at Hassan. In the semi-gloom, he

looked darkly menacing, only the snowy shirt and the whites of his eyes relieving the blackness clothing his body. He stared straight ahead, his classic profile carved from stone, as they took the Muscat road. There was a downward turn to his mouth and a sneer fractionally lifted the muscles of his face.

All that oozing charm and laughter with Josef had been false. He didn't like her, and there was no reason why he should like her son. Why, then, had he made contact with them both? Purely for the money? He could have done that without making a personal appearance.

Pride prevented her from asking. It would make it seem as if she was anxious or curious. So the head waiter himself had removed her coat—to an imperceptible intake of breath from Hassan, when he saw her no-holds-barred dress—shown them to a small intimate table, hidden behind greenery, and taken their order before Hassan spoke.

'You're desperate for work, aren't you?' he asked in a tone of velvet menace.

Assuming a cool and confident stare, Tiffany gave a slight shrug and looked as indifferent as possible. Her knee hit his thigh and she was aware of tightly muscled warmth beneath the soft wool of his trousers. The indifference slipped briefly. Their eyes met and she saw an unmistakable glitter of desire in his expression. She drew herself upright in her chair.

'Not that desperate,' she said calmly.

His mouth softened. Her pulses beat a little faster from an illogical sense of danger, mesmerised by the sexual threat pouring from his body, sweeping over her like a flash-flood.

'I could make you so successful that you wouldn't need to struggle for work any more,' he murmured, leaning forwards.

But there was an unpleasant ring to his voice and she wondered what the price might be. His eyes strayed to her bare shoulders and lingered with a chilling caress on the swell of her breasts. Tiffany felt hot and wanted to fidget, but kept her body utterly still, apart from taking quick sips from her glass of lemon tea.

'I don't think I'll have to struggle. Not as far as my work is concerned. It's good enough to warrant success,' she said coolly.

She handed him her designs. He abandoned the sauté pigeon breast and flicked through the folder with narrowed eyes.

'Yes, it is,' he said unemotionally, without any evident enthusiasm. 'Here's the contract for the Omani project. I want you to handle it personally. Sign.'

Her lips parted in amazement and his dark eyes dropped to them, the lines of his face becoming filled with sensuality. A small quiver ran through Tiffany as her nerve-endings sprang into life. The heat in the restaurant was overpowering. It seemed suddenly cramped and claustrophobic. She felt her heart beating heavily. In confusion, she scanned his face, and found to her dismay that his expression only intensified her inflamed senses.

There was such uninhibited carnality flowing from him that it was like a brick wall coming straight for her. It was impossible to escape, impossible not to be affected. The gold of his skin glowed smoothly in the candlelight. The carved nose, chiselled mouth…every feature spelt out his sensuality and his hunger. The pulses hammered within her body, fighting the drugging seduction of his eyes.

She battled her way back to sanity, still mesmerised by him, but forcing her strong will to overcome the terrible and unwanted attraction she felt. She had glimpsed a vast, untapped well of passion within herself and it frightened her with its potential to destroy her calm, well-ordered life and self-control.

'Sign,' he drawled, with a mocking twist to his mouth.

'Sign?' she quavered, then frowned and tried to control her cracking vocal cords. 'Just like that?'

He smiled. Tiffany's heart fluttered alarmingly.

'Don't you want the work?' he asked in a husky voice.

She sliced fiercely into her Gravad Lax as if it were a tough steak and counted to ten.

'That depends on the price,' she observed coolly.

'I approve of your perception,' he murmured. 'You know I want something very badly. I could have it for the taking, I realise, but it would make things less distressful if you agreed not to make a fuss and give in gracefully.'

'I bet it would, you arrogant bastard!' she breathed, white with anger. He was certainly blunt! Hassan wanted her body, stretched out and willing on his bed. 'I have utter contempt for men who are in a position of power and make threats to control women.' She rose from the elegant chair, her body proud, the carriage of her head almost regal as she looked down her nose at him. 'In my country, we call that sexual harassment and it's punishable by the courts. Do your worst!' she said shakily, realising what she was having to do. The business she and Charlie had built up so painstakingly would be ruined by this man, merely because of his disgusting sexual appetite.

'You'll fight me for custody?' he grated, as she bent to pick up her handbag.

Tiffany froze. Then she felt her legs give way and she sat down again, dumbstruck with horror, her limpid grey eyes widened. He was serious. Deadly serious.

'For…what?' she whispered.

The strain showed in her face. She didn't delude herself. Hassan al Sharif, she knew, wouldn't look so sure of himself unless he had good reason.

'Custody,' he said in a chilling tone. 'Of Josef.'

'Jo? But... Oh, God! What... I feel sick,' she whispered, holding her head in her trembling hands.

He came over and poured water on a napkin, kneeling down and pushing away her hands and dabbing her forehead with it. Then, seeing she could hardly support herself in the chair, his strong arms went around her and his face was distressingly close to hers, harsh, relentless, his piercing eyes searing into her tormented soul.

For she remembered. It was something Nazim had said, soon after Josef's birth—and repeated often. In an effort to stop her from leaving him, he'd threatened to return to Riyam. She would lose her son, he'd yelled. Custody was almost always given to men in his country.

Could Nazim's brother do the same? Could he demand her son, as the nearest male relative? Her stomach knotted.

'You won't take Jo!' she whispered. 'You can't! We have English passports. Besides, you've given me no proof of who you are—'

'Here,' he said curtly, handing her his wallet.

With fumbling fingers, she flicked through the credit cards, the airline tickets, all for Hassan al Sharif, and stopped at a photograph of three men. Nazim. Hassan. And an older man in the middle, who appeared to be their father.

'Josef is *my* son,' she said levelly.

'I could get custody without any difficulty,' he claimed.

'Influential friends and the Sultan's blessing?' she asked, lacing her tone with heavy sarcasm.

'More than that. Already I have a great deal of information which indicates you are an unfit mother. But...' his hands gripped her wrists tightly as she opened her mouth to protest; she closed it when she saw from the triumph on his face that there was more horror to come '...it is the payment of a debt I have come for.'

The sick hysteria within her receded a little. Money. He was apparently rich beyond most people's wildest dreams. Yet he wanted what he'd obviously lent to Nazim, that time in Turkey. How much would that be?

She turned her head defiantly and met his liquid eyes. An inch more and their faces would be touching. Her pulses drummed in her ears.

'Get away from me,' she said with icy contempt. 'Take your hands off me. Their touch makes me feel nauseous. Sue me if you must. Your name will lose respect if you do, a man of your wealth forcing a widowed mother and her son into bankruptcy.'

His mouth twisted and Tiffany had the extraordinary feeling that he reluctantly admired her strength. Quietly, he returned to his seat and finished his food. Tiffany couldn't touch hers. There was another smile playing about his honey-moistened mouth, and his mocking glance flickered over her constantly, forcing her to remain in her seat. He had another ace up his sleeve, she knew, and waited in an agony of suspense. He'd string her out till she was screaming with nerves; he would take pleasure in taunting her.

The discreet waiter removed their plates and they waited in silence while his beef was flamed and she was served with her lamb.

'I have some news for you that will test that excellent English self-control of yours,' he said quietly. 'In fact, I almost took you to my suite at my hotel, so we could be totally private, but I thought that unwise. For both of us.' His sultry eyes rested thoughtfully on her and she cut him with her glance. 'This was the best I could do,' he continued, indicating their privacy. 'Are you ready?'

'For anything,' she lied with a firm conviction. 'Tell me about this debt.'

'Very well. When Nazim contacted me, that time he was stranded in Turkey, I took advantage of the situation.'

'I bet you did,' she ground out.

He gave her an icy look. 'I arranged for him, his wife and child to be smuggled out of Turkey in exchange for the only thing he had of value.'

'You're too late if you want that consignment of Persian carpets. It was sold to pay off debts,' she said wearily. 'The money you lent him to set up again in England soon went.'

'It was a lot of money,' he frowned. 'It would take a great deal of extravagance to get through it.'

'I don't know how much it was—'

'Half a million pounds,' he drawled.

'Half—!' Tiffany gulped. She let out a sigh of despair. 'I can't possibly pay that back. There was a slump in the market for carpet importers. I have no cash to spare,' she said. 'Not now. But let me work on the project, without any strings attached, and I'll give you an agreed percentage to pay off what I owe you. I hate being beholden to anyone,' she added bitterly.

'Oh, you misunderstand. It's not carpets or money that I'm owed,' said Hassan huskily, pushing a document towards her.

Tiffany felt a change in the atmosphere. It had become tense and ominous. Her hand trembled as it took hold of the folded parchment.

'Well, if you're thinking to claim my body in part payment, it's not for loan, hire or sale,' she snapped.

Hassan gave her an indolent glance of sheer disdain. 'I'm not asking for it,' he said curtly.

Tiffany blushed. She'd thought…

'What was this item of value?' she asked coldly. 'Nazim had nothing. We were penniless.'

Hassan's face showed triumph. For several unbearable seconds, he kept her waiting for his answer, torturing her deliberately.

'What was it?' she cried in desperation. 'Tell me!'

'Your son,' he said softly.

'My son?'

'Well, to be legally precise, he isn't your son. He's mine. He belongs to me, you see. Nazim pledged him to me, as surety, to be surrendered if the debt was unpaid.'

Paralysed by what he'd said, all she could do was stare, her body as cold and stiff as if she were a corpse. And well she might be one, for all the life he had drained from her with his preposterous claim.

'He had no intention of repaying the debt,' said Hassan harshly, when she didn't answer, 'and to be honest, I banked on that, hoping to gain control of Josef.'

'Control?' she husked, aghast.

'Yes. To return him to his rightful culture, to people who could bring him up properly. But after a while I realised that, not only did Nazim not intend to repay the debt, he didn't have any intention of surrendering his son either. For a long time, I did nothing, giving him the opportunity to consider his position and honour his debt.'

'Nazim was right not to pay a debt of *dishonour*. My son isn't a pawn to be swapped around in payment, like a handful of coins!' Tiffany rasped.

Nazim had been even more of a worm than she'd thought. And so was his evil, callous brother.

He stilled her with a look.

'Someone had to rescue the child from his parents,' he scathed. 'I wish I'd done it sooner. I'd delayed because my father died and I was worked off my feet, taking over the business empire. He'd left it to me, not Nazim, the elder son, but felt all along that eventually the inheritance should also be Josef's. By then, Nazim had disappeared again.'

'How did you find us?' she asked resentfully.

'Pure chance. I saw the plans for your hotel and your name. I set out at once to discover if you were Nazim's wife, and, if so, what kind of woman you were.'

'And?' she breathed.

'My informants told me that my brother had died in a car crash,' he grated. 'They told me about the way you lived, in poverty, and that you'd provided no permanent home for Josef, wandering about Europe and Turkey like a vagrant.'

'I went where my work took me!' she seethed.

'Or your temporary...er...sponsors?' he queried. 'The men who put up the money for your fare—'

'They were reputable businessmen!' she cried hotly, flushing at his insinuation. 'Of course they paid—'

'For services rendered.' He nodded, with a mocking look in his eyes. 'You must have been exhausted, the hours you put into your job. I learnt you frequently were out at night.'

'Did you have me investigated?' she grated, incensed.

'I did,' said Hassan grimly. 'And I didn't like what I found out. I don't approve of a woman who spends money on expensive suits when her son goes about in rags.'

'But this is ridiculous! It's part of my job to have a good daytime wardrobe and to look smart—'

'This evening,' he continued relentlessly, 'my suspicions of your immorality were confirmed when I saw you with a man, silhouetted against your bedroom curtains in an intimate position.'

'Intimate—'

'He was on his knees,' hissed Hassan, his eyes boring into her. 'In my experience, that's pretty intimate.'

'Oh, for heaven's sake! I can explain—'

'Don't bother,' he growled.

She gave an exasperated sigh. 'He was getting an eyelash out of my eye.'

'You'd temporarily lost control of your hands?' he mocked.

'Yes.' She waved her fingers at him. 'I was doing my nails. They were wet. Mike is newly married and loves his wife.'

'I've seen her. She's not the sensual sort. He could easily be diverted by you,' said the sheikh in a low, matter-of-fact tone.

Tiffany faltered, disconcerted by the fact that he found her so attractive. It was flattering and worrying.

'Mike's in a rosy glow. He doesn't notice... Why the hell am I defending myself to you?' she asked in irritation.

'I don't know. I don't believe what you say. Too much has contributed to form an unfavourable impression of your character.'

'So now you have this false opinion of me, what bearing does this have on what you intend to do?' she demanded.

The lines on his face grew harsher. 'It means I must take Josef from you. It's clear to me that he should be where he belongs. In his father's country, learning his true culture, being groomed to take over his inheritance when he comes of age.' He leant back in his chair. Tiffany could not move. Hassan sipped his iced water, his eyes never leaving her face, and continued. 'That document gives me the right to take Josef whenever I like. He is mine, given to me by his father. In law, you have no rights in the matter, and if you decide to fight me I will make life unbearable for you. I will *not* allow my nephew to grow up in a slum. I mean to give Josef the future he deserves. If you care anything for him, you won't stand in his way.'

'Really. And where do I fit in?' she grated.

'That depends. I could ensure that you never want for work over here—'

'Wait a minute!' she cried, galvanised into life. 'You take Josef, and I stay here? Is that your plan? You honestly think that I'd part with him?'

'For money and the sake of your career, yes. You seem single-mindedly selfish. And I certainly don't want you,' he said bluntly. 'I don't want your influence. He's reaching an age when he can do without you and needs the company of men.'

'This is a nightmare!'

'I don't think you realise the gravity of your situation,' said Hassan in velvet tones. 'As far as my country is concerned, I have unquestionable rights to Josef. It may take a little while for me to prove my claim, but I can certainly show that you're unfit with the evidence I have.'

'What evidence?' she asked in astonishment. 'Mike in my bedroom? I've explained that—'

'That, the fact that you sometimes come home in the early hours looking as if you've had a heavy night in some man's bed—'

'That's preposterous! Your investigator hasn't done his job properly. Very occasionally, I work at the studio half the night!' she said angrily. 'I have to put the hours in, to bring in enough for us to live on. Josef doesn't suffer; he's asleep. He's properly looked after. Mike and Mandy are very reliable and need the money as much as… Oh, damn you! I'm doing my utmost for him!'

He shrugged. 'Even if you can prove that, I can put pressure on in another way. I can call in the debt. You wouldn't be able to pay it and you'd go to prison. Josef would have no one to care for him. Naturally, with the other evidence I have of your unsuitability as a mother, I would be given custody then, as a relative who can offer him an infinitely better life than an impecunious jailbird,' he said softly. 'Heads I win, tails you lose.'

She stared in horror. 'You rat! You really mean it!'

His eyes blazed black and deadly. 'With every drop of my blood, every beat of my heart, I swear I will not allow Josef to remain with you. I'll have him, one way or another.'

For a moment, she was speechless, wilting beneath his blistering gaze. He hated her enough to tear her from her son. It was a prospect she couldn't bear to think of.

'I won't let you separate us! It's out of the question! You can't!' she whispered, her eyes filling with tears. Hassan frowned and concentrated on forking up some mange-tout as if they were discussing the ownership of a dog and not her son. 'I love him!' she moaned. 'He's all I have in the world—'

'You have your career,' he growled.

'Oh, God! Without Josef, everything is meaningless.' She saw a glimmer of hope. Hassan's hand had hesitated in mid-air. 'I beg you,' she said huskily. 'Leave us alone, to make our own way in life. You've managed all this time without Josef. You can run the business yourself. Pretend we don't exist. One day you'll have your own sons. We don't care about this inheritance. I love my son and will die rather than see him torn from me, or hurt in any way. For God's sake, he's a child! Believe me,' she said vehemently, 'I will defend him, no matter what the threat.'

The hand she had flung out in her plea, was enveloped in Hassan's warm grasp. He shifted closer to her and his knee slid alongside her thigh, but she didn't care. All she could think of was the danger to Josef.

'How passionate you are!' muttered Hassan, his eyes filled with desire. 'Your whole body is alive. Marrying you was the only sane thing Nazim ever did. You are the most beautiful woman I have ever known. And so feminine that your challenge to my masculinity is quite unbearable.' He turned her palm over and kissed it, branding her flesh with the heat of his lips. 'You are as graceful as a deer, as sensual as a houri. The perfect woman. A woman I am reluctant to abandon and see only in my dreams.'

'Please,' she moaned, incapable of withstanding his cruel, mocking seduction. 'Leave me alone.'

He gave a cynical laugh. 'See sense. Josef will be rich. He will have no need to go hungry or cold, or live in a rotting building. Josef will have better opportunities, better care with me, not a working mother who has to go out all day and half the night, and can't even clothe him properly. Can you deny him a bright future where he can use his talents to their best advantage? Can you deny him the chance to ride, ski, sail, even fly his own plane? What right have you to condemn him to a life of pinching and scraping? How do you think he will feel when he knows what opportunities are his for the asking?'

'You wouldn't tell him!' she cried hotly.

'Why the hell not?' growled Hassan. 'He has a right to know. It's his life you're thinking of ruining.'

'God, how I hate you!' she seethed, her beautiful face tense.

'That's understandable,' he said, with a mocking lift to his black eyebrow. Then he leant forwards. 'I have a legal right to Josef and a great deal of influence. I'll fight you in the international courts if you like, cite the presence of would-be lovers, expose your debts, cite your extravagance which Nazim complained of, and which plunged you all into a spiral of poverty. I'll show his letter to me, which complained that you trapped him into marriage through your pregnancy and that you insisted on following your career when your son was born. Is all that true?'

She gazed at him in dismay. An innocent and naïve eighteen-year-old, she had been Nazim's victim.

'Some, not all—'

'You bitch!' he snarled. 'The sooner Josef is out of your incapable hands, the better.'

'The facts have been twisted! I'm not what you think. You can't do this to us!' she hissed. 'He's settled in school—'

'He'll adapt. Children always do, if they're loved enough,' said Hassan ruthlessly.

She closed her eyes tightly, shutting out his harsh, savage face. Hassan had no mercy. He wanted his pound of flesh and nothing would stand in his way.

Silence fell between them as Tiffany sought to think rationally. At the moment, her mind was in such confusion that her judgement was impaired. She couldn't tell whether Hassan had a water-tight case against her or not. She didn't know enough of Arab law. The Shariah, Nazim had called it. And she knew that it was very much in favour of men, who played a strong part in the upbringing of their sons. But would the fact that Nazim had virtually signed away her son be upheld in English law?

Oh, God! How could he?

'I can't give up my son,' she said in a barely audible voice. 'If you insist on demanding your rights, then you'll have to fight me for him.'

'You'd ruin yourself to keep him? Turn down wealth?' he asked quietly.

It seemed he held his breath, waiting for her answer.

'I am not immoral and I have made every effort to care for him. Let the courts judge,' she whispered.

Hassan's expression remained impassive. He swirled the wine in his glass, thinking rapidly, a dark scowl on his face.

'I see,' he said slowly. 'I am surprised. I have failed to convince you that it would be in Josef's interest. It's a pity you feel this way.' He gave a gesture of defeat and Tiffany's hopes soared. Incredibly, she'd won! He'd given up! All that fervour had been put on to frighten her! Hassan sighed. 'I admire your strength. You have defeated me, it seems.'

'What…what are you going to do?' she asked warily.

'What can I do?' he countered. 'Would I really get involved in a court case which could last years? It would harm my nephew, and you could easily turn him against me. He'd hate me if I upset his mother. Would I be that stupid?'

'No,' she admitted, still uncertain. After all, he'd sworn that he'd stop at nothing… 'I suppose you've got too much sense to do that.'

'Well. That's that,' he said heavily. 'I must return to Riyam.' He sounded genuinely regretful. 'However…I must provide for him.'

'I'll accept no money from you,' she said, with a proud jut of her chin.

His eyes flickered. 'Foolish woman,' he growled. Then he gave a shrug. 'In that case, earn it.' He scrawled his

signature on the Oman contract which he passed to her.
'I'll have a ticket waiting for you at the airport, by
tomorrow afternoon, together with the necessary details.
You can fly up the coast and see the site.'

Her grey eyes widened. 'What for?'

'I still need a designer. Why not you? Go there and
clinch the deal with my lawyers. You can stay in the complex and look around; get the feel of it. I want you to stay
for ten days and come up with some designs. Make a good
job of the interior decoration and your fortune is made
without any further help from me.'

'If I refuse?' she asked, her fine brows drawn together.
'If I want nothing to do with you?'

'You'd be that bloody-minded? Then I'll make sure
you're broken if you wilfully refuse to take steps to give
Josef a good life, even if that good life has to be without
me. I'll make sure that every opening is denied to you, as
it was with the Palm Sands deal.'

She shot him a look of loathing. 'You devious, manipulating rat!' she raged. 'You arranged for that to be cancelled, didn't you, so that you had a clear financial and
professional hold over me? How low can you get?'

He gave a cynical smile. 'Pretty low. As low as I have
to. Look at the sum your company will be paid.'

Tiffany stared. It was phenomenal.

'Well?' barked Hassan.

She let out a long breath. With that money, she could
probably manage comfortably. But…he was forcing the
pace again. Making her rush about whenever he snapped
his fingers. It galled her to jump to his bidding, yet she'd
be stupid to refuse. It seemed the only way to keep her
head above water and survive this ghastly nightmare.

Otherwise, she thought miserably, he'd carry on with

his underhand vendetta and Josef would have to leave his beloved school. She'd never be able to afford the fees.

'How do I know this is above board?' she asked sullenly, her mouth unconsciously pouting.

'Check with the Omani Embassy in the morning,' he said curtly. 'They'll vouch for the scheme, and me.'

'Why are you helping me?' she asked doubtfully. There must be a snag, but for the life of her she couldn't find it.

'I'm not. I'm helping Josef,' he snapped. 'He is of my blood.'

She tossed her head in a defiant gesture. 'I can't just leap up, pack my bags and go away for ten days. There's Jo to consider. I need a little more notice—'

'No. Leave tomorrow night, or not at all,' he snapped. 'That is my price. Explain to him what it means to you.'

She teetered on the edge of accepting. It was so tempting, the opportunity for so much. Everything she'd worked for lay within her grasp. She could check with the embassy that the development existed.

'You want every last bit of my humble pie, don't you?' she glared, her eyes slate-hard.

'Is it much to ask? I need to salvage a little of my pride,' he shrugged, 'since I will be returning home without my nephew.'

She realised that he hadn't expected to fail in his mission. He'd imagined she'd turn her son over to him, lured by the prospect of money. But who would look after Josef if she went?

Almost immediately, an idea occurred to her. His burning ambition could be realised. He could board at the school! Now, she could afford that. He'd be thrilled! Though she must warn the school not to allow him contact with anyone apart from herself. She had time to go there tomorrow and tell the headmaster that Josef must be supervised. Jo would be in his element; he would be with friends, and well cared for, and she could concentrate on the job in hand.

In a swift movement, she rose, leaving her meal untouched on the table. Her stomach was in no fit state for food. It kept lurching about virtually every time Hassan let out another devastating bombshell.

'I accept,' she said with a frosty stare. 'Don't bother to see me home in that ostentatious piece of scrap metal outside. I'll take a taxi. If I'm leaving for ten days, I have some explaining to do to Josef and a great deal to organise.' A thought struck her, and she paused, suddenly apprehensive. 'You are returning tonight, aren't you? You're not waiting till I leave the country and then go sneaking off to kidnap Josef?'

His chest swelled in offence as he stood up and fixed her with an outraged expression.

'I told you, I am leaving. On my soul, I would not dream of snatching Josef and causing him distress. I care for his welfare, unlike you.'

She was reassured. But as she stalked haughtily through the restaurant, her spine tingling from Hassan's watchful gaze, the doubts began to crowd into her mind and she wondered whether she was doing the right thing after all.

CHAPTER THREE

TIFFANY landed at Sohar at noon, two days after the fateful dinner with Hassan, weary from lack of sleep the night before, the frantic rush to tie up everything at home and a rapid top-up of her wardrobe. Charlie had been dumbfounded, but his delight that they might stay solvent had carried her through the hasty handing over to him the last few pieces of work remaining for the hotel.

She should have been feeling elated that the next year was financially secure, but she didn't. There was a strange flatness inside her.

The intense heat—unusual by the coast—was doing its best to flatten her, too. She longed for a shower to cool herself down. Not long. Cool herb tea and nutty pastries beckoned.

She followed an airport official across the tarmac, pulling down the brim of her straw hat against the glare of the dancing heat. The sun burned into her arms, exposed beneath a short-sleeved jacket-style cotton top, but a warm breeze moved her full skirt and gave a welcome relief from the intense blast for a while.

Boarding the small jet which was to take her to the development site, she was surprised to find it took off almost immediately and that she was the only passenger. The drone of the engine lulled her to sleep and she woke with a start when the steward quietly asked her to fasten her seatbelt for the landing.

The beautiful sleek Mercedes Benz which met her was blissfully air-conditioned. She felt partly refreshed from her sleep and examined the harsh landscape with interest through the smoked windows, hanging on to the leather strap as the driver swung along the desert road and chatted on his handset at the same time.

It seemed a long journey, through arid scenery with not a building in sight apart from a ruined caravanserai. To her surprise, they stopped at this, and the driver got out and leant against the car as if waiting for someone.

Tiffany eyed the man warily, then clambered out, meaning to ask what he was doing. As she did so, she saw him stiffen and shade his eyes.

She followed his gaze. Far into the distance, she saw the small, indistinct figure of a solitary rider. He was surrounded by a haze of heat and a cloud of dust. His shimmering white robes merged with the snow-white horse to give an impression of one pagan creature. She smiled faintly at the magnificent sight.

As the man neared, she could see that the horse was at a full gallop and the rider lay low in the saddle, guiding the animal swiftly and surely between the massive rock boulders strewn across the wild landscape. Man and beast were in perfect harmony, a fusing of natural animal grace.

Her secretly romantic nature thrilled to see the stallion's long mane streaming back like white ribbons, and his powerful muscles bunching and stretching. It was such an arresting sight that it didn't occur to her to wonder why the driver had stopped to await the advancing rider, nor what purpose the rider served.

Quite near now, and probably showing off, the veiled man had eased the breakneck pace and was lounging in the saddle. He was shrouded in a long white robe, edged with gold braid, and a traditional bedouin head-dress. His black desert boots were slipped into gleaming silver stirrups, hanging over bright red leather saddle-bags, and his hands lightly held the colourfully embroidered reins.

To her delight, the huge stallion was reined in near her. He fretted and pawed at the ground, evidently sulking that the glorious gallop was at an end.

Tiffany smiled at the rider, her graceful hand pushing back a strand of sun-gold hair which had escaped in the warm, dry breeze. His eyes were narrow slits, as she imagined all desert men's must be, and were only just exposed above the tightly wrapped cloth which had been flung across his face against the choking dust. His hand rested momentarily on the butt of his rifle which had been thrust into a deep saddle holster, then he gathered the reins purposefully in his hands.

Tiffany made to turn, thinking that the display was over and she would resume her journey to the coast. But the rider had jabbed his heels hard into the stallion's flanks and was making straight for her.

'*No!*' she screamed, realising in a split second what this must be. Hassan's revenge!

She flung a frantic glance at the curious but motionless chauffeur, as the massive horse bore down on her in a thunder of flying hoofs. She saw his eyes roll, his bared teeth, and then she was being whisked up into the air.

Rough, cruel hands crushed Tiffany's body as, rigid with terror, she was swung across to the rider's lap. Her hat fell off; the horse skittered, then she felt the hard steel of male thighs beneath hers.

And most unnerving of all was the vicious grip which held her a prisoner. So frightened was she that she could only scream soundlessly. Her whole body trembled, bending like a supple willow as she realised she was totally at the man's mercy.

Her eyes slowly lifted and a violent shock ran through her.

Hassan.

Tiffany's stomach lurched. She'd recognise those glittering jet-black eyes anywhere. Especially as they were laced with a savage hatred and a look of malice which pierced her body like a repeatedly stabbing knife.

'Hassan!' she croaked.

He laughed. 'Hassan,' he agreed mockingly.

She felt his thigh muscles tighten and swell as he brought the horse under control. One of his arms slid from her body and she was forced to cling to him, afraid of falling, hating the necessity of clutching at his chest like an adoring, desperate woman.

'What are you doing?' she yelled up at him.

He reached out and lifted the loose reins, collecting the horse. It seemed to her that suddenly man and beast became one hard, efficient powerhouse of energy, working in perfect unity, honed muscles rippling, wild natures barely held in check.

In a brief flash of realisation, Tiffany became truly aware of Hassan's immense kinship with the desert and all things natural, pagan, wild. And it terrified her.

'What are you doing?' she repeated with an authority she didn't feel.

'Abducting you,' he growled.

She cringed within.

'You can't! Josef—'

'He's safe at school,' he laughed. 'Whereas you have a different lesson to learn.'

Hassan's body throbbed with vitality and he seemed elated, causing her nerve-endings to spring to life. He was exuberant because he had a foul plan in his mind and its success seemed assured. She wanted to weep. The safety of her tiny flat, Charlie and Josef seemed a long, long way from this malevolent man and this hostile environment.

He leant forwards, holding her tightly, his right arm unnervingly stretched across her breasts, his fingers splayed insultingly over the rising swell.

Automatically she strained away, but the arm tightened over her ribs and she was crushed into a solid wall of unresisting muscle and bone. The long, tanned fingers pressed deeper into her side, and as the horse gathered pace his spreading thumb regularly met her rhythmically bouncing left breast.

'Hassan! Please!' she cried, finding her voice. It was torn from her lips by the wind and the heat, emerging like a choked sob.

'Save your breath!' he grated. 'You'll need it. Every last gasp.'

She dared not struggle. He was perfectly capable of letting her drop to the ground. She glanced down. It looked a bone-breaking distance away.

To Tiffany's frightened eyes, the stony desert stretched far ahead, glinting in the relentless sun, barren, featureless. She was in his territory now. He intended... She gulped, her imagination examining a number of possibilities.

'This won't get you anywhere!' she managed, feeling melodramatic as she shouted in the direction of the venomous eyes above her.

She felt his grunt reverberate through his chest, and then he had spurred his stallion on, bending her unwilling body with his dominant one as he leaned low against the wind, emphasising his authority and her submission. The weight of his head lay on her shoulder, the pressure of his chin bruised her flesh.

She felt an increasing apprehension about Hassan's highly physical presence. His body dominated hers in more ways than one. Alarm made her quiver as she realised his fast, heavy breathing and the rapid thudding of his heart were not entirely caused by the effort of riding.

'Now let me go!' she ordered. 'Stop this ridiculous attempt to frighten me!'

'Ah. Success. Is that what I'm doing?' he murmured into her ear, with a rush of hot breath.

Tiffany flushed, recalling the avid sensuality of his hot eyes when they had virtually stripped her the night she'd been wearing her kimono. He was capable of violence, with all those fierce passions held so tightly in check. He'd be like his brother.

Nazim had always seemed quiet and controlled on the exterior, only the terrifying way he had first made love to her betraying the savagery within him. And later had come frequent displays of his violent temper.

Her white teeth dug hard into her lower lip as the memory made her shudder with revulsion.

Hassan let out a low grunt. She was really afraid. He must know every curve of her figure by now. How shaming. If he was as lusty as his brother, he'd be quick to arouse. After all, she'd only permitted Nazim to kiss and caress her and he'd turned into a tenacious, unstoppable lecher.

Hassan wriggled slightly in the saddle, making her aware of every potent inch of his body beneath the thin cotton robe. And, to her dismay, he tucked his face against hers so that they were cheek to cheek, the fine material of his head-dress doing nothing at all to conceal the strong bones of his face and the fiercely clenched jaw.

She wrenched her head away, but it was too uncomfortable to stay in that position for long and soon it nat-

urally returned to lie against that despised face, though
every muscle in her body stayed tense.

'Relax,' he muttered. 'There's nothing you can do at
all. Nothing.'

'Just you wait!' she retorted hotly.

Relax! While she was being abducted, fondled in the
most insulting way! Tiffany drew in an angry breath, in-
flating her ribcage, and regretted it immediately as she felt
a movement in his cheek muscles and realised he was
grimacing at the result. For her breasts had risen, and,
beneath the flimsy material of her dress, had settled themselves so that their peaks were being rhythmically massaged against his arm by the motion of riding.

To her horror, she felt heat course through her body,
engulfing her in its flames. And no amount of arching her
back could disguise the fact that her breasts had swollen,
and their tips met Hassan's welcoming arm with an increasingly hard pressure, till they felt as hard as bone and
as sensitive as her wildly leaping nerves. Tiffany moaned.

'Patience,' mocked Hassan. 'Control your needs. Enjoy
the ride.'

'You rat! Stop touching my body!' she yelled back at
him, her eyes fevered.

'It's that, or fall,' he snarled. 'Keep still and don't tempt
me.'

'You're disgusting! Loathsome! You enjoy humiliating
me!'

She tried to change position, and became alarmed at
the heat in his loins which burned shockingly into her
buttocks. Her whole body went rigid. The horse stumbled
on a pebble and the iron band of Hassan's arm swelled
as the muscles expanded and held her firmly, with even
greater intimacy than before. Now she was completely

plastered against him and no secrets of touch remained between them.

'For your own safety, keep still,' he muttered. 'For my own sanity, don't *move*.'

The flames in Tiffany's body simmered wilfully. Unable to bear the constant survey of Hassan's embered eyes, she turned her head and buried it in his chest, hoping he would sense her feminine vulnerability, and pity rather than desire her. Cradled against the soft cotton robe which soothed her cheek, she breathed in the surprisingly pleasant scent of his hot male body, which was mingled with the faint perfume of rose-water.

'Let me go!' she moaned into the folds over his chest.

'Not yet.' His voice murmured through her hair. 'Not till we're alone.'

Tiffany gulped. 'Alone?' she husked, barely able to say the word. 'Where? Why?'

'Let your imagination run riot,' he said sardonically.

She did and it made her tremble uncontrollably.

His breath exhaled harshly, hot and tingling as it riffled through her hair and sensitised her temples. The big hand adjusted its hold, moving away from her breast, but still splayed in arrogant possession across her fragile ribs, claiming her for his own.

Tiffany tried to make her mind forget the disturbing sensations and think what action she might take when he stopped. There was no point in trying to run away; he was bound to be taking her somewhere isolated. Her only hope lay in appealing to any remnants of civilised behaviour he might have. She frowned. That wasn't much. Her lip refused to stop quivering.

Clutched in his ruthless arms, she felt incredibly vulnerable. She wouldn't have much chance against him if he tried to rape her.

When she refused his advances point-blank, her delicate bones could easily be crushed by a blow from that massive, cruel hand. Misery filled her eyes. Old memories of pain, from Nazim's petulant slaps, rose to sicken her. She bruised easily. Violence made her physically ill.

'Sheikh Hassan. I appeal to your sense of honour—' she began shakily.

'Shut up,' he snarled savagely, yanking hard on the reins.

The stallion jerked his head alarmingly, flicking back foam. Hassan gave an exasperated grunt and spoke to him in gentle, soothing tones which hummed through Tiffany's ribcage in a resonant rumble. He leaned to the right and the horse obeyed the sway of his body, trotting into the dry torrent bed of a river. It was surprisingly deep, and edged with tamarisk trees which rose directly from the pebble bed, as if they scorned anything as soft as soil.

A chill settled on her. This was a harsh land, where only the harsh survived. It was like Hassan himself. Beneath his sophisticated, smooth exterior lay an uncompromising lack of softness. In Hassan's heart lurked a nature in harmony with the unrelenting desert, a man equal to the task of surviving here in the most inhospitable surroundings, pitting his wits against nature itself. What chance did she have, with someone so accomplished in winning against all odds?

A shudder rippled through her, and Hassan's hand began to move, gently stroking. Its invasiveness made her shrink. Instead of soothing her, it was, she felt, causing the panic rising within her chest. And, she thought bitterly, struggling in his arms futilely, his touch brought her dormant sensuality to life.

Her whole love-starved body was tensing against his insistent caress. The hollowing physical need of a body incomplete because of its lack of a satisfying union mocked her shocked mind. She raised a flushed face to his, breathing with shallow gasps.

'You bastard! Don't touch me like that!' she grated.

'You don't want to be calmed down?' he murmured.

'I *am* calm!' she yelled.

He grinned, his eyes crinkling up above the veil.

'Lucky you,' he said softly, bending his head down.

Tiffany strained back, swaying alarmingly as Hassan adjusted his hold on her, laughing as he did. She was incensed. Part of that anger was for herself. When he'd bent his head, she had wished the barrier of his head-dress didn't exist and their lips could have met for one brief, crazy second.

Her eyes were drawn to the faint outline of his mouth through the fine cotton. It became serious. She badly wanted to drag her gaze from his lips, but seemed to be incapable of doing so. She clenched her jaw to prevent the overwhelming urge to wrap her arms around his neck. Her mouth felt parched for tender kisses.

A spasm of hungry pain lashed through her, condemning her wanton thoughts. This was what he had planned—an excuse to hold her with the utmost intimacy, her gradual awareness of his intense sensuality and her eventual surrender. Then he would be able to use his sexual hold over her to gain what he really wanted: Josef.

Tiffany's warmth turned to ice. Guilt and shame washed over her. Hassan's attraction was so insistent that she had allowed her instincts to respond, rather than keeping her head clear. Whatever he did, whatever he said, he had one aim only. She could not allow herself to be fooled for one moment.

Unconsciously, Tiffany had drawn her body into a ramrod posture. Her head had lifted from its position against

Hassan's chest where his heartbeat pounded so unnervingly fast and furious. He was aroused, that was embarrassingly evident, but now Tiffany felt strong. Coldly she suffered his unwanted embrace, her spine stiff, her face staring into the middle distance with a tight, closed expression.

'Thank you,' he said drily.

Startled, she flashed him a frost-bitten look, but he was serious. It puzzled her and she was left wondering what he meant.

They followed the river bed's twists and turns. Then she felt the tension of his muscles beneath her and he drew her upright body firmly into his.

'Stop that!' she yelled. 'I told you, I loathe your filthy hands—'

'Hold on tightly.' His hot breath hit her ear harshly, making her spine shiver with the sensation.

The horse was forced up the steep side of the wadi and she flung her arms around Hassan's waist, clinging on for dear life as the stallion slipped and slid on the polished rock-face. Above them, coming into view as they began to make their way up the slope, was a cluster of palms in a boulder-strewn desert, and behind them, rearing in a jagged wall, were stark mountains which stretched across the whole horizon.

The ringing sound of iron hoof on stone echoed in the vast empty desert, emphasising the unnerving loneliness she felt. They moved beneath feathery tamarisk, brushing beneath the twisted branches, and the unbearable heat on Tiffany's head disappeared.

As they came to the shady palms at a walking pace, she wriggled her hand from around Hassan's waist and felt her scalp. It was burning.

'I'll get sunstroke because of you,' she accused.

'Your hat fell off.'

As if that explained his lack of sense!

'You callous brute!' she snapped. 'Are you trying to kill me?'

'You survived, didn't you?' he growled.

His arm withdrew from her ribs and he stood in the stirrups, settling her in the saddle firmly. Then he swung down in a lithe movement, slowly unfolding the material wrapped around his face.

Tiffany eyed him warily, knowing her legs wouldn't hold her if she tried to stand. At least she was safe on the horse. There wasn't much he could do to her there, apart from touch her. Dismounting promised a greater danger.

'Get down,' he ordered, raising a hand to help.

'What for?' she snapped.

He scowled. 'Because my horse needs to recover. He's the only thing that stands between us and death. If he falls, we're done for. The next waterhole is forty miles away. Well?'

Oh, God! What was he planning? 'I can manage,' she muttered, pride getting the better of sense. 'Move aside. I don't want your sweaty hands anywhere near me.'

His black eyes flickered dangerously, but he moved back with a mocking bow. Tiffany grabbed the pommel of the saddle and dismounted. But her strong will wasn't enough to prevent her knees from buckling and she staggered.

Hassan didn't move. She flung out her hands to the ground to save herself from falling, grazing them on the sharp stones. Ignoring her smarting palms, she rose on trembling legs and faced him squarely.

'You cold-hearted monster!' she seethed.

He was smiling cynically. 'Don't glare. Much as I wanted to help, I respected your wishes. You said you didn't want my sweaty hands to touch you,' he remarked, moving towards her.

She shied away, but he had only come to see to his horse. She watched as he removed the saddle-bag and then the saddle, and loosened the girth, then spent some time seeing to the stallion's needs before he was satisfied and let the horse trot off to the water-filled channel which led into the pool a few yards away.

Tiffany licked her dry lips as she heard the stallion's muzzle swishing in the water.

'Cool yourself down,' said Hassan curtly. 'We're staying for ten minutes only.'

'Ten!' Tiffany's eyes blazed. 'I'm hot and thirsty and determined not to budge from here until you tell me just what you expect to achieve by this childish act.'

'Oh, it's not childish,' he murmured, unravelling his head-dress. 'And I don't think you see me as a child, either, do you, Tiffany?'

'No, I don't,' she agreed, her lashes lowered, knowing that there would be a satisfied smirk on his face. 'I see you as a foul and brutish animal.'

His sharp exhalation made her look up—and that was a fatal mistake. Hassan al Sharif made an arresting sight. Framed against a backdrop of gently waving palms in a searingly blue sky, he stood with his black desert boots planted firmly apart, his powerful shoulders squared in anger.

But it was his face which hypnotised her. In this setting, he was even more compellingly handsome than before. His hair lay blue-black and damp against his scalp, curling slightly where the head-dress had constricted it. Rage and pride shaped the lines of his face, bestowing on them a harsh beauty which caught her breath.

His eyes brooded on her, pure black like the desert

night, touched by a glint of silver fire which glittered dangerously. Tiffany couldn't look away, captured by the softening light which was changing the darkness of his eyes into a glowing warm velvet shot with stars.

Her lips parted, forced to do so by her rapid breathing. She took a step backwards, moistening her dry lips so that she could speak.

In two strides, he had covered the distance between them, and then he checked himself with an effort.

He flung his head back, breathing in the clean desert air noisily. And then his hooded eyes flickered down to where she stood like a bewildered gazelle, hypnotised by a predator.

'Refresh yourself,' he growled. 'Then you can change.'

'Into what?' she asked shakily, fighting for sanity. The desert was making her act crazily. 'A dancing girl? Your whore? Or would you prefer the added spice of resistance from your prisoner?'

'Don't be ridiculous!' he roared. 'Refuse to act sensibly if you must, but we'll be riding on in a few minutes whatever you do. And in two hours you'll wish you'd taken a drink and that you'd put on the clothes in my saddle-bag. Do as you're told.'

He swung on his heel and strode purposefully towards the pool. Resenting the truth of what he said, Tiffany drank from the channel which ran with fresh spring water, and splashed her head and neck with it, cooling herself down. A saddle-bag was flung at her feet and she studiously ignored it, wondering how she could change while he watched.

'Dress.'

'I won't be part of a floor-show for a half-crazed Arab,' she snapped, quivering a little at his appearance.

Water glistened on his skin, giving it a silver sheen in

the sunlight, and the black hair dripped small pearl-shaped, sparkling droplets. His wet robe clung to his body like a second skin, forcing her to acknowledge the unnerving breadth of his chest and the well-developed muscles there. She dared not lower her eyes further. He was drenched. The thin cotton had done little to conceal his body beneath when it was dry. Now… She swallowed nervously.

He regarded her sourly. 'Before I show you what a *completely* crazed Arab is really like,' he said with soft menace, 'put the clothes on.'

Sullenly she bent down and undid the buckle. Inside there was a large amount of fine black cotton material, neatly folded. Sulkily, she drew it out. Beneath lay a bright peacock-green Arab tunic and trousers. Her wary eyes turned to his, as her fingers sank into the soft, delicate material. It was disturbingly flimsy.

'You expect me to wear this?' she asked slowly in disbelief. 'Are you really asking me to dress up like an Arab girl?'

'I picked those clothes,' he drawled, 'because, strange though it may seem to you, after a few thousand years of living in the desert my people know the most suitable garments to wear. They will protect you.'

'From you? Then I'll put them on immediately!' she said scathingly. 'But it strikes me as odd that you should bother to protect me when I've been in the sun without a hat for so long. It's hardly surprising I'm suspicious. Maybe you have an ulterior motive for making me strip.'

'You weren't in any danger,' he retorted. 'It was a short journey and your hair is thick, especially piled on top of your head like that. But now we cross the dunes and the heat will be intense. It is a long ride, Tiffany, some hours.

You'll need every ounce of energy in your body to endure that.'

Her eyes widened. 'Hours?' she cried in dismay. 'Why, Hassan, why? Where are you taking me?'

'I'll tell you when I'm ready. Now hurry. We began our journey at an unfortunate time of day.'

'All right,' she said grudgingly. 'I'll protect my head with the black chador, but I won't put on the clothes. I'm darned if I'll play the part of your Arabian concubine!'

The black eyes narrowed ominously. Before Tiffany could turn and run, he had come up behind her and yanked open her jacket, pulling it down over her shoulders so that her naked back was exposed to the hot air and his equally hot eyes. Effortlessly he turned her around to face him and his big hands gripped the material, effectively trapping her arms.

Then her chin was gripped between his finger and thumb and tilted up, so that she was forced to look into his fierce eyes.

'Stubborn woman! Recognise what is best for you!'

'Never seeing you again would do for a start,' she seethed.

'Tiffany, I can strip off your clothes and those small lacy briefs you are wearing, in this undignified way, if you continue to insist on defying me, or you can be sensible and dress yourself. I will have no compunction in ripping this garment from your body. Whatever happens, you'll ride into the desert with me and you'll be wearing the clothes I have chosen.'

His voice was low and menacing. She had winced at his mention of her briefs. It enraged her that he knew so much about her body. He had held her with too much intimacy on that damn horse of his.

'You are without doubt the most bestial, most degenerate devil I have ever had the misfortune to meet,' she said coldly. 'Now turn away and show me that you have a vestige of human decency in you.'

'Tiffany—' he began.

'Turn away!' she cried hysterically, believing that the low-spoken word was the start of the seduction she feared. Her outburst worked. He frowned and went to prepare his horse.

But she didn't trust him. As if she were undressing on the beach, she draped the chador over her head like a tent and slipped her dress off. She discovered that the green outfit was balm to her hot flesh. When she had positioned the black garment over it, covering her head completely, she thought ruefully that they would look like man and wife to any stranger who saw them riding together.

'I'm ready,' she called flatly. Hassan led the stallion to her. 'And I want to know where we're going.'

'Eventually to my home,' he said, his eyes travelling up and down her figure in approval.

She cringed. 'No! Why—?'

He shook his head impatiently. 'We haven't time to discuss it. Here.'

His hand reached out and caught the end of her veil. If she pulled away it would be ripped, and she'd be left only with the close-fitting harem outfit to wear. Helplessly she stood while he drew the fold across her face, his eyes mocking her as he did so. His long, elegant fingers delicately fixed the end into a small hook which she hadn't noticed.

Mutely she waited, wishing his breath wouldn't fan her face in that sensitising way, wishing he didn't have such thick, fringing lashes and such an unfairly primitive appeal. Wishing… She gulped.

Slowly, the lashes lifted and his eyes slid to meet hers.

The fingers hesitated, hovering above the veil. His lips curved sensually and her own mouth parted in response to the hunger within her.

'Mount,' he said in a whisper.

Tiffany blinked, trembling, wondering what it would be like to be kissed by a man like Hassan, and rooted to the spot in confusion at her thoughts.

'God! You shouldn't have hesitated! Where the hell has my resolve gone? Tiffany,' he muttered huskily, 'I am unable to resist you. Every movement of your body has aroused me so that I can hardly contain myself. Damn you! Damn you to hell! You and that gorgeous body of yours have driven me to this!'

'Hassan…' Her throat shut off.

A lazy desire flooded his face, and she was so afraid and the flooding weakness was so overwhelming that her limbs refused to move, refused to let her run or even make any further protest.

She had been hypnotised, she thought numbly, watching the sweet parting of his arching mouth. With a delicate, lingering movement, Hassan unhooked the veil and deliberately let it float across her face, causing her skin to tingle with its gossamer touch.

'No,' she croaked, her eyes huge, and as clouded as a troubled lake.

But his strong head bent relentlessly and, as it did so, her lips lifted instinctively to his in a desperately pagan need, as if the desert had drawn from her all the layers of civilisation and left her only with primal desire. Dry, aching, she needed her raging thirst to be quenched. And Hassan was the man to satisfy the barrenness in her body.

The kiss was as deep as a well, as violent as a deluge. His mouth was cool and firm, moving with determination over hers, flowing smoothly, and she found herself responding eagerly, nothing but an impulsive passion driving her willing lips to seek relief from thirst.

Within her, it was as if a dam had burst. Inhibition had left her, defeated by the incredible hold Hassan had over her. And he seemed content to match her unbounded demand. Her fingers faltered on his shoulders, then drifted longingly over them, revelling in their strength and the curve of his back as it bent to her.

He was beautiful. Perfect. The man of her dreams.

Tiffany felt her body glow and become fluid, obedient to his masterful kiss. Then she jerked violently and stiffened. For he had begun to coax her lips apart and she remembered the disgust she had felt when Nazim had invaded her mouth so ruthlessly. Her whole being shuddered with revulsion.

And then the pressure of Hassan's body had gone. She lifted her heavy lids which had closed without her knowing. Looking at him with confused, dewy eyes, she thought he seemed pale and strained.

For several seconds they stared at one another, and then he passed a hand through his damp hair, not taking his eyes off her for one second.

'How much more humiliation do I have to take?' she whispered with scorn. 'You've made your point. I am at your mercy. My body is yours to assault, to rape. My life depends on you entirely at this moment.' Her glacial eyes searched his and saw him flinch. 'But whatever you do to me, Sheikh Hassan,' she said, gaining courage, 'you'll never touch me inside. My mind and my soul are mine and can't be hurt by you. If you plan to harm me, you might remember that.'

His mouth twisted and his expression became unreadable. He linked his hands and indicated she should get into the saddle. She vaulted up and he took the reins, walking along beside her in long, heavy-heeled strides as if he was taking out his temper in physical activity.

She refused to think. Didn't want to. Whenever a vision of Hassan, brutalising her, came to her mind she shut it out with a fierce effort of will. Josef was waiting at home for her. She would come through all this, whatever it might be. She would return home to him and close her mind to this terrible experience. Whatever it might be.

The saddle creaked beneath her and soon she became mesmerised by the steady, monotonous rhythm and the never-ending dunes which stretched into the far horizon, to the foot of the soaring mountains.

Hassan strode on, relentless with himself in the heat. It seemed nothing touched him, she mused, her resentful eyes lingering on his tense back and lowered head. He seemed to have the capacity to withstand any discomfort, scornful of normal human frailties like exhaustion.

She began to slump and found her back aching dreadfully. Her legs chafed, too, and she let out a gasp of discomfort as the stallion side-stepped to avoid a snake which Hassan had ignored.

'Tired?' he asked curtly, over his shoulder.

'What the hell do you think?' she snapped.

Without a word, he slipped the reins over the horse's arching neck and motioned for her to take one foot from the stirrup. He swung up and squeezed into the saddle behind her.

'Lean back,' he ordered grimly.

She wouldn't. Instead, she strained forwards.

'God! You're stubborn!' he muttered.

He crushed her against him and she was wrapped in his arms, her spine supported by his chest. It was blissfully comfortable after the strain of the last hour.

The sun blazed hotter and hotter, hitting the stones among the dunes like an anvil. The rays glanced blindingly back into their faces and she was glad of the veil that protected her. She was incapable of speech, her throat as dry as the sands.

Hassan adjusted her chador as they rode, so that the folds lay thickly over her head, then tucked one huge hand around her middle. Around them, the dunes sparkled with colour—orange, gold, rose, silver, as the grains reflected the sun. Despite her distress, Tiffany began to understand why some people revered the desert landscape.

It was true that it could be harsh and merciless. But it was also very beautiful. There was something pure and clean about the scene, as though the mountains and dunes had been cut out and stuck on a hard blue background. It was all so uncluttered, and the sense of space was majestic.

But the monotony of the pace made her drowsy. Several times she felt her head roll and Hassan's arm tighten around her. Eventually she longed for a change of pace to keep her awake.

'Can't we go any faster?' she asked irritably, her voice hoarse and cracked.

'We could.'

He did nothing to back up his answer. Her nerves rose to screaming pitch. She wanted this terrible, interminable journey to end so that she could know the worst.

With an impatient mutter, driven almost insane by the situation, she clapped her heels into the stallion's flanks. It took off immediately, launching himself into a full gallop. Tiffany clutched at the saddle with a scream. It was drowned by Hassan's roar. His body tensed as he fought to hold the animal.

In a moment they were stationary. Tiffany sat sobbing, overcome with an intense misery at the situation.

'Let me go home,' she moaned. 'I want my son. You can't separate us. You can't really mean to threaten me—'

She broke off as the lump in her throat prevented her from saying any more.

'This matter is far too important for me to be swayed by your tears,' rasped Hassan. 'The mountains are near. It'll be cooler soon. Let me decide how to get there and don't make my horse half kill itself by galloping in this heat again.'

'You care more for your horse than for people,' she said sullenly.

'Some people don't deserve my concern,' he growled.

'What have I done?' she asked, astonished.

'You ruined my brother,' he bit out. 'And I won't have my nephew brought up to be as callous as you.'

'I don't know what you mean,' she said wearily. 'You've jumped to conclusions—'

'Shut up. We'll have it out soon. I want to know everything about you. You'll tell me every detail of your life. Then I can decide whether you accompany Josef to Riyam or not.'

'But you admitted to defeat—'

'No. I said that it seemed as if I was defeated. Not that I *was*.'

Her mind whirled back to what he'd said. She went over it all. 'You have defeated me, it seems. What can I do?' The back of her neck prickled. Hassan was a dangerous man, devious and clever.

'Josef will live with me,' she said icily.

'Rest. You're tired. We'll talk about it later.'

Tiffany groaned. The heat was sapping her strength and her will. She could hardly stay awake. The mountains did seem closer. But at the moment, they were absorbing the sun's rays and throwing them back at her. The air was breathless, with an ovenlike heat she could smell. The sun now hung like a huge white ball in the sky, and the haze in front of them made the dunes appear to shimmer like heaps of diamonds.

She slept. Waking, she found herself cradled in Hassan's arms. He gazed down on her with worryingly softened eyes as she jerked upright and shivered in the chilly air. The sun had become a baleful crimson, staining the desert the colour of blood.

It was magnificent, glorious. Massive clouds hung stacked like red and purple blankets. It was the most incredible sunset she had ever seen. Her head turned to view the great coloured canopy over their heads and she marvelled at how insignificant they were amid its vastness.

Her normal world, that of the city, seemed narrow and confining. The horizon had always been bound by buildings, enclosed, and looking in on itself. She'd never known how immense an empty space could be, nor how beautiful.

Her eyes gentled and a languid feeling of peace swept over her, the warm strength of Hassan's encircling arms infinitely appealing. The setting was mesmerising her, playing on her yearning sensibilities for love and romance in the vacuum of her life.

'One of the three really breathtaking sights in the world,' murmured Hassan's deep voice, 'and a tantalising glimpse of infinity.' His breath fanned her face. 'It puts us in perspective, doesn't it?'

She nodded slowly, caught in the magic of the moment, watching with awe the great clouds roll across the heavens and seeing the crimson sands turn wine-dark.

'And what are these other breathtaking sights?' she asked quietly.

He was very still suddenly, as if he were somewhere else entirely. Then he spoke, so softly that she could hardly hear his words.

'A woman in love, and the face of a child,' he said huskily.

Tiffany felt her heart contract at the simple perfection of his answer. It had been beautiful, almost poetic, and utterly sincere. She trembled, aware that she had trespassed into his private, sensitive self.

Then she felt suddenly much more confident. If Hassan nursed thoughts like that, he couldn't be the monster he pretended. There was hope. A spark of humanity existed. She could appeal to his sense of justice and honour, and, if that failed, to his sentimental heart which placed children so highly. Unconsciously she relaxed into his arms.

They trudged up a steep crescent-shaped dune, and when they topped it she saw the dark shapes of palm trees, outlined in a black silhouette against the yellowing sky. The oasis was set in what appeared to be a huge salt-pan. She closed her eyes against the intensity of the light and then after a while the glare receded on her eyelids. Expecting to see that a cloud had passed over the setting sun, she found that they had left the desert and were passing beneath lush palms.

Eagerly she looked around for signs of habitation, a fort maybe, or small lime-washed houses, but there was nothing.

'Is this our destination?' she asked uncertainly, peering ahead into the thick plantation.

He gave a small laugh. 'No. This, Tiffany, is where you and I are going to get to know one another.'

Her face tightened with nerves. 'What do you mean?'

His eyes bored into hers.

'I mean that this is where we will spend the night. Just the two of us.'

CHAPTER FOUR

SLOWLY Tiffany turned her head to scan the scene. They were totally alone.

She had been expecting to arrive at his house by nightfall. Without knowing she did so, she'd hoped for a civilised, sophisticated house with servants, a place where she could appeal to Hassan's westernised side. It had never occurred to her that she would be trapped with him in the desert. He was a different man here.

So it was in this pagan setting that Hassan planned on acting out the climax to his little scheme. Whatever... She felt her throat constrict and she thought ruefully that her body seemed to know things before her mind did.

Of course. He wanted it all: Josef, her, and the complete success of his plans. His pride would accept nothing less than that; he'd want her to admit he had absolute power over her. And how better could he display that power than by sexual domination?

God, she was stupid, to let herself fall in his hands like a ripe plum!

Her eyes spotted the rifle in its deep holster which was buckled to the saddle-bag. The butt was close. If she could...

'Tiffany,' came Hassan's sardonic voice, 'it's not loaded. Forget it.'

'Never,' she vowed. 'Never.'

But her words belied her weak body. Misery, fear, hunger and exhaustion caught up on her in a black, sweeping wave. Her brain was careering around inside her head like an out-of-control carousel. Through a dark fog she felt herself being lifted from the saddle, and the next thing she knew was that she lay on the ground and Hassan's fingers were fumbling with the neck fastening of her tunic.

'No! Don't!' she cried hoarsely.

'Dammit, Tiffany, I—'

'How could you?'

She fought him like a wildcat, using her nails where she could, yelling in her terror, the material tearing and exposing part of her breast. With a moan, she drew the torn cloth to cover herself.

'Leave me alone!' she screamed, flailing with her hands.

Hassan's rough hands let her go and he got up, to stand glaring down at her as she lay in a tumbled heap on the ground.

'You bully!' she whispered, staring at him with pained eyes, her body turned to ice. 'I despise you!' she ground out vehemently with all the passion of her being. 'More than anyone I've ever known!'

He fingered his shoulder where she'd dug in her nails.

'Hell! You seem to have recovered with a vengeance!' he growled.

'I hope it hurts. Try that again,' she seethed, 'and I'll tear your face apart.'

'Get up,' he barked, his eyes blazing. 'Stop jumping to the wrong conclusions and stop being melodramatic. Bring the food from the saddle-bag. I'll light a fire. Obey me,' he said in a warning tone, as it looked as if she intended to defy him, 'or you go hungry. And I'm very tempted to abandon you right now. What chance of your survival without me?'

Holding her body erect, every disdainful inch showing her contempt, she stalked over to the well. Without a word spoken to her, he unhooked a silver scoop from his belt, which she dipped in the leather bucket, pouring the sparkling water over her head and body. She felt vehemently that she must wash away the imprint of his marauding hands.

Numbly she collected the saddle-bag. She had to eat. There were a few hunks of bread, some cheese, fruit and dates. Nothing else.

'Are you trying to starve me, too?' she shouted at him as he strode away.

His big body turned and he eyed her silently. Then his chest inflated with a deep breath.

'Anyone who eats heavily on a desert journey is a fool,' he said, and spun on his heel.

She glared at his retreating back and ate half the food, eyeing the rest with longing, but she didn't dare to touch it. She feared him. Damn him!

Hassan was some time. Tiffany waited, wondering where they would sleep. That was, she thought, with a gnawing agony inside her, if she was allowed to sleep at all. He had said that he wanted to get to know her. Her tongue slicked over her upper lip. It was unlikely that he meant a civilised chat.

However much she had to admit that he had briefly aroused her base desires—and hated herself for that humiliating fact—she dreaded what might come next. Hassan gave off an aura of such virility that she knew instinctively he would have an insatiable appetite. She'd gone through the pain of a man's animal lust before. She couldn't stand it again.

Her head aching, Tiffany drew the chador from her head and unpinned her hair, releasing the tension in her scalp where the grips clustered among the heavy strands.

Sex. It began pleasurably; it ended with disappointment. To her, it had been a perpetual sensation of emptiness, a nameless loss and failure, which pervaded her whole being and made her feel cheated. She never wanted to have that sense of despairing frustration again.

There was a sound ahead of her. She blinked in surprise, seeing that night had fallen as swiftly as if a light had been switched off. The utter darkness was unknown to her and she felt unnervingly vulnerable. It seemed to wrap her in a stifling cloak of dark velvet.

Hassan came into sight, pausing when he saw her. His flowing robes were white against the blackness, and above his head were the tiny flickering stars, looking for all the world like minute gemstones.

Tiffany steeled herself to her forthcoming ordeal.

'I've lit a fire,' he said abruptly, then turned his back on her and strode away.

Well! she thought, in astonishment. That wasn't the behaviour of a man who had evil designs on her! Emboldened, she hurried after his retreating figure.

The fire glowed comfortingly and she huddled close to it, suddenly cold, and thinking she ought to go and get the black robe—not that it would have been much good, because it was so thin. She looked back in the direction of the well where she'd stupidly left it.

It was very dark. She didn't want to search for something that would be so little use.

As she crouched by the fire, the front of her body soon became warm, but her back remained chilled. Hassan moved about busily, setting a brass-beaked coffee pot on the fire. She wondered how he had the energy, after urging his stallion and a reluctant hostage over miles of unfriendly desert. A scowl crossed her face. She resented his indifference to the elements.

'I'm cold,' she said, wrapping her arms around herself.

The peacock-green outfit shimmered in the firelight as she massaged her arms.

'It'll get colder,' he commented indifferently.

'So what are you going to do about it?' She frowned, then her eyes rounded as she realised that she'd given him an opportunity to tell her just what he would do to warm her up!

He slanted his eyes at her shivering body, the lower part of his jaw dark with beard now.

'You want me to change creation?' he asked mockingly. 'To make the desert warm at night for you?'

Relief flooded her face. She really would have to be careful in her choice of words. It seemed, however, that his mind wasn't on her body after all, or he would have taken up that challenge.

'I want something to wrap around me. Are you purposely depriving me of civilised comfort? Is this intentionally vindictive behaviour on your part?' she asked with scorn. 'I suppose you've read *The Taming of The Shrew*, and fancied putting some of Shakespeare's ideas into practice!'

He poured a stream of thick black coffee from the pot into two tiny brass cups and handed one to her.

'Are you really so used to living with all the benefits of modern life that you can't appreciate simplicity?' he countered, ignoring her jibe.

'You saw my flat,' she said sullenly.

He scowled. 'Yes. Squalid, wasn't it?'

'It wasn't that bad! You try being a penniless widow with an eight-year-old son!' she snapped.

'Don't feel sorry for yourself. You got yourself in trouble.'

She flushed scarlet. It wasn't her fault that she had become pregnant by Nazim. How dared he? She tried to think up something rude to say, but her brain was tired.

He sat cross-legged on the ground. He was a little too close for her liking, but she pretended that it didn't bother her and stayed where she was. She had no intention of letting him know she felt intimidated.

'I hate to think of Josef living under such appalling conditions because of your stupidity,' he said tightly. 'My God! You really made him suffer!'

She drank the hot sweet liquid before answering, irritated that she'd given him some more ammunition for his attacks on her.

'My son never went hungry or cold,' she said with quiet dignity. 'His diet might not have been as good as it is now, but he ate healthily, I saw to that. You can't deny that he's a smashing kiddie. And if his clothes were second-hand, they still kept him warm. I tried to give him the best education we could manage, so that he has the chances I didn't.'

She looked up at him defiantly. Hassan's face looked drawn. His bleak eyes met hers.

The trunks of the palms and acacia trees around them creaked and complained as they contracted in the cold. The heaped sand beneath the palms whispered, disturbed by a light breeze. The thin new moon had risen and shone its light on the crystalline crust beyond. Tiffany shivered at the eerie scene.

'Let's get down to business,' said Hassan grimly.

'*Business!* Is that what you call it? You unemotional swine!' she scathed.

'I want Josef,' he said bluntly.

A chill raised the hairs on her spine. 'So that's it! You're holding me hostage! The Batinah project was a ruse to bring me here, then,' she said bitterly. 'How could you raise my hopes about the future for Josef and me? You got me here under false pretences!'

'Not entirely. You can work on the scheme. I told you; it's yours for the taking. I'll fly you there as soon as you like.'

'Providing…?' she grated, with a querying eyebrow.

'Exactly,' he said with a grunt of satisfaction. 'I want your co-operation. When we arrive at my home, I want you to ring Josef up at the school and tell him you want him to fly out to us both. He'll come like a shot. Won't he?'

'Well,' she said sarcastically. 'It's all nicely worked out, isn't it?'

'I think so,' he said, with a maddening smile.

It didn't reach his eyes, though. They remained utterly hostile, as hard and glittering as black diamonds.

'And me?' she asked, her voice wavering. 'Where do I fit into your neat little scheme?'

'I told you before. Nowhere. I want you to gradually fade out of his life.'

She quailed. She'd been wrong about his intentions, then. He wanted only Josef, and she was to return to Seeb or even England, without her son, if his plans came to fruition. He was very single-minded, very determined, and his hatred of her was absolute.

'Aren't you afraid that when we reach wherever you're taking me I'll somehow give you the slip?'

'No. My fortress is impregnable. If I choose to keep you there, you won't escape. And since it's my bolt-hole, it is remote, in the middle of the desert, with no way in and no way out apart from the air, or this long, beautiful caravan route.'

'Beautiful?' she scathed. 'It's tortuous.'

'You hate my country?' he frowned.

'Your…?' Her senses sharpened. 'Wait a minute! I had
the impression that we were going to a home of yours in
Oman! Are you telling me we're in…in Riyam?' she
asked, her nerves climbing to screaming-point.

He smiled mockingly. 'Correct. The plane brought you
straight here. This is Riyam. My country. And it seems
that even on a short acquaintance you hate it.'

'Damn right, I do!' she cried, hiding her dismay by her
attack. 'And its people! Particularly its arrogant, ruthless
men! You enjoy wielding power over women, don't you?
Using physical strength and bullying tactics to intimidate
and frighten! Well, Sheikh Hassan, you might harm me,
but you won't get my son. And I swear to God you won't
ever crush my spirit!'

But he was close to doing so. The dark night hummed
around her. She was trapped. He'd won. Riyami laws applied here. He'd take her to his fortress and no one would
help her; no one would dare to. If she didn't agree to his
demands, she'd probably never see Josef again. The prospect was appalling.

Hassan's eyes were warm on her, shining, she thought,
with the light of grudging admiration, and that irritated
her.

'Tiffany,' he said quietly, 'understand why I'm doing
this—'

'I don't!' she cried hotly, tossing her hair with impatience and frustration. 'Why would you take a son from
his mother? Have you no decency at all? No finer feelings?'

She'd angered him. His big chest had risen and his face
was thunderous.

'I'm thinking only of Josef,' he snarled. 'He must come
first in all of this. My information is that you, his mother,

lured my brother into casual sex and then forced him to marry you by using blackmail.'

'No—'

'You ask me to believe you, rather than my own brother?' he said with a proud tilt to his head. He leaned forwards, contempt written all over his face, and Tiffany despaired of ever proving herself innocent. 'He wrote and told me all about you, remember. That you tried to kill your own child, and when that didn't work you sulked all through your pregnancy.'

'I was ill—'

'You are not fit to be a mother of any child, let alone my nephew! Apart from your hatred of motherhood and facing up to your responsibilities, there is the additional charge of wild extravagance and promiscuity. Is it any wonder I want Josef and will go to any lengths to get him? How do you think I feel, to know my brother's son, flesh of my father, blood of my blood, is learning about women and life through your roaming, amoral eyes?'

'But you're basing your actions on hearsay!' she cried vehemently.

'Not only that,' he continued, ignoring her interruption as if she hadn't even spoken. 'Your sluttish behaviour in your own home, with Josef in the next room, convinced me that I was right. I can recognise a woman who breathes sensuality from every pore. Normally I make no judgement on women like you—but you are corrupting an innocent child.'

'I deny everything you say about me,' she grated. 'All of it. Josef is happy with me—'

'He knows nothing else,' snapped Hassan. 'Listen to sense. Josef has every right to know of his father's culture, to be introduced to his only remaining kin. He has a right to live in comfort instead of poverty. You won't go away empty-handed. I'll see to that. It's a good bargain, Tiffany.'

'But here! It's so barren…'

Distaste on her face, she waved an expressive arm at the desert surrounding the oasis.

'Riyam is a country of contrasts,' said Hassan. 'Like its people. The desert has its own beauty to those who look. We have lush green valleys and oases too, full of plants and birds.'

'And you'd train him to be like you,' she said bitterly, making no secret of the fact that she thought that would be the worst thing he could do.

Hassan's brows lowered. 'I would make sure he was interested in the business and teach him how to handle it. And how to deal with people.'

'Oh, that's easy,' said Tiffany sarcastically. 'The Sharifs find what they love, take it, or threaten it. Then they have the power to do what they like.'

His teeth clenched hard. 'Only when the situation is desperate,' he grated.

'Desperate?' She glared. '*You're* desperate? How the hell do you think I feel?'

'You'll get what you always wanted,' he said stubbornly. 'Your freedom. I know you wanted that from the start, that Josef's birth came between you and your plans. You can pursue your career—and I have made a promise to you that my influence will put work your way. In a few years, you could be very wealthy from your talent. You'd like that, wouldn't you? You've never made a secret of the fact that you're career-minded.'

'I find it fulfilling, yes,' she said in exasperation. 'But what would that be, without my son? Knowing he was being taught your unethical methods of manipulating people, changing from the child I know to a ruthless, empty-hearted man like you?'

Hassan's temper began to fray and Tiffany felt she were sitting in the middle of a brewing storm. Between them, hostility crackled like an electric charge as they both fought for what they wanted.

'For God's sake, Tiffany!' he rapped. 'Stop pretending to be a devoted mother. Are you holding out for a share of my wealth? Admit that you were horrified to discover you were pregnant. Admit that you didn't want your child, that you tried to have it aborted—'

'No, no! That's not true!' she cried in despair.

'You almost lost your baby—'

'Yes, I fell…' She choked. 'Nazim pushed me, over-come with temper, after my mother told him I was car-rying his child.'

A glacial light flickered in Hassan's eyes.

'You bitch! Now I am certain that you lie,' he said with soft menace. 'Because no Arab would ever do anything to harm his child. A child is sacred, Tiffany. You're black-ening my brother's name, knowing that he can't defend himself. Well, I defend him as a Sharif, and despise you the more for making Nazim bear your own failings. I know that all through your pregnancy you were miserable, and insisted on trying to continue at art school. And even after Josef's birth, you were determined to continue with your career and couldn't care less about looking after your son!'

'You would stick up for him!' she raged. 'You would believe him, before me! It's all lies! Of course I was upset to find I was pregnant! I was unmarried and didn't want—'

'You didn't want a child to inconvenience you,' he said tightly.

'I give up. It's no use talking to you,' she said wearily. 'You'll never believe me.'

'No. I won't. What you think doesn't matter, anyway. Give in. You're beaten. Let's make Josef's arrival here a harmonious one, not with the two of us at daggers drawn, so that he's torn in half by our antagonism. If you really loved him, you'd agree. Besides, Riyami law will uphold my claim to him. Co-operate, or Josef will suffer,' he said grimly. 'I'll have him, whatever you do. Of that, I'm certain. Do it the easy way, or the hard way. It's your choice.'

'The judgement of Solomon, all over again,' she whispered. 'My son will be cut in two if I stand up for my rights. And I lose him if I don't.'

Her head lifted and she stared into the darkness with moist eyes. What chance did she have of fighting Hassan, now that she was here? He was without mercy. To make his point, he would cleave Josef apart.

'You're intending to keep me prisoner until you have what you want.'

He didn't answer her statement. She made a helpless gesture.

'I agree,' she mouthed, unable to speak the words aloud. 'On one condition.'

Tears sprang from her eyes, cascading down her face as misery rose to conquer her self-control. Somehow she'd get herself and Josef out of this mess. But for the present...

'You're in no position to make conditions,' he growled.

'Listen to me!' she begged. 'I'll make it easy for us all by accepting the inevitable. I'll do anything you ask. Only let me stay with my son. If you have an ounce of pity within you, grant me that. You've beaten me. I give in to your foul demands. But be generous in your victory. Oh,

God! Don't deny me the right to stay with my own son, my own flesh and blood. He'd be unhappy without me. I couldn't bear to think of him pining.'

She raised her tear-stained face, knowing that her sanity depended on his answer. Her heart would be broken if she never saw Josef again. Anything, even living as a virtual prisoner of this merciless man, would be preferable.

Separation would be a torture more violent than mere physical blows. She couldn't keep her shaking body still. Her emotions had been ripped to shreds. She tipped her head back in hopelessness at the situation she was in. Her hair fell like a golden river down her back.

'Please,' she croaked. 'Oh, please, please, Hassan! I beg you from the depths of my heart!'

The stars twinkled cruelly at her from the vast black canopy, making her feel very lonely. There was a deep silence, so intense that it seemed her ears ached with it. The slow flames on the fire licked at the acacia, which filled the air with aromatic scent.

'I couldn't trust you,' he said in a slow, thoughtful voice. 'You'd have far too good an opportunity to make Josef hate me. It wouldn't be difficult for you to persuade him that life in England would be sweeter. You and I would be strangers with opposing aims, quietly destroying Josef between us. You see, there would be nothing that bound you to my purpose, nothing to ensure you made a genuine attempt to help Josef adjust to life with me.'

Tiffany wanted to scream. He hadn't refused outright. He was weakening in his resolve to send her away, but she didn't know how to make him relent. He wouldn't want to be seen to lose face. Curse his pride. What could she do?

'Oh, Hassan!' she moaned, feeling her chance to see Josef grow up slip away. 'If you ask me to crawl on hands and knees, I will if I have to. I have a hell of a lot of pride, but not where my son is concerned. You profess to care about him; can't you see that he'll be unhappy without me? I've brought him up; you're asking him to start a new life in a new country without the one person he loves.'

'I don't want him unhappy. I don't want you to crawl,' he growled.

She grasped his arms and threw every ounce of her heart into what she said.

'What do you want, then? Ask me. I'll do it. I'll do anything! Anything you want! Name it, it's yours!'

His wickedly white teeth drove deep into his lower lip. 'Anything?' he repeated hoarsely.

Shudders ran through her at the naked desire in his voice and the sexual threat which sent her nerves singing. Now that he had Josef, his mind and body were turning to her. Nazim's demands would be nothing compared with this man's smouldering sensuality.

'Even…' His hand reached up to touch her cheek. Tiffany closed her eyes tightly. 'You see, there is only one way. You would even give yourself?' he murmured.

The very air became charged with his raw need, surrounding her in its relentless seduction. It made her shrink into herself with an involuntary movement.

She didn't dare to stop him. Not yet. She must not make him angry. Once she had his agreement, she could make it clear that she wanted nothing to do with him and that he'd have little pleasure in forcing her against her will. It was a slim hope, but one she had to believe in or she'd crack up.

His fingers pushed gently through the silk of her hair. A touch like a butterfly's wing trailed across the bones of her face, over her neck and along her shoulders.

Hassan's face had lost its cruelty, its granite-hard determination. Now he was all man, flesh, blood, beating pulses. The desire driving from his body terrified her.

'You're so beautiful,' he said huskily.

She flinched. The warm, soft pad of his thumb outlined her quivering lips with all the skill and expertise of a master at seduction. And, more than she could have believed possible at this terrible moment in her life, his dark, sultry eyes and potent masculinity were awakening her stupidly responsive body as his relentless fingers sought her arousal.

Tiffany groaned. She'd never felt this kind of need before. He was using her hollow, unfulfilled womanhood with skill, knowing his expertise, relying on the lure of the promise of satisfaction which poured from his skilled fingers and his knowing eyes.

The cruel knives of desire were driving into her and she had to dig her hands into his shoulders to prevent herself from crying out. She had to get away from her own destructive longing. Another shudder ripped through her.

'You ask for that?' she whispered.

'It's what I want, at this moment,' he growled.

His mouth had a sultry arch which all but mesmerised her. She felt that her turbulent emotions were no longer under her control.

'God!' she breathed, incapable of understanding why her body melted at the mere thought of his naked body. It was indecent. Unladylike. Unstoppable.

'You said anything. That's what I want. You,' he said in a remorseless tone. 'Hell!' he groaned. 'Whatever I think about you, my eyes, my hands, my lips seem incapable of keeping off your irresistible body. I am obsessed by you, Tiffany. I have been consumed with desire for you since that day I first set eyes on you and I loathe you for that alone. I must either get rid of you, or take you. There is no middle way as far as I am concerned. The fierce contrasts of the desert. It's all or nothing. And I want all. Till you have nothing more to give and I have nothing more to take.'

His mouth touched her throat, forcing her head back, and she felt the burning of his lips on her flesh. Tiffany fought the unwelcome surges of warmth in response to the savagery beneath his gentle assault. Her head strained back in an effort to increase the distance between them.

'I couldn't surrender and keep my self-respect. You'd have to rape me,' she warned in terror, her breath coming fast and heavy.

'No. I wouldn't. You'd join with me in enjoying every touch, every movement. Every new path my fingers, my lips, my teeth, my tongue, may find.'

'No,' she denied, every inch of her tingling with anticipation.

His palm splayed out on her back and ran down the soft material, making her hollow her spine away from his touch. It was impossible for her to stop trembling. Deep within her lay a pool of molten heat, waiting to rise in her veins, waiting to erupt in an explosive surrender.

And she wouldn't allow it to. She tensed her whole body.

'Submit to me,' he murmured against her ear.

'No! I won't,' she moaned.

'Then you are of no use to me,' he said softly, staring into her eyes.

She slicked her tongue over her lips and, mocking her, he did the same to his. An agony of sweet pain coursed through her body. She wanted him, God help her, she was hooked by the first man who'd managed to arouse her.

Sex seemed to have more impulsive, irrational power than sense.

'For the last time, let me stay with you and Josef!' she whispered. 'Don't degrade me, your own sister-in-law, by demanding my body as a payment.'

He held a lock of her hair and was rubbing it sensually between his finger and thumb, lost in its silkiness. A sinful ripple ran through her veins, making her breath quicken and her lips part softly.

'I want your submission, Tiffany. I want you to offer yourself to me.'

'No,' she whispered.

How she hated him for what he was doing to her! she thought bitterly. He was making her come to terms with the fact that she wasn't cool and controlled at all, beneath the surface. Hassan's charismatic sensual nature had destroyed all her barriers like a heat-seeking missile.

He was in complete control of his sexuality and was able to use it to his advantage. Tiffany screwed up every muscle in her body, hoping to dissipate the shameful desire she felt for him.

'There is one alternative,' he said slowly.

Tiffany grasped at the straw of hope.

'Name it,' she snapped, giving him a hard look. 'Anything would be preferable to being abused by you.'

His lashes hid his expression and he dropped the strand of hair as if he'd been scalded.

'There's only one way you can stay with Josef if he is in my house. I do see the wisdom of letting you remain with him. Maybe after a while you won't wish to stay; we can come to some arrangement about that. You could have respect, and my protection. You would have a considerable influence over Josef's upbringing and a life of comfort.'

She was almost willing to let him ravish her, if it meant all that. Her protective instincts towards Josef were fierce enough to do almost anything to keep some kind of say in the formation of his character, so that he didn't turn out as dissolute as his father, or as ruthless as his uncle.

'What would I have to do?' she asked in a chilly whisper.

Hassan smiled hungrily. 'Become my wife.' She gasped and made to speak, but the grip on her arm stopped her. 'Not a bad exchange, a veneer of respectability, for spending days and nights of pleasure in my bed, is it?' he said with a voracious look.

Days and nights? she thought in horror.

'Wife number one? Two? Three?' she snapped scornfully.

He shook his head. 'I am a Christian, of course. The Sharifs have been Christians for a hundred years. One wife at a time,' he said with a low laugh.

'Why...why bother to offer me this farce of marriage?' she asked. 'You could force me.'

'I could indeed. But I want you like hell. I want your abandoned responses. I want absolute surrender and to know that you find my lovemaking impossible to resist. I want you to beg me to take you, to need me. I want to see you weak and defenceless from my kisses. Only then might my obsession fade. Until that time comes, when I tire of you, our union will be infinitely more enjoyable if you are willing,' he growled huskily.

'I'd be passive, not willing!' she declared hotly, tossing her shimmering head.

He laughed again, his teeth dazzling white, and she resented how handsome he looked when he did so.

'Your body would never allow you to stay passive,' he smiled.

She stared at him in silence. He was right. It wouldn't.
But her head would hate every second.

'You want it all, don't you?' she said in an acid tone.

'Oh, yes. I want it all. I've never gone for anything
less. Well?'

'What choice do I have?' she said bitterly. 'You know
I'm forced to agree. It's the most barbaric, cold-blooded
proposal. If I don't agree, you'd keep me here anyway as
a revenge, wouldn't you? And if I never went back to
Oman, the authorities there would have to send Josef back
to England or put him into a children's home. We'd lose
each other if I refused your monstrous suggestion. Oh,
yes, I agree. But with every inch of my body I resent
doing so, and hate and loathe you for putting us in this
situation! How clever you've been. You'll have no legal
battles. No expensive, long-drawn-out court appearances,
no sullen nephew who's missing his mother. And, on top
of all that, you have me to paw any time you choose.'
Incensed that he had cleverly managed to get everything
he wanted, she fixed brilliant steel eyes on him, her voice
husky with emotion. 'I agree, you bastard. Just remember
that I won't pretend to like you and I won't pretend to
enjoy what you do to me.'

'Oh, I think I'll overcome your reservations,' he said
softly, his mouth lightly running down her cheekbone.
'Easily,' he growled. 'I'll make you forget Nazim's lovemaking!'

She gave a deep shudder, remembering. 'No,' she said
in tones of ice. 'I won't ever forget. No woman could.
That will remain in my mind and my body till my dying
day!'

Hassan went very still, and when she looked at him she
saw he was white-lipped. His hands dropped away, pain
shadowing his eyes. She had, it seemed, successfully

fended him off. He disliked thinking of her and his brother. It doused his arousal effectively. She must remember that. It could be her only defence.

'I have your word?' he asked grimly.

'Yes.'

She felt better now. He could be diverted from assaulting her. She had very little to hang on to, but now she wouldn't entirely lose Josef. It was better than nothing.

'Then get some sleep. Make a hollow in the sand to fit your body. It will be warm underneath the cold surface,' he said in a distant tone. 'Try to rest. We ride early tomorrow.'

She stared at him, trembling.

'You're not…you're not going to…'

His eyes gleamed in the darkness.

'You want sex?' he asked, in a hard voice.

'You bastard! No!'

'Your mind is overcoming your body at last,' he mocked.

'I loathe you, Hassan al Sharif, brother-in-law or not,' she grated. 'And don't you forget it!'

She scraped furiously at the sand to make herself a warm hollow, relieved that he was settling down a short distance away.

'Don't you have a blanket for me, or anything?' she asked, when she'd finished.

'No.'

He rolled over, turning his back on her. Soon there was that dense silence again, the kind of silence that broke the nerve.

Tiffany curled up by the fire, turning her body this way and that, trying to get comfortable, trying to keep every part warm, and failing. Fatigue claimed her limbs. She lay in a lethargic, frozen daze, miserable, unable to stop her teeth chattering.

Her spirits were low. A small sob broke free of her lips. Hassan rolled over with a grunt.

'Hell. What's the matter?' he asked curtly.

'I—I'm cold and miserable. What the devil d-do you think is the m-matter?' she stammered through her sobs. 'You've stripped me of all d-dignity and forced me into a horrible marriage.'

'Come here,' he snapped.

'You're *evil*!' she cried, with all the feeling she could muster.

When Hassan came over and stood above her, she stared numbly at the pair of black boots, too tired to do anything. If he took her now, he'd get little pleasure, she thought dully.

He bent down and picked her up, still curled into a ball, and she was so worn out that she couldn't even struggle. His strength of mind and body was impressive.

A long, blood-curdling howl echoed through the clarity of the night, and then another. Tiffany gasped and her arms flew around Hassan's neck. She buried her head in his shoulder, shaking violently.

'Don't be afraid, Tiffany. It's only wolves,' he said gruffly. 'In the mountains. Now to sleep. I'm tired, even if you aren't.'

Against the glorious warmth of the hollow of his shoulder, she tightened her mouth angrily. But she let him lower her to the ground and settle himself with an impersonal efficiency, drawing her to him so that she rested her head against his heart. And her eyes were closing against her wishes, her mind becoming drowsy, and she slept almost immediately.

Some time in the small hours, she half woke, to find

Hassan's hands wandering over her body. He was muttering something in Arabic which she didn't understand. But she did understand what he meant to do. Imprisoned in his arms, she wriggled her hands free to defend herself.

Resisting, his fingers slid to explore the curves of her waist and she pushed against him forcefully.

A hand drifted to her thighs and she felt the old sensation of panic she had felt when Nazim had reached that point.

'Oh, God! Don't touch me! I'll feel sick,' she moaned.

Hassan's eyes snapped open, startled.

'What is it?' he asked muzzily, his face unnervingly close to hers. 'What's the matter?'

Although he released her immediately, she remained defensive and bristling with outrage.

'You were mauling me,' she said furiously.

His face became cold. 'I didn't know. I was dreaming,' he muttered.

'Of your dream woman, I suppose,' she scathed. 'A female who is always ready and willing, who enjoys your touch.'

The light was dim, but Tiffany could have sworn that his skin became faintly flushed.

'Do you still feel sick?' he rasped.

'Not any longer. Not now you've stopped fondling me,' she answered with a baleful look.

His brows drew together in a savage scowl. 'It's not long till dawn. There's no point in trying to sleep. We'll ride on,' he said abruptly.

'Oh, no!' she cried in exhaustion, tipping her head right back.

She should never have done that. Before she knew what was happening, Hassan had given a groan and had pressed her back to the ground. His mouth drove into hers ruthlessly, taking her breath away in a bruising kiss which her body welcomed if her mind railed against it.

Fiercer and fiercer his mouth ground down, and, under his passionate onslaught, her own lips began to respond in desperate need, devouring him, her hands lacing into his glossy dark hair and driving his head hard downwards so that all the terrible passion within her could be released. His mouth slid over her jaw and then returned, tenderly this time, drifting tantalisingly so that it just touched her skin, while his hand lifted to fondle the nape of her neck. A thrill of sensation shot down her spine and she gave a small moan.

Hassan spread out her golden hair on the sand, lifting it from her nape with delicate, incredibly electrifying movements of his fingers on her scalp. She luxuriated in the freedom and sensuality that this gesture gave her, small, throaty moans escaping from her in wanton, uninhibited ecstasy.

Hassan's languid, long forefinger lifted to the corner of her mouth, sliding delicately, tortuously over the soft down of her cheek and sweeping back to press her murmuring lips. Her chest tightened at his caress. It was gentle, tender… She whimpered. Her whole body seemed to be welcoming him. And no wonder. He knew instinctively how she wanted to be touched, and that his hands and lips were slowly but surely increasing her arousal to an exquisite level.

'I tried,' he whispered. 'God help me, I tried!' His mouth slid, kiss by kiss, to the lobe of her ear. 'I know this is unfair. That you hate me. But… I want you. Heaven is my witness, I want you!'

'Please—' she tried to protest, feeling a spear slice through her at his impassioned words. He sounded shaky and driven by dangerous desire.

'Tiffany!' he groaned, devouring her ear. 'Tiffany… Let me ease my madness for you. Let me please you,' he coaxed. 'I've wanted this for too long.'

She jerked in response to the incredible sensation of his lips and tongue. Suddenly, her mouth was covered by his in a fierce, never-ending kiss that took her breath away. She sank willingly into its warmth, crying aloud for him, her arms frantically holding him, enjoying his strong body as she pressed herself boldly against him.

Aching inside, almost explosively freeing herself of all her pain and frustration, she hardened her mouth as he had, and they took refuge in savage kisses which fuelled their fire, till neither of them knew what they were doing, only that they couldn't get enough of each other's lips, nor could they ever be too close.

Flesh to flesh, bone to bone, they sought mindlessly for unity. Frantic, breathless, Tiffany clung to Hassan, her wilful hands gripping his shoulders as his mouth swept masterfully over every inch of her face and down over her throat, and to the hollow at its base. There it lingered, moistly, and he became ominously still.

'Now we know,' he said thickly. 'Now we know, Tiffany.'

CHAPTER FIVE

TIFFANY'S humiliation was complete when she heard the quiet, exultant note in his voice. Hatred surged up to rescue her and she gathered the threads of control. Her self-respect was non-existent. She had to find it or be in his power. Her head went up.

'You can't tell anything from what has just happened,' she said scornfully. 'Have you ever considered that I might be using you? Maybe it was a test of my own power to arouse you, to see how much I could use my own sexuality to dominate *you*.'

Hassan winced noticeably. 'You bitch!' he seethed, his eyes flickering with lethal fire. 'You vicious little slut!'

'I feel no compunction about the way I behave towards a man like you,' she said coldly. 'I'll use any means I can, to win. And if you do force me to marry you, then you'll never be sure whether I'm responding to you or faking. You know what I felt about my late husband. One can't help but make comparisons.'

'My God!' he muttered thickly.

'I said, Sheikh Hassan,' she added tightly, 'that I could swallow all pride if necessary. That includes letting a man I despise make love to me.'

Straining her eyes in the black night, she thought his face looked racked with pain. But it was probably only a grimace of frustration that made his teeth flash like that.

'You wanted me—' he said hoarsely.

'Do you really imagine,' she asked in contempt, 'that I could want the man who has treated me so cruelly?'

'If I can hate and…want, so can you,' he muttered. 'They are close emotions. They can be mistaken for each other.'

'I'm not as hot-blooded as you. I think we established that early on. I certainly don't have your animal appetite,' she said scathingly, knowing with despair that what she said was untrue. It seemed she had, and it was a discovery that appalled her. She'd enjoyed everything he'd done, his touch, his passion…

Hassan's mouth twisted in a wry, mirthless smile. 'I'll saddle my horse,' he said abruptly.

Tiffany felt all the breath leave her body. She was safe. Her scorn had beaten him again. She felt limp from the effort.

When they moved on, into the heady, scented desert night, he walked alongside her, his head close to her thigh. He navigated by the stars, taking them over the cold sands, the swish of the horse's tail and the soft fall of shifting grains the only sound that broke the stillness.

Guilt at her response to him swept over her in flooding waves of embarrassment. She thought of her future and of spending each night of her life in his arms and was startled at the intensity of her excitement. It shouldn't be like that! She shivered and his eyes glinted at her. She could do nothing without his knowing. He was beginning to see into her soul.

To the east, the sun had crept over the horizon. For a magical few seconds, the sky was awash with pink light. Then it turned a bright cloudless blue.

Ahead were high dunes which rose like the softly rounded breasts of a woman's body. Swirling sand drifted from their peaks in small feathery gusts. As the horse moved into the sharp black shadow of a dune, she raised her face to the welcome breeze.

'Not long,' said Hassan quietly.

She thought his face looked different, despite the dark shadowing beard. Softer. Perhaps because their journey was nearly over. The future was daunting.

'Your new world. Your new life,' he said suddenly.

She looked at him in surprise.

'I suppose so,' she said heavily. 'I dread it. It'll be a living death.'

His mouth hardened and he made no comment.

'You—you'll be kind to Josef, won't you?' she ventured.

'He is my brother's son,' he said enigmatically, and she didn't push him any more, seeing he didn't want to talk to her.

Beyond the plain they were crossing, where the air danced with heat, lay a lush green valley. It was backed by a gigantic wall of jagged peaks.

'Tawi Atair,' said Hassan curtly, pointing to a faint irregular hill hanging behind a curtain of hot air. 'The Well of Birds.'

'Birds?' she asked in surprise, recalling that he'd told Josef something of this place.

He shrugged. 'Bee-eaters, purple sunbirds, hawks, magpies, herons—'

'Herons? There's a lake?'

Perhaps his home wouldn't be as harsh and unwelcoming as she had imagined.

'Thirty fathoms deep. Formed, so legend has it, by a falling star,' he said in clipped, flat tones.

In any other circumstances, she would have been delighted with the legend—and her surroundings. But fear nestled destructively within her body and she was in no mood for enjoying Hassan's country. Its pleasantness only served to emphasise her own desolation.

Gradually the hill turned into a huge fort looking as if it grew from a plug of rock, a sand-coloured castle, as in a fairy-tale. It soared into the air, flaunting its Crusader battlements, narrow window embrasures and huge ornamented arches. Tiffany saw it as a prison.

The tall towers rose over a hundred feet above a sea of palm groves, and surrounding those, like darkly moving waves, were fields of lucerne and indigo, spreading out in a challenge to the yellow desert. Tawi Atair was obviously self-contained; an island in a sandy sea.

Her eyes lit on a small dusty landing-strip, where two tiny planes gleamed in the sunlight. She must remember that. Maybe there would be a pilot who would fly her and Josef out, one day.

'Don't consider it,' murmured Hassan.

She flicked him a swift glance, hating the way he read her mind. It felt invasive.

'Oh, you're going to be wondering all the time,' she said, taunting him in defence. 'Wondering whether I've sold my body to this man or that, perhaps to a lorry driver, or a pilot. After all, we both know that I'm a cheap whore. I could easily seduce my way out of here, Hassan, and you'll never rest when we're apart.'

'That's why I intend to teach you such a thorough lesson in bed,' he snarled, 'that you'll have nothing left for any other man.'

'Impossible,' she said haughtily.

'We'll see,' he threatened.

Tiffany's face grew taut with strain. Hassan meant to rid himself of all his anger and sexual frustration on her. It would be a terrible revenge on an innocent woman. She *had to* persuade him that Nazim had ill-treated her and that violence would never win her over. Her stupid attempt to hurt Hassan by sarcastically suggesting she would sleep her way to freedom had back-fired on her. Damn! He won every time.

She tried not to slump in the saddle, though she desperately wanted to. Discipline kept her body upright. The years of pushing herself through the pain barrier to dance, to hold herself erect and graceful, were paying off again.

The white stallion walked through a line of frankincense bushes, their needle-thin leaves springing straight from contorted branches. Sap oozed from them, dropping into pots and filling the air with an exotic perfume.

And Tiffany's face softened a little when she saw the wild flowers beside the track. There were pansies, celandine and violets. It was almost like being home in England. Home! She gave a low moan.

'Josef!' she muttered. 'You said I could ring him—'

'At noon.'

'It's a long time to wait,' she said, defeated. Disappointment filled her face. Almost six hours. What could happen in those hours?

'We'll fill that time,' he said grimly.

She stiffened. He intended to slowly torment her with the hold he had over her. She'd fight every inch of the way.

'How far are we from other settlements?' she asked in a low voice.

'About a hundred miles,' he answered laconically. 'Don't think of running away. You'll never make it. The nearest town is far to the east, across the desert over there.'

He waved an arm vaguely towards some distant hills. There was no road, no track, only open desert. Tawi Atair was perfect for his abduction. Tiffany frowned. If she spent the rest of her life here, she'd go mad from the isolation. No wonder he behaved in such an extraordinarily arrogant way, if he was used to lording it over the locals in his own little world.

The massive iron-studded door of the fortress swung open and the stallion's hoofs clattered over ancient cobbles. Smiling-faced servants in white robes ran to greet them, and Tiffany looked for obsequious, fawning servility, but saw only friendliness and what appeared to be an easy relationship between them and Hassan.

Their smiles extended to welcome her and she found herself being swept along by Hassan and his chattering servants through a lush garden past hibiscus, daisies and camomile, beneath shading acacia, olives, and juniper. Its beauty was all the more poignant to the weary, apprehensive Tiffany. It ought to have been hard, ugly and uncompromising, to fit in with her situation.

In a small turret-room, at the top of a spiral staircase, the servants finally left her alone with Hassan. A wave of subtle perfume tantalised her nostrils as they entered, and she cringed at the thought that another woman, perhaps Hassan's last mistress, had inhabited these rooms. She shut her eyes to the wonderfully exuberant impact of the architecture and fabrics in the room and spoke before he got any ideas.

'I want a bath and a sleep and something to eat,' she said coldly, with as much authority as she could muster.

He threw her a mocking look and sat on a sumptuous divan, easing off his boots, dropping them on the soft oriental carpet and looking thoroughly at home. She didn't like the implications of that at all.

'Help yourself. That's a bathroom over there.'

He nodded towards a carved wooden screen between pale peach-coloured curtains which softened the honey stone walls.

She hesitated.

'There is a lock on the door,' he said sardonically.

'I should hope so. I want my own clothes back. I hate these second-hand, ethnic things.'

'I don't think Faridah would like to hear you describe them in that derogatory tone of voice,' he retorted. 'One of my cousins,' he continued, when she opened her mouth to ask whom he meant. 'She works for me here.'

'In this house?' she asked in surprise.

'Oh, she doesn't sleep here. She comes here every morning. We always have a working breakfast together. She's my public relations officer. Faridah usually goes home for dinner. Would that bother you, Tiffany?' he asked, his gaze sliding insultingly over her, his lips arched in a wicked smile within the black ruffian's beard.

'I'm not interested in anything but Josef and his safety. My mind is dead to everything else—particularly our relationship. Do what you like with me. After Nazim, no man will ever be able to earn my love,' she answered, with a challenging look.

His eyes flinched and she felt she was constantly scoring victories now. He was scowling at her comparison of him to his brother. Her confidence increased.

'I think you ought to make arrangements for your cousin to stay,' she said boldly, using his own sense of honour against him. 'Your servants will gossip otherwise. Do you want everyone to think your future wife is not to be respected?'

'I intended to ask Faridah to stay,' he said shortly. 'Even if you and I know what your reputation is, to the outside world it must be as if you are above suspicion. But I don't want you to mention our…arrangement. Not to her, or to anyone.'

'Why not? Is this some kind of trick?' she asked, her grey eyes alert. He couldn't be trusted, not one inch.

'I've said we'll marry, and we will,' he said in a low voice. 'But I think that for the time being people should imagine you're here of your own free will, as the woman who's working on a project of mine. I want them to think that we've decided your son should come here to join you.'

'You want me to act a part?' she asked incredulously. 'To pretend that I don't hate the very air you breathe?'

Hassan drew in a deep, angry breath. 'What will it do to my nephew if he arrives here, only to find that your hatred for me is public knowledge? How will he feel if gossip also tells him we are to be married? He'll be so confused he won't know what's going on. He'll be bewildered, incapable of handling the situation.'

He strode over to her and she backed away, wary of his barely leashed temper. But his long arm reached out and caught her shoulder, bringing her spinning towards him. She withstood the pain from his grip stoically, vowing that she'd die before she acknowledged he was hurting her.

'You have to pretend,' he snarled. 'As I will. Do you think I'll find it easy to show you any respect or courtesy? Everyone must think that we are falling in love gradually. If you love Josef, really love him, you'll make that sacrifice. He needs to get used to it here; to feel at home, before we drop any more bombshells on him.'

He was right, damn him! 'And if he doesn't like you? If he doesn't like it here at all?' she asked coldly, meeting his blazing black eyes fearlessly.

'That's one of the reasons we mustn't announce our arrangement too early,' he said grimly. 'I wouldn't keep him here against his will—it would be a waste of my time teaching him the business if he left the moment he could, as Nazim did.'

'Did Nazim hate you and your father, and this place so much, then?' she asked in a low tone.

Hassan's mouth thinned. 'Get this straight, Tiffany,' he said harshly. 'I don't want you to keep referring to my brother. He's dead.'

'If Josef doesn't want to stay, we wouldn't need to marry, would we?' she asked, her throat tightening again at the thought of being his wife and lying in his bed every night, waiting for him.

He smiled nastily, encircling Tiffany with his arms, his hands pressing with arrogant possession into the small of her back so that she was forced against him. Their bodies met and Hassan's hot masculinity all but swamped her senses. She kept herself as rigid as a ramrod, and let herself shudder in disdain.

His hand shot up to her chin, making her look at him.

'You sly bitch! If I am given cause to think for one moment that you are turning Josef against me,' he hissed, his breath jerking out at her, hot and harsh, 'I will make you wish you were dead.' His eyes terrified her. She couldn't move for fear. Every word was bitten out in a savage fury. 'You agreed that Josef ought to have a chance—a fair chance—to see if he liked it here. You accepted that he should be given the opportunity to know his true inheritance. *Didn't you?*'

She nodded, incapable of speaking.

'And you accepted everything that went with that.' He shifted against her, the dark brooding of his smoky eyes flaring into a cruel desire as he deliberately branded her with the knowledge of his arousal. 'That includes warming my bed when and where and how I want. And how often I want,' he breathed.

Tiffany quailed and tried to shrink back from him. He wouldn't leave her alone, she could see that. She would be locked into a rerun of her soul-destroying marriage to Nazim. She'd stayed with *him* for Josef's sake, too, crushing her own loathing in order to bring her son up with some semblance of decency towards women, and with some morals. Oh, God! If only there were another way... Could she escape, so that he no longer had a hold over her?

If she did, then she'd have to take Jo from school and fly straight back to England; she wouldn't feel safe so near to Riyam. That meant disappointment for Josef— both in losing out on an uncle, and leaving his beloved school. Then there was her partnership with Charlie. She'd be letting him down. It was no use; the complications were too great. If she could, she'd stick out the marriage, providing Josef wanted to stay.

Hassan gave her an impatient shake. 'Pay attention to me!' he snarled. 'You have to allow my nephew to make a reasoned choice: comfort and a future here, or poverty with you. Not a choice based on your scheming lies and selfish hatred. Because that's what it would be, Tiffany,' he growled, his hand going to her hair and catching hold of a handful. Her head was pulled back and her vulnerable throat was exposed. 'So if you prove to me that you're totally selfish and are not truly concerned for Josef's future, I'll fling aside any remnants of civilisation within me and kick you out. But before I do, I'll destroy you. Physically, mentally, emotionally. You can be sure of that.'

'You vindictive bastard!' she muttered with difficulty. 'Let go of my hair!'

The hand, still on her back, now bent her into an arched bow so that he dominated her completely, his menacing face savagely dark as it leant over her.

'You will swear to be straight with Josef, and keep your

opinions of me strictly to yourself. Let him make up his own mind, for his sake,' he growled.

'I swear!' she moaned, and he immediately let her up and released her. Desperately she sought for composure. 'I doubt,' she continued proudly, reaching up to arrange her hair again, 'that you'll be able to keep up the façade of being a charming uncle for long. Your foul temper will erupt and Josef will discover what a swine you are without any help from me.'

'You have nothing to worry about, then, have you?' he murmured.

'Nothing,' she said vehemently. 'You can't fool a child for long.'

'I'm banking on that,' he snapped. 'Now get yourself cleaned up. I want to shave and have some breakfast. Come down the turret stairs when you're ready. Here are your clothes.'

He began to stride out.

'Isn't this your apartment?' she asked with a frown.

She'd thought he had installed her here to be available for him, despite what he'd told her about his cousin.

'No. My mother's.'

'Oh, that's her perfume, then.' She sniffed the heady air.

'No. Mother died on the day I was born. The perfume is part of the walls. This was once a room in the women's quarters. When they were built, five hundred years ago, the clay was deliberately kneaded with the essential oils of flowers, instead of water.'

Tiffany's eyes widened at the sensuality of such an action. The very air she was breathing demanded her surrender.

'Was...?' She hesitated. 'Was your mother *loved*?'

Hassan frowned. 'Yes. By everyone who saw her.' He

made to leave, and then added, 'I took her from Nazim by my very existence.'

Stunned by the emotion in his voice, she watched him leave, noting the raised shoulders and clenched fists. Both sons had been brought up without a woman's guidance. That explained so much, suddenly. The cycle of deprivation mustn't be passed on to Josef.

Numbly, she went to the bathroom he'd indicated, locking the door and running a bath, clambering into the blissfully silky water. She stayed there a long time, thinking of nothing, blanking her mind. She'd take one hour at a time. It was the only way she could cope. And there were over five more of those hours before she could speak to Josef.

On a roof terrace looking over the Well of Birds, Tiffany sat down to an uneasy breakfast. Hassan had shaved and the pirate beard had given way to his smooth, infinitely touchable, golden skin. Once again, Tiffany was to marvel at his changing image and moods. For with the pale grey suit he appeared the epitome of the successful businessman, instead of the lawless desert barbarian. But she must remember that he was both of those, and more.

Faridah arrived, beautiful, with a rich flawless complexion and dark brown almond-shaped eyes. Her age was difficult to assess; she might be in her late twenties, or early thirties. Immediately Tiffany felt at a disadvantage in her crumpled cotton skirt and the simple jacket.

Tiffany had been introduced as Nazim's wife, so it was likely that Faridah knew what Hassan was up to. The woman was certainly hostile, and so probably knew Hassan's version of the facts.

Faridah's scrutiny had been unnerving.

'*This* is Tiffany?' she'd said, in a warm husky voice,

her eyes sweeping contemptuously over the creased cotton. Faridah herself was wearing a cool Egyptian cotton suit, dazzling white, perfectly cut, and shaped beautifully around her curvaceous body. 'Hassan, she looks a little the worse for wear.'

Tiffany bristled at the venom-laced remark.

'I am,' she began grimly, intending to tell her why.

'Tiffany found the journey exhausting in the heat,' said Hassan smoothly, spooning up a dish of fresh strawberries, his dark eyes warning her.

'So I see,' said Faridah. 'Poor dear. You look *wrecked*.'

'Thank you,' said Tiffany politely. 'But I'll recover shortly. I will have regained my poise and my customary grooming when my luggage arrives. When might that be?' she asked Hassan with a faint smile.

Inside, beneath the cool mask, she wanted to throttle them both. Deception always made her feel guilty, and she had no idea whether or not she could pretend to like Hassan, let alone make sheep's eyes at him. Though it did give her a perverse pleasure to show him that she was in control of herself, and he wasn't crushing her as he'd imagined he might.

'Your things have arrived,' he said quietly, watching her carefully. 'They'll be in your room now. We wish to do everything to make you feel comfortable.'

Hypocrite! her eyes said to him. He seemed amused and sprinkled a little more sugar on his fruit, lifting a strawberry in his fingers and reaching across the table with it, so that it hovered an inch from her mouth.

'No, thank you,' she said pleasantly, with a false smile. 'If I eat that it'll bring me out in a rash. It would be like poison to me, you see.'

A lazy, mocking grin made him look wickedly seductive.

'I'll have it, Hassan,' said Faridah huskily, catching his wrist.

His lashes flicked down to her and his mouth lost its smile. Faridah dropped his wrist immediately, flushing. Tiffany stiffened. Even his cousin was afraid of him. She'd stepped over the line and he'd rebuked her with a mere movement of his eyes.

'You have your figure to think of,' he said suavely to Faridah. 'The strawberry is drenched in sugar. Besides, Tiffany isn't eating much, and after the desert ride she needs to eat. Particularly sugar, to give her energy.' He turned his dark eyes on Tiffany. 'You had little to eat on the journey. You mustn't make yourself…weak. That would never do, would it? We want you to be fit and strong.'

'I'm not weak,' she said firmly, realising, however, the truth of what he said and helping herself to a few slices of fresh pineapple. She did want to be strong, though not for the purpose he had in mind.

'You look washed out to me,' said Faridah languidly. 'I suppose Hassan only let you have a few meagre dates on the journey.' She looked sourly at Tiffany and her next words indicated that she didn't know how forcibly Tiffany had been abducted. 'I'm surprised you didn't object, travelling all that way with an unmarried male. If word gets out—'

'It won't, will it?' frowned Hassan. 'You and my driver are the only two people who know how far we travelled together. No one else will question my movements. Ahmed won't pass comment and I don't expect you to. Remember, Tiffany is my sister-in-law.'

'You shouldn't have spent the night out—'

'That's enough!' commanded Hassan sternly. 'You question my honour and Tiffany's, too.'

Faridah looked him up and down, her eyes betraying hunger. 'You are a man, Hassan,' she said softly. 'No one could deny the power that—'

'Faridah, I forbid you to speak of this any more,' he rapped, his face tense with anger. 'I'm going to start work. Join me when you've finished. Tiffany, I am not intending to burden you with my presence till you have rested after the journey. Make yourself at home. Sleep, wander around, borrow a costume from the clothes in your room and swim, if you wish. There are books in the library. I'll ring you in your room at noon.' His eyes glinted with a warning light. 'But I wouldn't step outside the confines of my house and gardens, though.'

'Why's that?' she asked brightly, deciding to test his reaction. 'I thought I might explore the oasis, perhaps take a brief camel ride into the desert while I was waiting for the hours to pass. I had a few camel rides in Turkey. They were fun.'

His hooded eyes hid what he was thinking, but Tiffany detected a slight twitching at the corner of his mouth.

'You have the stamina of an athlete,' he murmured.

'A dancer,' she corrected. 'That's what I was, before I had to give it up.'

'A dancer?' cried Faridah, with a look of distaste. 'That does explain a lot, doesn't it, Hassan?'

'Yes,' he said, his mouth twitching. 'It does.'

'Ballet dancer,' said Tiffany firmly. 'I had to forget everything but practice. We worked at something until we succeeded. We learnt never to consider failure, that the body—and mind—is capable of anything.'

'How interesting. It opens up all sorts of possibilities. It would be a shame to waste your talents on a camel.

However, if you insist, I think it would be better to wait till I can be on hand to instruct you. I could give you a lesson and teach you the skills, if you like.' His tone had become husky. Tiffany knew that he was thinking of a more intimate teaching.

'I thought horses were your speciality,' she said icily.

He smiled. 'I'm very versatile.'

'Nazim was a good teacher,' she said, trying to sound wistful, and hoping Hassan would see the double meaning and leave her alone. 'A past master.'

A past master in demolishing her spirit, in subduing her with violence, she thought miserably. She must not let that happen again! Her eyes filled with unshed tears and she turned them on Hassan. The effect was astonishing. His sexual mockery was replaced by an icy rage.

Tight-jawed, and with a face of stone, he was having some difficulty in controlling his voice.

'Tiffany,' he growled, 'you are not to go out, for your own sake. You might stray a little too far—and then you wouldn't be able to ring Josef, would you?'

'What do you mean?' she asked, her heart thumping.

His whole body taut with menace, he laid a hand over hers, flattening it on the table.

'Only that you might lose all track of time and it will be too late to disturb him and take him away from his lessons,' he said, with a sinister light in his eyes. 'You wouldn't want to risk that, would you?'

He was bargaining with her. It was clear that she had to stay inside the fortress and behave herself, or she'd never be able to make that telephone call to Josef.

'I'll stay, as you suggest,' she said casually, then glanced down at her imprisoned hand. 'Don't you think you're being a little forward?' she reproved, in her best haughty English tone.

Faridah was seething. Tiffany felt uncomfortable about that.

'My concern for you made me forget my manners. Excuse me,' he said abruptly.

Tiffany watched him walk away, and realised wryly that Faridah was eyeing his broad back and tapering waist with open admiration. The woman's eyes were filled with desire and for a moment Tiffany felt sorry for her. Then felt worried for herself; Faridah would loathe her if she knew there was a marriage of convenience arranged.

'He makes my insides curl up,' breathed Faridah throatily, as Hassan's tall figure finally passed through the door at the far end of the terrace. Faridah fixed Tiffany with calculating eyes. 'And he's mine,' she said sharply.

Tiffany shrugged. 'You saw him first,' she said, assuming indifference. She'd have to talk to Hassan about this.

'I certainly did.' Faridah's hand banged down on the table. 'I belong to him!' she said fiercely. 'A female cousin always belongs to a male one! So keep off the grass. I have grazing rights.'

Tiffany bit her lip. She wanted to say that Faridah was welcome to them, but dared not. She'd promised she'd go through with this pretence and she was determined to keep her part of the bargain. And yet...

Joy flooded through her. If he and Faridah could get together, it would make all the difference; for surely, if he was married to *Faridah*, it would be all right for her to stay in his house, with a wife around. She brightened. Her own marriage to Hassan might not be a foregone conclusion after all! And yet, contrarily, she hated the idea of Hassan's marrying his cousin. It stuck in her throat to admit it, but she didn't want that at all.

'Watch him,' said Faridah, observing the changing expressions on Tiffany's lovely face through narrowed eyes. 'He's up to something.'

'Oh, yes?' enquired Tiffany, sipping her coffee with a studied air of casualness. Her heart began to thud. Faridah was thinking along the same lines as she was.

'Don't trust him. He's not being entirely honest about Josef.'

Tiffany stared, aghast. 'What do you mean by that?' she whispered hoarsely, every one of her senses jangling with alarm.

Faridah shrugged. 'It's perfectly clear to me. Hassan wouldn't spend most of his life and all his energy on the Sharif empire, only to hand it over to some kid, would he?'

'He has to leave it to someone—'

'You don't understand. When you've devoted your soul to something, as Hassan has, with a single-mindedness that's breathtaking, when you've let your personal life take second place, you won't rush to give it up. Besides, he'd lose the power and authority. He likes that.'

'Then why on earth did he seek Josef out?' puzzled Tiffany.

'My dear, you're very slow! Work it out. It's better to have potential trouble under your own roof. Hassan fears losing absolute control of his empire which he's built up so painstakingly. It's his whole life, Tiffany. Everything.'

Tiffany frowned. Faridah knew nothing of the arranged marriage. As far as she was concerned, Hassan was taking Josef into his house as a long-lost nephew.

'But Josef is just a child!' she cried. 'How can he be a threat? It'll be years before he can take over from Hassan—'

'Not years. Soon. When Josef is nine, he has the right to half the company because he is Nazim's son and it is his lawful inheritance. You, as his mother, will act for him and Hassan will have to consult you on every move he makes. That would be time-consuming and against Hassan's belief that a company is more efficient with one boss.'

'Surely Hassan knows that? Didn't he search for Josef in order that he should inherit—?'

'He's probably thought of a way around the problem of handing over half the company to a child in a year's time. He'll have worked out some way to keep everything under his control,' said Faridah slyly, standing up. 'He wants total domination.'

Tiffany heard the echo of Hassan's voice and knew the woman was speaking the truth. He went all out for what he wanted.

'Ever since he was a child, Hassan has set himself impossibly high standards. And met them,' continued Faridah. 'He's harsh with us all, but harsher on himself. A man of great strength and of a great will-power. He wants to be the boss. I don't think he'll gladly give up half the company. To my mind, there's someone else more deserving than your son. Do you honestly think that a passionate and ruthless man would hesitate to trick the child of his estranged brother and a whore?'

Tiffany's mouth opened in astonishment at the insult. Her head whirled and she didn't even notice when Faridah quietly rose and left her alone. Faridah had laid her cards on the table; she resented the presence of a potential rival and sought to undermine her. She'd succeeded in doing more than that.

Tiffany now knew why Hassan had been so keen to marry her. As mere relatives, she and Jo would have control over half of the Sharif empire. Marriage, however, would bring them both under Hassan's control. By becoming Josef's stepfather, Hassan would be able to tell Josef what to do as far as the company was concerned. As time went on, he could mould Josef to his image and only allow him a say in the running of the business if, and when, he wanted. No wonder Hassan looked so pleased with himself. No wonder he rode roughshod over any opposition she might put up. The stakes were very high.

And no wonder he insisted that she should pretend to fall in love with him, so that no one knew of his scheming.

Hassan was prepared to marry her for the sake of his rotten companies. What else might he do, to ensure no rival interference? Bound to her seat by the impossibly heavy weight of her own dread, she didn't run after Faridah and demand more information, nor did she move for several seconds. For within her was such a turmoil that it was all her body could cope with.

Hassan, she had to remember, was a particularly merciless man. He didn't behave like people she knew; out here there was a different law and it seemed he might be powerful enough to make his own. He had tricked her several times; deception came easily to him. Now he'd lured her into his den and she would have difficulty in escaping without being eaten alive.

Tiffany knew she had to play for time. Everything had happened so fast that she hadn't been able to chew things over. Somehow she had to put off Josef's visit without arousing Hassan's suspicion. And then she might have to manage her own flight, and face all the consequences.

She turned the matter over and over in her mind, trying to be level-headed, finding only confusion and panic instead. The garden beckoned, cool, calm, soothing. It might help her to sit there and think.

She had to play Hassan at his own game, but play a

better one. If she could lull him into a lax frame of mind, she thought, slowly descending to the peaceful courtyard, she might convince him that there was a good reason why Josef shouldn't come just yet. Then she could find out a little more about Hassan and make a rational decision. She bit her lip. She'd have to be *nice* to him.

Could she do it? Could she butter up the man who intended to use her to his own ends?

Tiffany sat down and leaned her head against the stone wall, listening to the joyous bird song. It was ironic that here in this lovely garden she was so unhappy and that the peace only served to emphasise her chaotic thoughts.

A man's voice drifted through the window grille, close to her head. Instantly Tiffany tensed up inside, recognising Hassan's brusque tones. He was speaking in Arabic and seemed to be making a lot of curt arrangements. And then she heard a door slam and the sound of Hassan tapping out a long telephone number.

'Hassan al Sharif. Get me the legal officer, please,' he said. Tiffany lifted her head. Normally she would never listen to a telephone conversation. But this might be something to do with her. 'Marcia? I want you to do something for me, fast…yes, yes, I'm fine, and no, you're right, I don't waste time on preliminaries,' he said irritably. 'Listen, this is absolutely top priority. My US companies are to be handed over and I want you to start preparing the necessary paperwork. I'll no longer keep a managing interest…'

Tiffany's mouth opened in surprise. It was something to do with her, and Faridah was wrong! Hassan was already arranging to turn the companies over to Josef! A rush of relief hit her stomach in a warm glow. Whatever his attitude towards her, he did feel fond of his nephew. Thank God! She needn't worry about Josef's safety.

She heard Hassan talking again and tiptoed away, strolling into the beautiful building with its graceful arches and rich furnishings. Everything would be all right for Jo. She, well, that was another matter. She still needed *time*.

Tiffany went to her room, her mind a little calmer, but nevertheless pacing up and down restlessly, waiting, waiting, for the hour when she could ring Josef at school. Exhausted by the strain, she finally flung herself on the bed and slept a little more, wondering if she'd ever get back into some kind of routine. Hassan had turned her world upside-down.

He intended to do the same to Josef. What would her son think when he learnt that she intended to marry his uncle? She grimaced, knowing Jo would be thrilled, seeing it as some kind of fairy-story come true. For her, it would be a horror story, played in slow motion. When she was with Hassan it seemed that, although parts of her body raced out of control, it was as if she were living life at half-speed, every sense inflamed and intensified.

As the muezzin called the noon prayer, she had found her way to Hassan's study and was about to knock when he opened the door.

'Come in,' he said quietly. 'I was coming to find you.'

He stood aside and she swept past into a room lined with books, many of them antique. But there was nothing antique about the communications in this desert oasis. A bank of computers and machines, printers, photocopiers, fax, and a shredder were arrayed on a huge table running the length of the room.

'Give me the number and I'll get it,' he said.

'No, thank you. Give me the code and I'll do it myself,' she answered stubbornly.

He smiled, silent and watchful, assessing her in that calm, still way of his.

'Here.'

She turned the dial away from him so that he couldn't see what she was doing and rang the number, waiting while one of the masters went to find Josef, and his breathless voice answered.

'Mum? Is that you?'

Tiffany's eyes grew moist and a lump welled into her throat.

'Oh, Jo, hello, darling! It's wonderful to hear your voice! How are you? Everything all right?'

'Terrific! We had sausage and marmalade sandwiches, and when we went to bed we had a pillow fight. It was great. How are you? Is it nice there? I missed having a story...'

'I missed telling you one,' she said huskily, smiling fondly at his torrent of words. 'I'm fine.'

Tiffany looked up in alarm as Hassan picked up a phone.

'Hello, Josef,' he said in a warm, affectionate voice.

'Who's that?' asked Josef uncertainly.

'Hassan. Your uncle.'

'Oh, terrific! You there too? Are you keeping Mummy company?'

'Something like that,' he said, amused, his eyes lingering insolently on Tiffany's furiously quivering body.

'Jo,' she said, glaring at Hassan for interfering in her private call, 'have you got a match on Saturday?'

'Oh, Mum! I told you!'

Tiffany dropped her eyes. She'd known the answer to her question. It was all she could think of, to delay Josef's arrival here, till she'd thought things through. She needed to be certain of Hassan's intentions, and as yet she couldn't be certain he would treat her with some degree of respect.

'There's one on Wednesday afternoon here, and an away match on Saturday. I'm in the Colts, Uncle Hassan,' he said eagerly. 'I wish you and Mummy could come over and see me play.'

'We will, one day, I promise,' said Hassan.

Tiffany seethed. Already they were a couple!

'Jo,' she said, 'your uncle was thinking that you might like to come and stay with him soon—'

'Oh, brilliant! Will you be there?' cried Josef enthusiastically.

Her heart raced and she was about to reply when Hassan interrupted.

'How about coming to my home on the next plane?' he asked smoothly.

'Wow! Will the job be finished then? Can Mum be there too?'

'Jo—'

'You could see the new pony I've bought, and come hawking with me in the desert,' continued Hassan relentlessly, challenging her with his eyes. 'Bring a costume, because we'll swim—'

'Oh, I'd love to,' said Josef, evidently torn, 'but you see, I mustn't let my team down. I'm the hooker, you see. That's awfully important. I'm bang in the middle of the scrum, and—'

'Josef, of course you must play your matches,' said Tiffany quickly. 'I wish I could be there. Perhaps, Uncle Hassan, I could pop back to watch the match?'

'Sadly, there's too much to do here,' he said, his eyes looking daggers at her. 'However, we could arrange for you to come after your Saturday match, Josef. Then you can tell me all about it.'

'Oh, yes,' cried Josef. 'I'd love a holiday. All the other boys have them but I've never had one.'

'I want you to come and see my home very much,' said Hassan in his velvet voice. 'I'll go and make arrangements for the flight now. After Saturday, then. I'll let you know the details. Will you be all right to travel alone, or—?'

'I'm used to moving around,' said Josef. 'I like flying. The airlines have got people who look after children my age. Oh, thank you! That would be great. Just great! I'm so excited, I could explode!'

'If you do, we could get your headmaster to parcel up the pieces and send you air freight, then,' joked Hassan.

Josef giggled and to Tiffany his laugh rang like a death knell. Her son was usually reserved, but he'd responded to Hassan with a natural and enthusiastic ease. Hassan said a fond goodbye to Josef and left her to continue the conversation alone, though her son wasn't interested in talking about school, only his forthcoming holiday and what they would do. Tiffany felt caught up in the web of deceit again: trying to pretend she liked Hassan and everything was fine.

It was painful ending the call. She missed Josef so much. Starved of love, she had poured all her passion into loving him. But soon she'd be with him again, one way or another. The first hurdle—preventing him from flying out immediately, as Hassan had wanted—was over. Next, in case she did want to run away, she had to gradually become familiar with the house and the surrounding countryside. Especially her escape route. Just in case.

On the roof terrace, she searched for the hills which Hassan had pointed out to her when they first arrived. Then she noted where the camel park was, and the airport, and imprinted it all on her mind. It was the first step. Next, she had to gain Hassan's confidence and make him trust her so that she could wander around Tawi Atair freely and learn the times of flights out, any daily lorry departures—anything she could glean which might help her plan.

It was a precautionary measure, one she hoped might never be needed. Perhaps she and Jo could make a good life out here. It all depended on Hassan.

And soon, she must suffer the ordeal of the evening, with Hassan making passes and Faridah hating her because he did so. Her only way out would be to bore everyone solid with motherly chat. She might be able to divert Hassan and get him to stop thinking of her as a woman.

Because she didn't want to think of herself as one. It was bad enough being cornered by Hassan in Oman. Here, where he had the potential to do whatever he wished, it was even more unsettling. Already he'd swept her into agreeing to marriage, and extracted from her a promise to give his outrageous plans a chance. What would be next?

CHAPTER SIX

LUNCH had been a solitary meal in the garden, and Tiffany longed for company, even Hassan's, to alleviate the monotony. The long, interminable afternoon was spent reading beneath the shade of palm trees there, and a kind of peace did finally descend on her, brought by the gentle warm breeze rustling the palm fronds, and the scent of herbs and roses drifting through the air.

Occasionally, a servant would wander out and ask if she wanted anything; coffee and cardamom, some halva, a dish of nuts, pastries, or fresh sherbet. There seemed no sense of haste in the servants' movements, and they took some pleasure in extending Tiffany's knowledge of Arabic.

Ideas began to crowd into her head, shapes, colours, fabrics, all for the leisure centre and all stimulated by the essentially oriental atmosphere around her. She missed working already. It would be infuriating never to work in the Middle East again because she'd had to run from Hassan's clutches.

Dinner was less of an ordeal than she'd expected. She'd wistfully eyed the bedouin garments in the wardrobe, and decided to stick firmly to her own clothes, putting on a neat green softly curving suit which would have won prizes for its modesty.

Faridah seemed subdued, as if Hassan had told her not to be rude, and he was in a good mood—probably because everything was going his way.

'You look better,' he commented, when she was shown into the dining-room.

'I did as you suggested, and relaxed,' she said pleasantly, looking around in awe. It was as if they were inside a vast bedouin tent, of pale gold silk, the sun filtering in through a glass roof and striking the circular brass tables beside richly embroidered ottomans.

'Please sit,' said Hassan, sinking gracefully on to the low seat.

His eyes travelled as if hypnotised up her long legs, and she felt the heat rise up her shins to her thighs as surely as if he'd slid his hand there. Her lips had fallen into a soft, treacherous pout and she wondered how much of his behaviour was for Faridah's benefit. He raised an eyebrow, and she tried to act as if she was just beginning to find him attractive. It wasn't difficult.

'I'm afraid I have the wrong outfit, for these low seats,' she said with a small laugh.

'Oh, I don't know,' murmured Hassan with a piratical grin, his eyes switching between her knees and Faridah's gold trousers.

'That's typical of a man's double standards,' said Faridah, with a smile she plainly didn't feel. 'You complain of the immodesty of some women and enjoy it at the same time.'

'I hope you're not suggesting that Tiffany is immodest?' he said mildly. 'I didn't give her the measurements of our seats and I presume she imagined we'd be eating western style. Besides,' he added, his dark eyes thoughtfully on Tiffany's face, 'a man does like some hints of a woman's attractions.'

'Clothes are important,' said Tiffany, trying to diffuse the undercurrent of resentment coming from Faridah. 'Particularly for me. I've been admiring your robe; is it traditional?' she asked, of his black sleeveless coat, edged with embroidery in gold thread. Its soft folds spread over his white tunic and trousers and she longed to feel the material.

'I forget,' he smiled. 'You're interested in cloth and design.' He shrugged it off, and passed it to her, making sure that he held on to it for a fraction too long so that they exchanged glances.

Tiffany hoped Faridah wouldn't be too hurt by what was going on. If she did decide to leave, it would only be a short pain. If she didn't, then it was best Faridah should have some inkling of what was to happen. As Hassan said, it made it easier for others if their 'romance' developed in public.

The meal was served, and Hassan took care to move closer to her and help her eat delicately with her fingers, his voice caressing, working its way into her senses. She found her body beginning to tingle every time he lifted his expressive hand, every time she became the object of his attention. He knew just how to appeal to her baser instincts, she thought resentfully.

'Tiffany,' he said smoothly, touching her shoulder, 'there are a few days till Josef comes, and Faridah and I have some business to do. Why don't you do some work in my office? Perhaps some preliminary sketches and notes.'

'For the leisure complex?' Her face had become elated. 'Well, I've had so many ideas since arriving here—I'd really like to be able to capture them.'

'If she's in your office, where will you work?' asked Faridah sullenly.

'There's enough room for the two of us,' he said calmly.

Both women shot him a suspicious look, but he seemed

harmless. Tiffany's mouth quirked. Hassan would never be harmless.

'I'll hardly notice you're there. It occurred to me that you'd be bored, Tiffany, hanging around, waiting for the hours to pass,' said Hassan innocently. 'And it would be nice, getting to know one another like that, wouldn't it?'

'Yes,' she said warmly, letting her glance linger on him. 'It would be nice. Cosy.' She smiled brightly.

It was a good idea. She might learn a few things about his character. If he was worthy of being Jo's uncle, then the bizarre arrangement might work.

'Having said that,' mused Hassan, 'I need to call in to the souk tomorrow. Come with me, if you like.'

She did, and loved it, not worrying that his invitation had been an excuse to be seen with her in public. It didn't matter; she had his company and it turned out to be enormously pleasurable. She took her notebook, collecting samples of material from willing stallholders, making sketches and enjoying the chaos and noise, the hectic impression that she was in a tale of *The Thousand and One Nights*.

'Is Jo keen on markets like this?' asked Hassan, guiding her by the elbow and nodding in a friendly fashion at everyone they saw.

His changed manner astonished her. He was a different person—nice, warm, dangerously attractive. He'd reminded her beforehand that they must appear to be very friendly, because gossip travelled around the market like wildfire. So maybe it was the fact that she was responding to him as if he was very dear to her that made her feel weak at the knees. Her acting was even convincing herself!

'I could never take him in alone,' she said. 'I didn't like to risk it, not the kind of places we lived near.'

'No. Very wise. There are many times when you need a man, aren't there?' he said warmly, his hand briefly slipping up her arm in a blatant caress.

She stiffened, but he'd withdrawn his hand and was examining some carved wood, running his fingers lovingly over the flowers and leaves, his expression rapt. How sensual he was. He needed to touch. Nazim had just grabbed.

'What was your relationship with Nazim?' she asked suddenly.

Hassan started and threw her a dark look. 'He was my brother.'

'I meant how did you get on.'

'Don't all brothers quarrel?' he said lightly. 'Would you like some shoes made for you?'

'No, thank you. Did he resent you?'

'You have no right to pry into my past,' he said quietly.

'If we are to be married, I have every right,' she answered, a tremor betraying her nervousness about her future.

He walked her over to a low wall at the end of the market and brushed the whitewashed top for her to sit down. He placed a booted foot beside her and leant on his knee, staring at the green barley in the fields beyond. Water gushed down a small aqueduct below the wall, cooling the senses.

'We'll make it work, Tiffany. I promise you that,' he said in a low-pitched voice. 'My methods have been questionable, I know that, but they were for the best of purposes. And I think, now we've stopped fighting one another, our lives will be enriched.'

'By Jo,' she said quickly, hearing a compelling warmth creeping into his tone.

'Of course.' He smiled happily down at her. She had

to smile back; he looked so delighted with life that it was catching. 'I had a long talk with him before we came out today.'

Her face became pained. 'You might have asked me if I'd like to speak to him—'

'I wanted to talk to him alone,' he said quietly. 'Be glad that I did. He worships you. I think I should forget the circumstantial evidence about your morals and look to the future. Jo and you and me. I'll be a good husband. I won't ever replace Nazim, I know that, but we do have a certain…rapport. Don't we?' He laughed, a little wickedly.

So that was the reason for his change of attitude. Jo had charmed him. The sun glinted on the hairs of his arm, turning them to threads of gold like the cloak he'd worn the night before. She had a terrifying urge to stroke his arm and feel the strength and the silky covering of hair.

'We ought to be getting back. You said you were busy,' she said hastily.

'So I did.'

He held out his hand to her in a gesture of friendship. Taking it, she felt his warm grasp and found herself wishing that he would never let her go. He drew her to him and she swayed pliantly in his arms.

'Is this real or are you faking?' he whispered.

'You told me how to act,' she said with a gulp. He must never know how strongly she was affected by him.

'Make it more convincing,' he said tightly, a glacial light appearing in his eyes.

So it wasn't real for him, she thought sadly. Just as well.

Yet for the next two days they worked in a companionable harmony. Tiffany became very engrossed in working on her ideas and found colour and pattern blending effortlessly within her head. She longed to get started in earnest.

Being with him was an eye-opener. Maybe he was working hard to impress her with his courtesy and business flair, but it did seem to come naturally. He was hard but fair. Her respect for him grew.

And there was the Majlis.

'I'm holding an audience,' he said, late in the afternoon of the second day. 'Come and see it. I think you'll be interested.'

'You're doing a variety act?' she asked flippantly, to disguise the rush of warmth at his eagerness to include her.

'As sheikh of a thousand tents in this area, I am bound to make myself available for minor official acts,' he said, pride bringing an offended reserve to his face. 'Don't make fun of an ancient custom.'

Tiffany walked with him along marble corridors towards the largest salon, thinking about this.

'Will Josef inherit the title of sheikh?' she asked, trying to imagine her son as lord of a thousand tents.

'Only if he deserves it. It's not a hereditary title. You have to earn it.'

'How?' Tiffany felt pleased. That counted for something, didn't it? Hassan's character must be special for him to have been chosen.

He shrugged. 'Courage, generosity and mediating skill.'

'Oh.'

He smiled to himself at her contemplative face and motioned her to a seat where she was hardly visible. For the next two hours, people of all descriptions and all walks of life came to Hassan for his help. She knew nothing of what they said, but later he explained that he'd settled water disputes, arranged pipeline rents, grazing rights and oil concessions, and patched up grievances. And Tiffany could see how well he listened and that everyone looked up to him. It wasn't an act for her benefit and she felt the tug of ungovernable longing and admiration mingle with hope.

That evening, he came closer and touched her more boldly, speaking to her gently, smiling, heating the very air with his evident sexual attraction, bombarding her senses till she could hardly think straight. Of course, she was forced to play along. Forced? She had to admit that she was more than enthusiastic. Not many men aroused her admiration. She smiled wryly. She found him irresistible.

Every hour that passed, she fell more and more under his spell. She began to give in to her feelings, knowing with a sense of excitement that they could have an incredible relationship. For his part, it was clear that his antagonism and contempt had gone, and for Josef's sake he was burying the hatchet he'd wielded against her.

Despite her nagging uncertainty about Josef's well-being, and the fact that she missed him and looked forward to her long chats with him, she also looked forward to the days cloistered with Hassan in the big, cool office, revelling in his comments on her work with an almost childishly glowing pride.

Even more, the bittersweet moments when they pretended to be falling in love brought her equal measures of joy and pain. She almost believed that the sensual crescendo he was working towards flowed naturally from him, and wasn't part of a calculated plan. His affection seemed too real. It made her yearn to trust him and to give in to her instinctive longing to release her suppressed love. But she dared not, yet.

It was just as well. For, one morning when they were

in the study together, there came a fatal telephone call and Hassan walked innocently into his own snare.

'Hassan here...New York? Put them on... Morning, Marcia! You've worked fast... What about the US holdings...? Oh, the new owner! Didn't I say? His name is Abdul al Sharif.'

In a split second, Tiffany's warm glow turned to a hard, cold lump of nausea, clawing at the pit of her insides. Looking down on her shaking hands, she listened on in consternation.

'Bring the papers over yourself immediately. The matter must be completed by that date I gave you... Fine. See you then.'

The receiver dropped down and Hassan continued with his work, whistling cheerfully under his breath. Tiffany sat numbed with shock. She didn't know whether to say anything or not. It dawned on her that he didn't know she'd heard his earlier conversation with Marcia and would therefore be able to put two and two together.

It added up to disinheritance, of course; Hassan was shedding ownership of companies so that they weren't under his name any longer. In the event of her marriage not going through, Josef could never claim them, because they would no longer be owned by Hassan. But why give up ownership? Wasn't Hassan sure of his hold over her?

There would have to be another reason, a strong one, for him to hand over something he valued so much. Abdul al Sharif. The same surname. Who could be so important...? Her hand leapt to her mouth, as she realised the full implications. There was no other possibility. Abdul must be the person Faridah had referred to when she'd said there was someone more deserving of the inheritance. Hassan wouldn't hand his beloved business over lightly, not to anyone. This person would be someone very close, if he was to be given the US companies.

She considered the possibility which had sprung into her mind. Hassan would hardly have led the life of a monk. One of his women might have produced a child. For to whom else but a bastard son would he transfer his precious companies?

And if Abdul was older than Josef, that might be another reason why he'd been so all-fired eager to marry her; the *elder* son would inherit the whole Sharif empire, not a mere stepson. Jo would have nothing.

Whereas he did have a strong claim at the moment, as Nazim's child, and that was probably why Hassan was taking precautionary measures to safeguard his bastard son's future, transferring some of the companies before Jo took his rightful share.

Tiffany's mouth tightened. That scheming, devious, sly swine!

She passed a weary hand over her forehead. The situation had changed. Hassan wasn't to be trusted to do the best for her son. The sooner she and Josef got out of his clutches, the better.

Her eyes glittered. She wanted to confront Hassan, to have a blazing and satisfying row. But she dared not say anything. Her plan must be to allay his suspicions. Otherwise he'd put a guard on her and she'd never escape.

Misery filled her heart. The last two days had been enjoyable. Even…special.

'Tiffany?'

She jumped. Hassan's hand had descended on to her shoulder.

'What is it?' she said, trying to smile.

'You've been dreaming for the past minute or two. And

I see you've been doodling with your pencil all over your design for the powder-rooms.'

She looked down in consternation.

'Oh! How stupid of me! I was wondering about the fabric for the curtains.'

'Were you?'

Nodding brightly, she tipped her head on one side, as if still thinking. But Hassan twirled her chair around and tilted up her chin.

'You find it hard to put aside your feelings for Nazim?' he queried. 'Won't you let me help you get over him?'

His eyes dropped to her mouth and she felt his breath rasp a little more harshly. It was unbearable having him so close. Every one of her nerves screamed to be set free by him, from him—she didn't know what she wanted, only that he disturbed her more than any man ought to. Especially a clever, manipulating one who pretended to be charming in order to hide his convoluted plans.

His fingers slid smoothly over the hollow below her cheekbone and along her jaw. There was a fierce message in his eyes; one of tenderness and love, of burning desire. And she was caught up in it, unwillingly, incapable of dragging her gaze from his, incapable of preventing her face from flushing with warmth.

If he'd done this one hour ago, she would have responded differently. He was too late.

With a reluctant effort, she reached up and held his hand, meaning to remove it, but he plundered it with kisses and it was all she could do to prevent herself from crying out in despair.

'A couple of days can make all the difference between love and hate, can't it?' he mused, with a winning smile.

She wasn't won. Her heart had to be hardened against his easy charm and effortless sex appeal.

'All the difference,' she said wryly, seeing the irony of his words. An hour ago, she was falling in love. Now she wasn't. Simple. 'I think I'll go up now,' she said. 'I want to wash my hair and so on before dinner.'

'There's only the two of us tonight,' he said huskily. 'You don't have to be so modest in what you wear. Put on something…gorgeous for me. Please.'

She pushed him away with a light laugh.

'I would have thought that was just the occasion *not* to wear anything that didn't button up to the neck,' she said, managing to grin convincingly.

'I haven't attacked you, or treated you badly,' he said with a slight frown. 'Please. To prove you trust me. And for me to prove I can admire and sit on my hands at the same time,' he added with a rueful grin.

She tried to sound normal. Flirt! she told herself.

'Not all the time, I hope,' she smiled, trying to look provocative.

Hassan drew in his breath. 'Do you need any help to change?' he asked huskily.

Faridah saved her, by walking in on them.

'You won't be much use to me,' grinned Tiffany with a supreme effort. 'Not if you're sitting on your hands. See you at dinner,' she finished with a light laugh.

Outside, she let her body slump with fatigue. But the battle wasn't over. The worst was to come. As she toiled unhappily up the stairs, she concentrated on working out her actions for the next few hours. It was Thursday already and she had to find a way to get out of Tawi Atair. He must feel certain of her devotion, even if it meant she had to let him ogle her all evening. For Josef's sake, it was essential that Hassan never suspected what was in her mind. And then she'd find a means of fending him off after dinner. She had to.

Already her stomach seemed full of butterflies at the prospect of striking the right balance between enticing Hassan and perhaps inviting her own rape, and offending him with her reserve. Not easy. For that, she'd need an elegant outfit and a cool head—and perhaps a well of scorn, ready to pour on him if he ventured too far.

Hassan was nobody's fool, and he might just take what she offered, without caring about her feelings at all. Still, it was all she could think of to put him off the idea that she might be secretly plotting to get away.

Slipping into a satiny bra and briefs, she dragged her clothes out and laid them on the bed. Naturally she had been expecting to be working in Oman, and had brought one or two elegant items for the evening.

Not the black sheath. Although it had a bolero jacket, Hassan had X-ray eyes and impertinent fingers. She couldn't risk his discovering that beneath the jacket the apparently demure dress had a boned, strapless top which revealed a great deal of her breasts. It would have to be the cinnamon suit, she decided. It struck the right note between sophistication and allure, with its deep V neck-line—which could be buttoned high or low—the cinched-in waist, and the hip-hugging skirt.

She put away the rest of her clothes and did her face carefully, enlarging her soft mouth deliberately and en-hancing her eyes with soft grey shadow. It was still very warm, and she decided to dispense with her new bra and wear a thin camisole top instead. It was halfway over her head when it caught on a loose link of the safety chain on her watch.

And that was when Hassan chose to knock on her un-locked door.

'Tiffany?'

She struggled furiously with the top, her arms trapped and her head in its folds.

'Tiffany!' he called again.

'Hassan! Don't come in!' she called out in a muffled voice.

To her horror, the door opened. She froze in shock. There was a silence. All she could see was his shiny black shoes, but the atmosphere had heated more than a few degrees. She wriggled, hoping the camisole would free itself, stupidly not thinking of the obvious solution to her over-exposure.

'Later, Hassan,' she called in cool amusement, remembering not to antagonise him. She regained her senses and turned her back on him. Her throat was dry from nerves as she tried desperately to free herself in the deafening silence.

'Later? Any reason why not now?'

Tiffany was more caught up in the camisole than ever. And in her own deceit, dammit!

'I thought you enjoyed waiting,' she said in a muffled voice, feeling hot and uncomfortable, knowing he must be staring at her naked back and enjoying the way she wriggled. 'You said that could be exciting.'

'Well, well, well. Faridah was right about you after all. Trust a woman not to be fooled,' murmured Hassan. The door slammed. 'You make a very enticing sight.'

'No—!'

'Tiffany,' he said huskily, 'I'm not made of stone. You can't expect me to turn down an offer like this.'

'Oh! It wasn't an offer! Oh, damn this top—'

'Let me help. You seem to be badly tangled up there.'

'Go away,' she said mutinously, abandoning her attempt at coaxing him to leave. 'I can do it.'

'But I want to,' he husked. 'I can't stand the distance between us, nor stop my hands from touching your skin.'

She gasped as she felt his hands boldly cup her naked breasts and then he had pulled her hard against his rapidly breathing chest, the whole of her back burning from the heat of his body.

'Beautiful, beautiful,' he crooned into her ear.

The relentless movement of his hands made her groan aloud in rage, and then she had torn her top free and was trying to settle it down on her body. It dropped to cover her a little, but his mouth savaged her neck, hungrily sweeping it with passionate kisses, increasing the ache within her as his freely roaming hands explored her curves.

'Let me go, Hassan!' she said huskily.

'No,' he growled. 'You can't tease me and get away with it. You knew exactly what you were doing, didn't you?'

'No, I didn't! And you know how I feel—'

'Hell! I'll make you forget!'

He spun her around and his mouth drove into hers, savage, hating, and they were locked as if in combat, an elemental rage hurting them both. She tore her mouth away.

'Hassan, what has Faridah been saying?'

'That you're a tease. That your coolness is callousness. That you bet her you'd bring me to my knees with wanting.'

'No!' she cried in horror. 'She's lying! She wants you for herself—'

'You bitch!' he growled. 'That's a lie. I know who she mopes over and it's not me. You're trying to wriggle out of the truth. You enjoy throwing out your body as bait to helpless men, don't you?'

'Helpless?' she cried incredulously. 'You're about as helpless as a wolf in a sheepfold.'

'I should have kept faith with my brother's word, with Faridah's, with my investigator's, with the evidence of my own eyes,' he snarled. 'Not let myself be duped by you and your poor, innocent son. There's a name for women like you,' he breathed, his eyes impaling her with their venom. 'You've probably left a trail of broken men, haven't you? You certainly spoiled my brother's chances of ever making anything of himself. So…'

She gasped as he thrust her down on to the bed, his teeth tugging urgently at her bottom lip, and as she cried in protest his tongue slipped into her mouth with an unbearably erotic movement, inflaming their mutual need.

She seemed to be swamped in sensation. There was a hand curving, stroking, over her velvet hip; fingers shifting with intoxicating halting movements beneath the silky camisole, around the curve of her breast; Hassan's mouth filling hers with sweet hunger; his groans and his breathing, his muted growls, eloquently tormenting her sense of hearing; and his eyes, his damnable eyes, scorching, searing into her brain till it dissolved into mindlessness.

His plundering mouth moved relentlessly, savouring, gentling now, less voracious, but no satisfactory substitute for the act she longed for. And she felt the heat of his body and the dangerous power that lay so hard upon her with a sinful thrill of pleasure.

'No, you can't—'

'I damn well can!' he breathed.

His hands had roamed to her bare shoulders, revelling in the buttermilk softness, his lips following them, across her throat, her collarbone—

'No, Hassan!' she cried, her voice raw with need. He

had aroused her so easily that she could have wept with shame.

'Yes,' he said hoarsely. 'I will. I will have you. You're not a young virgin. You enjoy sex. And,' he growled, 'you can't deny that you invited me in, knowing how naked you were. I only came up to ask if you'd like to eat out. Now, I suggest, I eat in. Here…and…here…and here, here, here…'

Tiffany moaned at the exquisite demand of his mouth. 'I didn't—'

'I'm not going to argue. I am here and here I stay. Till I have what I want. Unfortunately,' he said, insolently cupping her breast and rubbing it with an intolerable rhythm of his palm, 'you won't be able to twist me around your little finger. I will be the dominating one in our relationship.'

'Dinner—'

'Is served up on a plate,' he mocked. 'A little earlier than expected.' His hands ripped away her bodice completely.

He shuddered as her naked body was totally exposed to his lusting eyes. Tiffany's hands reached up to thrust him away, but he effortlessly caught her wrists and she was only able to writhe helplessly beneath him as he drank his fill.

'You are very, very lovely,' he breathed harshly.

One wondering mouth dropped to a taut dark peak and her anger and fear were swept away by the agonising sharp pains of exquisite need which rocked her body. He was making her head spin; she was out of control, only able to concentrate on his devouring mouth as it captured each hard rosy centre, savouring hungrily, creating an impossible emptiness within her.

'You bastard!' she moaned, arching her supple back.

He grunted deep in his throat and she felt the hard ridge of his hip shift slightly. The tugging on her breasts softened, deepened, became more impassioned, and she could stand his tender, expert loving no longer. Small moans erupted from her lips, her head turned from side to side, and she became aware that Hassan's lips were drifting upwards, sliding over her skin, to her jaw, her lips, sweetly moving in a trail of soft fire.

'I—I—can't bear this,' she jerked haltingly. 'Please don't. I beg you.'

'I want you,' he muttered. 'And as long as there is breath in my body, I intend to make sure I take you, and see if you're worth all my desire. I have to know. We both have to know.'

'I don't understand!' She shuddered as his hands slid up the length of her thigh.

And she was encouraging him, amazingly, hopelessly, conniving in her own ruin, as he slid his savouring hands over her thighs, edging his knees between them. Tiffany squirmed as the sweet moistness within her signalled its unmistakable message, the wanton voluptuousness of her sinuous body making his mouth arch in carnal curves.

'Hassan!' she urged, closing her eyes so that she couldn't see what she was allowing. But she could feel. Oh, she could feel—a hotly inciting movement of his fingers, which scattered her senses to the four winds.

'Tiffany. God, we create fire between us!'

His mouth grazed her shoulder, savaged her nipples with brutal tenderness, and then she felt his tongue slicking around the curves of her breast in a light touch so delicate that she kept straining towards it.

The raw emotion within her and the pure, physical response were new. It was frightening. She had no idea that her body could take over so completely and deny her mind, nor that a man could be so gentle and so infinitely desirable because of that. She fought for consciousness, but Hassan's lovemaking was too passionate to allow that to surface.

There was only her dark need.

'Kiss me,' he murmured. 'Kiss me, Tiffany. I want you to. Hard. With all your passion, all your desire. Tell me what you want. How you like it.'

She gloried in him. Her treacherous mouth rose to his, her starving lips lush and full in expectation.

The telephone rang.

The lifting of Hassan's body from her, and the sudden cool air on her breasts came as a cold shock—and a terrible loss. One of his hands had remained on her breast, teasing it, exploring, enticing. She gave a sharp, involuntary moan and his eyes melted into hers.

'Yes?'

Tiffany blinked, her racing pulses making the blood roar in her head, as Hassan answered the phone.

'In a minute.'

He slammed the receiver down and for a moment was silent, his chest heaving with ragged breath. Then his storm-laden eyes turned to her and ran slowly over her body, leaving shock-waves in their path. Unconsciously, she lifted her body a little, desperate for his touch.

Hassan's breath exhaled noisily.

'I daren't touch you,' he said harshly, as if he knew what she wanted by a mutual sexual instinct. 'Not now. I hadn't meant…' His white teeth ground into his lower lip. 'Hell!' He stood up shakily. 'You make me lose all self-control! Well, at least there will be something to enjoy in our marriage,' he said cruelly.

Tiffany's eyes widened and she felt a stab of fierce despair. She had made herself cheap and he felt fully entitled to treat her like a slut. She lay there and tried to tell herself that it didn't matter. Soon, very soon, she would be out of his reach.

'Faridah has been trying to get hold of me,' he said, sounding husky. 'She's very angry that she found me here, I think.'

Tiffany groaned. 'You bastard,' she said in a flat tone.

He leaned over her and she shrank into the mattress.

'Hate me?' he queried, his eyes glittering.

'You know I do!' she breathed with venom.

He laughed and bent his head to her breast, feeding greedily, and her hands automatically went to his shoulders, smoothing over their gold satin, her whole body alive once more.

'Want me?' he growled in his throat.

'No!' she quavered, her hips jerking with the intolerably tantalising movement of his fingers.

'No,' she said desperately, as he slid down her body, his shockingly intimate kiss breaking all her resolve in a blazing furnace of wanting.

'Oh, you devil, you devil. Yes,' she moaned, lifting her hips in response. 'Yes, damn you, damn you!'

'Yes?' he whispered, in a simmering voice, shaking with passion.

Tiffany whimpered, driven beyond endurance at the lightly feathering kisses, the moist heat of his mouth.

'Please,' she begged, unable to stand any more. '*Please*, Hassan!'

He moved up her body, his eyes holding her, quickly easing his tie and flinging it aside, removing his shirt, unlatching his belt… She gasped with anticipation, as his hands twined in her hair, his desire-laden eyes mesmerising her beneath the heavy lashes, and she fell into a spiralling whirlpool of emotion.

'We can't…'

'We must,' he breathed hoarsely.

She shuddered at the tantalising distance of his sultry mouth.

'Kiss me,' she moaned. 'For pity's sake…'

A gossamer touch brushed her lips.

'I hate you,' she sobbed with need.

'Hate, want, they seem to be one and the same thing for us,' he rasped.

Her hands were helping him to slide off his remaining clothes—hands that moved without any conscious will on her part. He shuddered as his body lay on hers and for the first time they were skin to skin, knowing every inch, every aching, longing inch.

'Oh, my darling,' he husked. 'You are wanton, beautiful…'

She felt a delirious sensation at his words and then he was drowning her in his kisses, with more passion than she'd ever known could exist.

'You've taken over my whole mind, my body. I can't think of anything but you, can't envisage life without you near me, enticing me. This is the only thing that's been on my mind for days,' he said harshly.

And suddenly he had lifted his hips and the hard, infinitely desirable heat against her loins drove into her with a sweet, welcome thrust. Deep within her, she felt her muscles begin to contract rhythmically in automatic response.

'Beautiful,' he croaked. 'Slow me down, Tiffany, oh, slow me down!'

'What?' she mumbled dazedly. 'How…? I don't…'

'God!'

His fingers caressed sublimely, taking her to the brink and beyond. They rolled on the bed and she matched his frenzy, scorching him with her kisses, their mouths murmuring, suckling, nibbling, biting...

And he moved. Moved like a gentle, slow piston, till she yelled for more and she demanded her own satisfaction from him. Their rhythm was perfect. He called her name hoarsely, in agony, and faster and faster he possessed her, flooding her with sensation after sensation, leading her to a terrifying crescendo of emotion which made her bury her head in his neck and sob with relief.

But instead of stopping, he moved delicately, marginally, subtly, while she moaned for him to stop, and then he twisted her around so that she sat astride him, her breasts dropping heavily in his hands, and new trickles of arousal were beating at her body, his mouth sliding seductively over every inch of her skin. Again, with a quickening hunger, he drove her to a climax, leaving her clutching blindly at him for support.

He laughed softly in exultation, falling back with her on the bed, stroking her gently, muttering soothingly as she sought to control her senses and breathe normally again.

But he turned her deftly on to her stomach and gently massaged her back and her buttocks until she was helplessly tormented, begging him to continue. Only when she had reached almost total physical and emotional exhaustion did he relent and then he finally released his own restrained virility.

'Watch me, Tiffany,' he said thickly, as his head dropped back in an intense sexual need. 'Watch me love you!'

It awed her. She watched him, every second of his pleasure, every subtle change in his face, as it became suffused with passion. She had never known she possessed such heightened senses. She felt the muscles in his pelvis

and legs tense up, one by one. Every part of his body
seemed to be throbbing, humming. Beneath her fingers,
his shoulders bunched and flexed; her mouth lingered
softly over each fine, curling hair on his chest. The look
of pure, unadulterated ecstasy on his face tore at her heart,
wrenching it open, as a sweet tenderness flooded through
every vein she possessed.

It was a moment of miracles. Of a blinding, terrifying
realisation that if this man only loved her, if he had one
ounce of affection for her, she would love him until her
dying day.

'Oh, Tiffany!' he groaned.

Slowly, very slowly, bewildered by the depth of her
emotional response, she watched him return to sanity
again. His body relaxed, muscle by muscle and now she
knew every one of them.

They lay entwined, bathed in sweat, and he languor-
ously licked her with his tongue, letting it rasp on her skin
so that she shivered. Then he caught her in his arms and
held her tightly as if he never wanted her to be separated
from him.

'Tiffany,' he whispered, 'I make no apologies. We both
needed each other. We were made to be bound together
for all time. I've never made love like that before.'

She was too indolent to speak. He cradled her in his
arms like a child and she nestled up, bemused and spent.

'I knew it would be like this,' he murmured, stroking
the sun-gold of her hair. 'The moment I saw you. The
moment your eyes flashed at me. And when I saw your
body...' He kissed her forehead. 'It was inevitable, wasn't
it?' he mused. 'That we should possess each other.'

Tiffany lay supine, letting him caress her lightly, her
mind a blank, not daring to think, her body as still and

her brain as emotionally battered as if it lay in the aftermath of a storm.

Mutely, she let him carry her to a rose-scented bath, and she shared it with him. He soaped her body, gently, tenderly, adoringly.

'Hassan—'

He stopped her mouth with a light kiss.

'Forgive me,' he said in a low voice. 'If I hurt you, if I frightened you, it was because I always knew how completely you would captivate me. I still feel anger for that. No one rules me, no one. I understand why Nazim had to love you.'

'He didn't,' she said, her tremulous mouth parted. 'Not in a normal way. Oh, Hassan!' she lifted her arms to him and he wrapped himself and then her in bath robes and led her back to the bedroom, lifting her shaking body on to the bed. She couldn't bear his gentleness.

'What is it?' he asked gruffly, cradling her in his arms. 'Do you still think you yearn for him? Or can you admit that at least you feel a powerful emotion for me?'

'I-I—desire you,' she said hesitantly.

'No. It's more than that,' he said fervently, murmuring against her hair. 'There's a deeper feeling, isn't there?' he coaxed. 'Admit it.'

'No,' she said, reluctant to accept that she felt anything more than a sexual attraction for him. Anything else was impossible.

'Something has drawn us together, overcome all our hate and gone beyond it. Whether we like it or not, you are my life's blood, Tiffany. And I am yours.'

'I don't want—'

'Neither do I,' he growled. 'But it's useless denying our feelings. Fate has tied us together, and we are helpless in its path.'

'How can I trust you?' she cried piteously. 'I want to believe—'

'We have just been honest with each other,' he said softly. 'Our bodies have told us what we will learn one day to be true. Giving yourself to someone makes you vulnerable, Tiffany. I don't lightly trust myself with a woman—not as I did with you. Believe that. The rest will come in time.'

Her soft grey eyes kindled at the gentleness in his face. Her heart wept in hope. Wordlessly, she lifted up her arms and he held her very tightly. When they parted, her eyes were filled with emotional tears.

'I can't,' she whispered. 'I daren't.'

'Can't…love me?'

'Hassan—I don't know what to think. I—'

'Let your body and your heart speak,' he husked, kissing away her tears.

'I'm so confused,' she mumbled. 'There's something inside me I want to reach and I can't find it.'

'I know,' he said, in a choking rasp. *'I know.'*

They lay together, curled into one another, talking. Tiffany felt released from her defences, stunned that they could share confidences and dreams so easily. And even more surprised that Hassan seemed prepared to be patient, to wait until she felt secure and could trust him.

That wasn't yet. Soon she would have to start asking him to explain his actions about Abdul, and she was subconsciously putting off that moment. Her dreams might disappear like sifting sand.

'Are you hungry?' he asked softly.

She widened her eyes and opened her bruised mouth in alarm. But he laughed, his grin dazzling her and making her heart lurch.

'No, sweetheart,' he said. 'Later. I wondered if you wanted some dinner.'

She sat up in horror. 'Faridah! She rang—'

'Yes.' Hassan grinned at her disarmingly. 'I fear she'll be putting two and two together.'

'Oh, no!' moaned Tiffany, her body flushing a soft pink.

Hassan bent and kissed as much of it as he could reach, while she tried to push him away, grumbling gently.

'Don't worry,' he murmured. 'We'll just have to tell her straight away what has happened.'

'She'll be upset… She does love you.'

He laughed. 'No.'

'She does,' insisted Tiffany. 'That's why she's been wary of me ever since I arrived.'

'No. It's because you married the man she loved,' he said gently. 'Nazim. You won his heart.'

Tiffany was silent, wondering what to say. Faridah had lost Nazim, and now it must appear that she was about to lose Hassan too. All because of a blonde Englishwoman. It wasn't surprising that there was hate in Faridah's eyes. Had the woman deliberately misled her?

'This has changed everything, though,' continued Hassan softly, kissing Tiffany's nose. His lips brushed the full softness of her mouth and she trembled. 'We can't live together in this house for long without everyone finding out what we're doing each night. We must get Josef here immediately, and be married as fast as possible.'

She felt a chill settle within her. 'Don't rush me—'

His smile vanished. 'You agreed. Surely you must see we need to hurry the ceremony along? After all,' he said, his voice becoming agonisingly husky, 'you could already be carrying my child.'

CHAPTER SEVEN

TIFFANY felt the ice move down her spine. Their love-making had been so urgent, so impossible to stop, that she hadn't considered taking precautions, and neither had he.

And now he sounded so keen to get Josef into his power. How could she believe that he was being honest with her? What if he'd deliberately made love to her, so that she was bound to him—as she had been with Nazim? Oh, God! Had she led herself into a trap? Exactly the same one as his brother had laid for her? How could she be so stupid?

She had no reason to trust him, and every reason to be suspicious. Hassan now had what he wanted: her sexual submission. With that, he would soon manipulate the situation so that he also had Josef in the palm of his hand.

'It's all right, Tiffany,' Hassan was saying. 'I'll deal with Faridah. Don't shake like that. It'll be all right. I'll go down now and talk to her. I'll send up some supper for you, and be up later. I want to sleep with you, tonight,' he purred, his hands threading through her soft hair.

The sensually sweet brush of his mouth and hands induced a drowsy liquidity on her sensitised flesh, slow ripples of warmth making her shiver.

'I think I'd better go,' he said in a bemused voice. 'Before Faridah comes up here.'

'Hassan!' she said hoarsely, her eyes huge.

'Mmm?'

She struggled to sit up and he made a low, male growling sound in his throat.

'Go!' she pleaded.

He sighed and moved away, dressing quickly, her heart beating fast to see his superb body. She wanted to touch him, and when he turned he saw that and smiled, making her heart ache.

'Tell me you want me and then I'll go,' he said, in a voice harsh with tension.

The words hurtled out, wild and tormented. *'I want you!'* Oh, she moaned inside, the unfairness of it all!

'Yes,' he said, his eyes a blazing jet. 'Oh, yes. Wait for me. Hold on. I'll be there.'

Without a backward glance, he strode hastily from the room.

She ate a little supper when it arrived. However distraught she was, Hassan's lovemaking had sapped her strength and Tiffany must have slept, for when she woke she was still lying on the bed, totally naked, and Hassan lay beside her, caressing her body, the darkness of his skin contrasting with hers. He smiled.

'Please don't touch me,' she whispered.

'Sleepy?' He gave an indulgent laugh and curled her body into his. Immediately she felt safe in his strong arms. Safe! How wrong could her instincts be?

'Relax,' he crooned. 'You're as tense as a high wire. I'm perfectly capable of sleeping with you and not making love. There's more to a relationship than that.'

'Trust,' she quavered.

'Ah. Yes.' His mouth murmured against her temple. 'I can wait for that. It's a small word but has a huge meaning. I can't deny that I'm unsure of your motives. Still, you were young when you married Nazim and became pregnant. I can understand how you resented being tied down.'

She blinked, upset at his arrogance. She'd meant that she didn't trust *him*!

She lay very still for a long time before she spoke, knowing how important this was. Her first chance to clear her character in his eyes.

'You want the truth, you'll get it,' she said bitterly. 'I'll tell you about Nazim. I met him when I was eighteen. I was emotionally young. When you train for the ballet, you have no time for boyfriends. I was pitifully ripe for his attentions and his domination. We met at a dance, in the School of Oriental and African Studies where I was doing a course in oriental design. He came as a guest of one of the tutors. I let him drive me home and he stopped the car in a dark spot to kiss me.'

'That's enough. I don't want to hear what you did with him.'

Hassan had rolled over. She stared miserably at his back.

'You have to,' she cried. 'God! I don't want to talk about this! But you must know the kind of man your brother was and the kind of woman I am!'

'Tiffany,' he said urgently, turning to face her again, pain etched in the lines of his hard mouth. 'I refuse to listen to your account of his courtship.'

'Courtship?' She let out a rasping laugh. 'Nazim only knew about having sex,' she said tightly. 'Not love. Not romance, or courting.'

Hassan's eyes narrowed. 'What do you mean? I thought—Tiffany! Tell me!' he demanded roughly.

'He seemed to imagine that, because I'd let him kiss me, he could go on from there as far as he wanted, as if I'd given him unlimited permission. I didn't know that by giving in to his pleas to touch me I was storing up trouble for myself,' she said bitterly. 'I couldn't stop him, Hassan. He was like a maniac…' She gulped and Hassan enfolded her in his arms, soothing her shaking body.

'He all but raped me,' she said harshly. 'I called out but no one came. It was late in the evening and no one was around. He took what he wanted. He said I'd driven him to it, that I'd enticed him with my body—the way I'd danced with him, swaying, with my hair falling over my eyes, the way I walked past him, the way I provocatively lifted my breasts when speaking passionately about something…I didn't know! I swear I didn't!'

He stared into her eyes, and she wished she knew what he was seeing there. Could he recognise her anguish?

'Did he touch you again?' he asked grimly.

'No. I made sure of that. But he kept pestering me, day in, day out. And then I discovered I was pregnant.'

'And?'

'I told my mother and she found his address and went straight to him, saying he had to marry me or he'd be in trouble. It wasn't my idea—'

'But you married him,' growled Hassan.

'I didn't want to! At first he was angry. He came to my home and we had a blazing row. That's when he struck me and I fell down the stairs. But the fact that I nearly lost my baby changed Nazim—and me. We were both appalled. He felt terribly responsible and did, at least, care about our baby. He visited me in hospital and…well, we both really wanted our child. He seemed so devoted, so sorry—I thought he loved me.' She bit her lip, speaking in an almost incoherent babble, desperate to convince him. 'I had to believe in his love. Mother made it clear that I was guilty of immorality and lack of control. I could hardly forgive myself. There were flowers and chocolates, and he was gentle, Hassan, kind and thoughtful. And I wanted the best for my child. He said love would grow, that we'd make a fresh start. I was young, with no qualifications and a repressive mother. I couldn't bear the idea of bringing up a child under those conditions. Nazim was very persuasive in the picture he painted.'

Hassan gently stroked her hair, his eyes dark.

'Nazim was always persuasive. I must remind you, though, that he said in his letter that you hated being pregnant.'

'I hated being constantly sick. I hated living in a one-room bedsit. I hated the discovery that I'd made a terrible mistake about Nazim. Because once we were married, he didn't have to bother to be nice to me and we quarrelled incessantly. He wanted my body and didn't care if I felt like making love or not. Sometimes he was so rough that I was afraid for the child within me. You must believe me, Hassan; I continued with my studies because I could see that one day I'd need to support myself and my child—and maybe Nazim too. We were already in debt from his extravagance.'

A frown crossed his face. 'I can't recall that flaw in his character as a young man,' he said in an accusing tone.

'You don't believe me,' she moaned, twisting away.

He brought her back to him, holding her so that she was forced to look into his relentless, questioning eyes.

'You have to tell me your side of it,' he said, his face cold.

'Hassan,' she said in an impassioned voice, 'Nazim had everything he wanted, living with you and your father. Money could buy everything. Maybe when he left and had to manage on his own, he found it hard because he'd never been taught to budget. He really had no idea about keeping accounts and paying bills promptly. We lived well above our means because he'd deny himself nothing. What he wanted, he had. Including me,' she said bitterly.

'Let's get some sleep,' muttered Hassan. 'I find it painful in the extreme to think of my brother making love to you.'

'He never did,' she said in a small voice. 'Not love. He never did.'

For a moment, Tiffany thought he was going to take her in his arms. But then darkness shuttered his face and killed all expression.

'I have possessed your body,' he said quietly. 'I'm not sure I'll ever possess more. My relationship with Nazim is too close, isn't it?'

'I can't be sure if you're like him,' she whispered, her eyes rounded in distress.

He shrugged. 'Then you must find out. It will be enough to begin with—to have you as a wife, for us to know that Josef has a bright future, and that we can find pleasure in bed together. More may come, but we can't expect it, Tiffany.'

'Why am I destined to make loveless marriages?' she cried.

'Go to sleep,' he muttered.

She lay for hours, staring miserably at the great breadth of his back, the golden skin shining in the moonlight which filtered through the carved shutters. Her eyes travelled down his spine and across the wide shoulders. He lay very still, hardly breathing.

Her brilliant plan to allay his suspicions had probably worked. But at a terrible cost to herself. She'd virtually offered herself as a sacrifice. How it had happened, she didn't know, but whenever he came near all sense disappeared, to be replaced by a helpless surrender, as if destiny was telling her that this was the man she must devote herself to whether it destroyed her or not.

In the early morning, while it was still dark, they woke and made love, exploring, plundering, savouring each other's bodies. And it was tearing her apart, inch by inch, breaking her as he had sworn he would if she played false.

Later, as dawn tinged the room with blushing gold, she stroked his rosy-hued face, her mind drifting in all directions. It was as if they were already married and Jo was next door, and at breakfast he and Hassan would fill the house with laughter.

'Thinking of last night?' Hassan murmured, his hand reaching out to stroke her thigh.

She blushed, reminded of her abandon. He chuckled and leapt out of bed, striding to the shower.

When he whirled around and caught her admiring his perfect body, he grinned. Tiffany lowered her lashes.

'I was thinking of Jo,' she said quietly. 'How you made him laugh on the phone yesterday...' Her voice trailed away, wistful. He was wonderful with Jo.

'You miss him very much, don't you?' he said, coming over and taking her in his arms.

She looked up at him, pleading that he'd believe her.

'Yes, I do! Terribly! I want...' There was a catch in her voice. 'I want to be with him again.'

'It won't be long. A couple of days.'

He tucked her head into his smooth shoulder and rocked her gently, stroking her hair. Tiffany felt a wonderful feeling of peace. It filled her with anguish to think that she might soon be running away from Hassan. Very soon; it had to be. Or could she stay? Her head ached with her see-sawing decisions. She'd never been indecisive before. Hassan had reduced her to this. He'd taken away all her strength.

'Be patient,' he continued, murmuring in her ear. 'Life waits for us as a family together. Standing on touchlines, yelling ourselves hoarse, skiing in Switzerland or Morocco, lazing on a yacht off the coast of Zanzibar, coping with Josef's taste in music when he has birthday parties—'

'You make it sound wonderful,' she said shakily, wishing that the world he described could belong to her. Inside, a small voice was telling her that it could, torturing her remorselessly.

'It will be. We've grown above our misunderstandings and hate, Tiffany. You've seen a little of the way I am, day by day. I couldn't pay my staff to behave towards me as they do. I must have some redeeming features for them to be at ease with me, mustn't I?' He smiled.

'I can't understand why you want to take on Josef and me.'

His hands cupped the sides of her face and he gazed at her long and tenderly.

'Losing my brother was hard enough,' he said. 'My father never fully recovered from the shock. But at least I can make everything straight again, and ensure Josef carries on the Sharif name. And you know why I want to "take you on" as you so romantically put it,' he teased.

'Why did Nazim leave?' she asked.

That was the key to all of this. Instinctively she knew that it would explain something of her late husband's character and behaviour, and throw light on Hassan himself.

His lashes dropped to hide the wary light in his eyes.

'I can't answer that. I dislike having secrets from you, but someone else will have to tell you the reason, not me. And somehow I doubt that you'll ever know. I can't risk causing distress to another person who is an essential part of my life.'

'Faridah.' She looked at him hopelessly, torn with jealousy.

Seeing that she trembled uncontrollably, he abruptly removed his hands from her face and moved to the shower.

'Faridah does mean something to you, doesn't she?' cried Tiffany piteously. 'Oh, God! How can I bear this?'

'Faridah is my cousin and under my protection because I'm the oldest living male relative,' he said stiffly. 'I can't discuss her business.'

'Not even with me? Not even if it's partly *your* business?' she cried angrily.

His head went up. 'I'm going down to breakfast in a few minutes. Join me there if you want to.'

Tiffany couldn't. She stayed immobile while Hassan showered, dressed and went out.

Her mind kept vacillating, tormenting her with memories of Hassan's lovemaking and persuading her that they could have a marvellous life, the three of them.

Abdul had the first claim on the Sharif name and fortune—far more than she or Josef. In fact, she didn't care if she had nothing other than Hassan himself and Jo.

Confused, she slipped down to the garden, hoping to find some mental space to think. But she found Hassan sitting gloomily on a seat, his head in his hands. Her heart went out to him. He looked so miserable, so haunted, and when he saw her compassionate face his expression of joy burned so deep into her soul that she knew she had already fallen in love with him and everything was too late to be stopped.

She was his, body and soul, heart and mind.

His past was not important. Only their future.

He held out his arms in a pleading gesture and she gave

a low moan and ran into them. For a long time they didn't move, but held each other tightly as if afraid a small part would escape and not be included in the fervent expression of love and need.

'I want to tell you, sweetheart,' he whispered to her. 'But I can't. I'll speak to Faridah. I'll tell her it's coming between us.'

'No. I think she's been hurt enough,' said Tiffany, her eyes shining with unshed tears. 'And, in any case, I think I needed that time to myself. I came to a decision.'

Slowly he drew back, his face anxious. 'Go on.'

She was about to tell him that she loved him, to pour out all her feelings and put herself completely at his mercy. But the sound of Faridah's voice cut through the still air like a knife and thrust into her heart.

'Tell me,' urged Hassan.

'Not now—'

'Damn! Over here, Faridah!' he yelled in an angry tone. 'What the hell is it?'

'A phone call. Urgent. From Marcia,' she said coldly, eyeing Tiffany up and down.

'I must go. I've been expecting this. It could take some time. Meet you at noon to chat to Josef.' Hassan gave her a quick kiss on the lips, and followed it with a helpless, more lingering one.

Tiffany clutched at him, not wanting him to go. Faridah gloomily watched him stride away and then sat down beside her.

'He has us all in the palm of his hand,' she muttered. 'He runs our lives and we hardly know he's doing so.'

'I'm sorry if my presence—'

'You'll be sorry, if you don't get away,' Faridah burst out.

A nameless fear raised the hairs on the back of

Tiffany's neck. 'Are you threatening me?' she asked, her eyes worried.

'I? Threaten? My God! You've got more to worry about than a mere jealous woman! Oh, yes, I'm jealous. I don't deny that. I love Hassan. I've known him for years and you walk into his life and into his bed in a matter of moments.'

'Oh, Faridah! It isn't quite like that—'

'Your morals aren't my concern. Hassan is a healthy man and took what was on offer.'

'No—'

'You think there's any other reason? I pity you!' scathed Faridah. 'More, I pity your son and the danger you place him in.'

'What?' she cried, alerted by the woman's genuine fear.

'Oh, for goodness' sake!' cried Faridah impatiently. 'Pull yourself together! Hassan has softened your brain. I suppose he pretended he was going to marry you?'

'Pretended? He…what do you mean? Why do you say that?' demanded Tiffany.

'He's spoken for. I told you that, but you wouldn't listen. It's a long-standing arrangement,' said Faridah.

'But he said—'

Tiffany stopped, aghast. How could he have denied the existence of the arrangement? Faridah must be lying.

'He's not likely to admit it, if he wants to get you into bed, is he?' scathed Faridah. 'He won't touch me, of course, till our wedding day. Think; you've got a brain. Is he likely to marry his brother's wife, a used woman? He'll visualise Nazim's hands on you every time he looks at you. Besides, you're English and have a questionable reputation. He used you to sate his hunger because he couldn't approach me. I'm not that kind of woman.

You're different. He's making the most of you, while you're around and so easily available.'

'Using me?' she repeated faintly.

'Of course. You've underestimated him. A disastrous mistake where you're concerned. He's been enjoying your sexual favours and blinding you to his real intentions.'

'Are you suggesting that he's been deliberately allaying my suspicions?' Tiffany laughed incredulously. That had been *her* plan! It was too ludicrous for words!

'He succeeded, didn't he? All your anger, all the fight has gone out of you. You're putty in his hands. He can do anything he likes with you now. Soon you will innocently invite Josef here, and that'll be the end of him.'

She went cold, unable to move, searching Faridah's face. It was remorseless.

'The end?' she whispered, suddenly petrified.

Faridah's face twisted savagely, making her look ugly. 'There will be an accident,' she grated. 'I know it. How else will he make sure your son doesn't live to make any claims on the business?'

Tiffany began to shake. 'Doesn't live? An accident? But—Faridah, you can't mean…no, no,' she moaned.

Faridah was talking about the man who'd made passionate love to her, who'd shared the days in friendship, looked at her with loving eyes. Lying eyes. Lying hands, mouth, fingers…

'See sense,' said Faridah. 'He wants you out of the way. And your son. He has other plans.'

Tiffany's head jerked up. 'Oh, my God!' she whispered. 'Abdul!' she cried wildly.

'What?' snapped Faridah, her eyes narrowed.

'Abdul! I know of his existence, you can't deny it! Abdul al Sharif. He's Hassan's illegitimate son, isn't he? Are you his mother? You must tell me!'

Faridah looked taken aback. Slowly she nodded.

'Abdul. Yes. How did you find out?'

'I heard Hassan talking on the phone about your son,' croaked Tiffany. 'He's planning to switch some of his US holdings to Abdul. And I suppose Josef is a problem because he stands in Abdul's way.'

A slow smile spread over Faridah's face. 'How generous he is! Oh, yes,' she nodded. 'How clever of you to find out. Yes. Abdul is the reason for all this. Hassan directs all his passion towards getting what he wants, as you know.' She ran her eyes insultingly over Tiffany's body.

'He wouldn't stoop to hurt Jo! It isn't true, say it isn't true,' cried Tiffany desperately.

'As you please,' shrugged Faridah, standing up to go. 'Be it on your own head. Does it sound likely that he intends to marry you and let your son inherit, when Abdul can do so? If you don't come to your senses, it'll be too late. You'll have a dead child on your hands.'

'*Dead!* Oh, my God! Wait!' Tiffany's legs shook so much from terror that she couldn't stand, but was reduced to sitting helplessly and pleading with Faridah with her eyes. 'Help me,' she begged. 'Help me to escape from this terrible nightmare! Help me to leave this place and find some sanity!'

Triumph flared in Faridah's face. 'You want to leave?'

'Yes! Now!' cried Tiffany wildly. 'I must get back to Josef at once; I don't ever want to see Hassan again, to hear his voice, to feel…' Her voice broke and it was several seconds before she could continue in a desolate, bleak tone. 'I must get away before Hassan shames me any more. I have to prevent him from holding me here as a hostage and blackmailing me to get Josef over to Riyam. Please, Faridah! It's in your own interest to help me!'

'It is. I need you out of the way too,' she acknowledged sharply. 'Tonight. Meet me in the garden after midnight. I'll show you where to find a camel,' she offered. 'I'll bring food and water for you. All I can do is point you in the right direction. I daren't do more. I'm afraid of his anger. Well?'

'Please,' mumbled Tiffany, swaying with the enormity of what she was about to do. 'How safe is it, in the desert?' she asked, in a dry, ragged voice. 'How will I know where to go?'

'Stick to the trail,' said Faridah. 'He'll be tied up tomorrow, with his legal officer who's flown in from America. If you can keep him out of your bed tonight and escape, then it'll be ages before he notices you're gone. And then you'll be safe.'

'Why not now?' urged Tiffany, her eyes huge. She couldn't face a whole day and then evening here with her son's potential murderer. And if she had time to think of the terror of the desert journey, she might never make it.

'Because if you didn't come down to dinner, he'd notice you were missing, you fool,' said Faridah scornfully.

'Oh, yes. Of course.' Tiffany's brain seemed to be filled with a dense fog. 'Faridah, I can't spend the evening with him.'

'You have to,' she said in a hard tone. 'He must never suspect. Don't you think he'll be wary if you avoid him? Don't you realise he'll come up to see you, and maybe take advantage of you again if you're lying on the bed pretending to be ill?'

Tiffany let out a sigh of utter despair. 'I can't pretend—'

'For the sake of your child, you will. You must let him think nothing's wrong,' snapped Faridah.

In fact, Tiffany was able to spend the day alone. Hassan

had sent someone to meet Marcia who had arrived at Shirbat airport and they both stayed in his office, working on papers and taking lunch there.

Shortly before dinner, with Tiffany once again steeling herself to get dressed and face Hassan with a bright mask, Faridah came to her room, carrying a tray.

'I thought you might need a drink,' she said.

'Damn right I do,' muttered Tiffany, taking a good gulp. Faridah laughed at her expression when the alcohol hit her throat. 'What is that?' croaked Tiffany, feeling as if she'd swallowed neat turpentine.

'Local brew. It's OK. It'll give you courage.'

'It'll give me a sore throat.'

'Drink,' insisted Faridah. 'It'll relax you. Tonight you've got to make sure Hassan really believes he's landed you in his net. And then you've got to stop him sleeping with you. Can you manage that?'

Tiffany took another cautious drink and felt her stomach warm and her courage grow stronger. Faridah was eyeing the neat blue suit on the bed with distaste and strode over to Tiffany's wardrobe, pushing back hanger after hanger as she assessed the clothes inside.

'Be a sexy ice-maiden. You've got the face for it.'

She threw the strapless black sheath on to the bed.

'There's a jacket I wear with that—' began Tiffany. She sat down. The drink was paralysing her legs.

'Wear it without. Don't you see? If you look seductive and yet rebuff his advances, he'll realise you're not going to be easily dominated.'

Tiffany passed a hand over her head. She didn't understand the logic. Her brain buzzed.

'Wouldn't it be better if I wore something demure?' she puzzled.

'Do as I say. You're in no fit state to think straight.

This is a much more subtle method. He won't suspect anything this way. Get it on. If necessary, I'll keep him from slipping up to your room, but it'll be better if you can cool him down yourself.'

Faridah stayed to help the dazed Tiffany get ready and made sure she went down the stairs to the salon. Tiffany didn't know what she was doing, only that she felt numb with cold and terror. Soon she'd be travelling across a hostile desert. She was mad. But desperate.

Hassan, in a dinner-jacket, was talking to a curly-haired blonde woman wearing an elegant green silk suit. Suddenly Tiffany felt cheap in her dress, and gazed down on the considerable swell of her breasts and deep cleavage in dismay. What was she doing? Why had she listened to Faridah? The woman's motives couldn't be entirely innocent.

It was too late. Hassan had turned at the woman's surprise at the sight of Tiffany and his startled look was overlaid with a predatory hunger which made Tiffany melt within as if her bones flowed.

He made the introductions and she was aware of his eyes on her, piercing into her muddled brain.

'Marcia, would you excuse us for a moment? Tiffany and I have a quick arrangement to make,' he said smoothly. 'Please make yourself comfortable in the salon. I'll be in shortly.'

'Sure,' smiled Marcia. 'I'll wait for you there.'

At Hassan's steady, serious gaze, Tiffany swayed a little and clutched at a curtain for support. Then she felt his iron grip on her arm and she was being hustled into an ante-room, her body strangely unresponsive and heavy. She stumbled and he drew her up roughly.

His curse made her flinch and widen her eyes.

'Say something,' he rasped, his face close to hers.

'What? Hassan—'

'I thought so!' He frowned. 'You've been drinking! What the hell has happened? And for God's sake, what on earth made you appear half-naked tonight?'

She tried to shrink away from him, but he pulled her to his body ruthlessly.

'Am I now beginning to see the real Tiffany Sharif?' he asked. 'Are you truly a loose, sex-loving, promiscuous woman? After all, you haven't yet explained away Mike to my satisfaction.'

'Mike?' She tried to remember who he was, her mouth pouting in effort.

The grip on her arm tightened. 'So many men you can't remember? You've got me so I don't know what I'm doing! I hardly know what to believe about you, only that you throw out a carnal challenge to me which I can't resist.'

His head bent to her high rising breasts, his hands pulling down her precarious top, and she threw back her head and let out a groan. It was unbearable to have him hating her like this, but it helped her to keep control of herself.

What had Faridah said? Stop him sleeping with you tonight. Inspiration leapt into her mind.

'Don't touch me,' she said in a voice of loathing. 'I've tried to forget him, but I can't. Every time you made love to me, he was in my thoughts. It was he whom I held in my arms, who kissed me, not you.'

Hassan had let her go, and she felt his heavy breath rasping through his bared teeth.

'He?' he whispered hoarsely.

She fixed slightly glazed eyes on him. 'Why do you think I got a little tipsy tonight? I can't carry on unless I obliterate my conscious mind. He. Nazim.'

'You said that you hated him, that he raped you—'

'How else could I get your sympathy?' she asked recklessly.

There was a deathly silence. Tiffany couldn't bear to look at his ashen face, drained of life.

'I've got a headache,' she muttered. 'I'll give dinner a miss.'

'Wait.'

Racked by the anguish in his voice, she tried to understand why it should be there. This was the man who wanted to harm Josef. Yet it seemed he had really felt affection for her. Had Faridah been wrong? If only her brain wasn't so fuzzy!

'Go up to your room and stay there,' he said coldly.

'You won't come—'

'No,' he whispered. 'I never want to touch you again. You've caused me too much heartache, Tiffany. You were right. I will never be sure if you're faking or not. You cold bitch!' His hand thudded down hard on a table, making everything on it jump, and she cowered back a little.

'I suppose you want me to leave in the morning,' she said as casually as possible. Hope and despair battled within her. She might not have to go the hard way. He might send her packing himself. How could she want that and feel so miserable at the same time?

'Leave?' he snarled. 'When I don't have Josef? Oh, no. The situation is as it stood when you first arrived. I want my nephew and I'll go to any lengths now to get him. You stay here. The difference is that I won't marry you. Instead, I'll take my revenge on you for the way you've treated me by attacking you where it will hurt most.'

She met his glittering eyes with a terror-stricken look.

'Not Jo!'

He smiled a slow, cynical smile.

'I won't be beaten by a conniving, deceiving whore,'
he said softly.

Swaying, she struggled for strength. Damn Faridah and
her whisky! With a few shreds of dignity, she tipped up
her head and carefully put one foot in front of the other,
till she had left the room. The die had been cast. She
would escape from this living hell.

Upstairs, she stripped off the black sheath and crawled
into bed, shaking, waiting. The hours dragged. Near midnight, she dressed with fumbling, trembling fingers, putting on the green tunic and trousers and picking up the
chador.

The garden rustled with sounds of the night and a light,
whispering breeze. She sat on a bench and waited. A small
lizard ran splay-footed near her listless hand. This beautiful garden, this lovely house, would be denied Josef.
And Hassan—the only man, she knew, who could ever
rouse her to such heights of passion—was to be denied
her. A sob broke from her lips.

She wanted him; she had loved him. She wanted to
repeat that wonderful moment when passion had been
spent and they lay in each other's arms, cradled tenderly,
as if they loved one another.

'Come.'

She jumped at Faridah's sharp voice. Casually they
strolled past servants as if going for a night-time stroll,
and through the main gates to the camel park. Faridah
gave some money to the man and they helped Tiffany on,
packing food and water into the panniers.

'It's only a few hours,' said Faridah. 'Go! Hurry!'

She slapped the animal on the rump. It lurched up and
Tiffany made herself secure in the saddle, her heart in her
mouth. She pulled on the reins, following the direction of

the man's pointing finger, along a well-marked trail into the night.

After a little while she felt confident that she could handle the swaying movement and urged the animal into a shambling trot.

She had no idea how long it would be before Hassan discovered she was missing. She'd have to get out of Riyam fast and lie low for some time. For one thing was certain—all hell would be let loose.

Uncomfortably, she joggled on the camel's back, every rangy, loping stride taking her nearer to Josef and further from the rapacious Hassan.

Dawn filtered the sky with rose, red and purple. Soon the hard light of day beat down and she slowed the camel to a walk as the warm sun warmed her bones.

But almost immediately, the camel started snorting and bellowing, tossing its head alarmingly, and it was all she could do to keep her balance. A sixth sense made her turn around.

The sky was an unusual colour. A band of bright yellow stained the horizon, far to the north, on her left. It wasn't the dawn. She frowned, wondering.

Small spirals of sand twirled and coiled in the distance, like miniature whirlwinds. An uncanny sensation crept down her spine. The minute tornados were too tiny to harm her, but the air seemed to be tense, as if holding its breath, and she felt oddly nervous and jittery.

Thunder rolled in the south, where the sky glowered with dark navy thunderclouds. Tiffany eyed them anxiously and drove the jumpy camel onwards at a furious pace, clinging to the saddle for dear life.

The light grew dim and the air thickened, increasing in density and temperature until she was fighting for breath in a wall of suffocating heat. The sky had become an eerie yellow ahead, but she thought she had to continue, to avoid the thunderstorm. She looked up as a chill settled over her and discovered that the sun had disappeared. It had been obliterated by the yellow sky.

A bitter cold and damp wind swept over her, freezing every inch of her body. And it was then that she realised what was happening.

Her stomach lurched. Nausea clawed in her throat.

A brown wall of dust was coming towards her, closing with a petrifying speed. Amid the vast emptiness, she felt frighteningly alone, nothing more than a tiny, lone figure, a minute speck in the vast desert, easily swept away by any capricious force of nature. The cloud rolled inexorably on, and now she heard a mind-numbing wailing and grinding—the noise of sand being picked up and forced into the billowing blanket.

It was a sandstorm, and it was coming straight for her.

The years of self-discipline as a dancer, and of fighting for survival when Nazim had left her, came to her rescue. Her natural reaction was to fight trouble, especially as Josef was far away, depending on her.

People didn't die in sandstorms. They became lost if they went off course. She must keep her head, and when it became too difficult to carry on she must dismount and hang on to the camel's reins so they weren't parted. It was her lifeline.

Her terrified eyes never left the great column of swirling sand. It grew every second, whisking up small stunted trees and bushes in its path, and she could see them being hurled into the air. Panic rose within her.

Josef. Her beloved son. She had to come out of this for his sake! *Hassan!* Oh, dear God, she'd loved him! She'd needed him to live, as a dying man needed water. Without him, she would be only half a woman.

Her emotions were one turbulent storm, wrenching her apart by the violence of intense feelings which would never be calmed, but would blind her cruelly to any other man's affection, wearing down her spirit like rasping sand until she was left raw and wounded. Hassan was destroying her. And here, in this terrible desert, the sandstorm was finishing the job.

The camel balked beneath her, tossing its head, bellowing in rage. It wanted to go in the opposite direction and Tiffany had to force it to stay on the right path. Gently she urged it to kneel, intending to shelter and trusting in its instincts. It was built to withstand conditions like this. Didn't it have extra eyelids? Or was it some kind of special nostril? she thought wildly.

The animal wouldn't kneel. Frantically, weeping with frustration, yelling out loud, she pulled on the reins.

And then, over the roar of the fast-approaching cloud, she heard the unbelievable, wonderful sound of an engine.

Turning, the wind tearing away the shawl over her head so that her hair was whipped into stinging lashes over her face, she saw a green truck driving hell for leather towards her. She held up the shawl and let it stream in the wind like a banner. The camel folded its legs under and she slipped out of the saddle, still clutching the reins and her banner.

Then her hand faltered. The truck was by now close enough for her to recognise the dark head which was thrust out of the window. Only one man could have that same broad face and sweep of forehead, the terrible, glittering fury.

Hassan was driving fast, and with such hatred on his face that she drew back against the camel's flank.

The material slipped from her frozen fingers and disappeared in a trice with the icy wind. The truck stalled and he cursed loudly. He was angry. Violently angry. And Faridah had warned her of his vengeance.

The truck started again. Her hair was half-blinding her as she fumbled for the saddle, hoping to mount, running like a frightened rabbit from the man who was almost upon her, and shouting at the top of his voice. He was merciless and single-minded. He would stop at nothing.

CHAPTER EIGHT

TERROR blocking her mind, Tiffany fumbled with the reins, trying to mount in the teeth of the fierce eddies which brought stinging sand to blast into her face and the corners of her mouth. She shut her eyes tightly.

A strong gust buffeted her and she fell, only to scream with panic at the hard jolt of Hassan's body against hers. Grains of grit lashed into her mouth, half choking her. She struggled, but her endurance had been tested to the limit and she could fight no more.

Hassan dragged her roughly over the ground and pushed her into the truck in a bundle of limp arms and legs. The door slammed. The merciless sandpaper gale ceased and she felt soft leather against her back and thighs and a blessed warmth.

'You fool! You stupid fool!' roared Hassan.

She turned her face away, but he caught her head and made her look at him. She blinked to free her lashes from sand and gagged on the grit in her mouth. He reached behind him and drew a soft cloth over her face, delicately sweeping sand from her hair, brows and lashes, grimly tipping her head back and tousling her hair so that no more grains would fall on her face.

'Why?' he barked, his finger and thumb gripping her chin so hard that she cried out.

'Because I know what you feel about me!' she cried hysterically.

The truck rocked alarmingly, battered by a blast of

wind. An involuntary scream escaped from Tiffany's lips and Hassan half crushed her in his arms.

'Don't touch me!' she said, cringing.

The wind-borne sand screeched across the dark green paintwork of the truck like an electrical sander. Hassan ignored her attempts to avoid him and drew her down beneath him.

Her body was plastered against his as violent gusts lashed the windscreen, scraping it with a terrifying sound. She spoke, but didn't hear her own voice. The wind was roaring louder than she could yell.

Protest was useless. They were trapped there together and when the storm ended he would make sure she returned. Or he might leave her there to die. Her brain cleared for a moment. Why hadn't he done that? Why not leave her outside?

A rush of pebbles fell on the roof and bonnet, for all the world as if they were knocking to come in. The noise of the shower deafened her. She let her arms creep around Hassan's neck and his embrace tightened. Shifting his position, he moved so that his entire body protected hers and he was lying across her. His cheek lay against hers, their mouths a mere movement of the head away. Tiffany's lashes fluttered, signalling her agitation.

Hassan's eyes slanted over to hers.

The pounding of her heart sounded as loud to her as the roar outside. Something heavy careened into the car, making it shudder and bounce on its springs. She screamed soundlessly, her vocal cords paralysed with fear.

Hassan was saying something. She frowned. Then her mouth was covered with warmth—soft, seeping warmth, which calmed her and made her think of other things instead of the danger they were in.

His lips moved away, to leave her bereft. But she felt the racing of his heart against her breast and her pulses quickened in exultation.

Madness! A wild elation was surging through her body; the storm outside and within were somehow merging, making her want to fire off all her energy. And then she realised. He hadn't wanted to kill her, or he would have left her to suffer the sandstorm alone. He wanted her badly enough to drive hell for leather over the desert and save her.

She couldn't quite make it out. The noise outside was too great for her to think clearly. All she knew was that Hassan held her with a fierce, protective tenderness, and although she couldn't hear it she could feel his breath as his voice soothed her.

There was an explanation. She would find it.

The hammering of the pebble storm abated. In its place, accompanied by a sudden rushing sound as if a waterfall hit them, came torrents of thick mud, driving at them in a horizontal brown mass. It drove so hard into the truck that it shuddered with the force and mud splattered through a dozen hairline gaps, covering her face, her hands and arms, all that was exposed. She could feel it clinging to Hassan's body, plastering him in brown sludge in seconds.

A howling wind arose, deafening her, ringing in her ears and through her head till she felt her brain must explode. Nothing, surely, could withstand this relentless beating—neither the truck, nor its occupants. They were certain to die. Any moment now, one of the gusts which perilously rocked the truck would turn it over and batter the vehicle until their bodies were exposed to the merciless storm.

'Hassan!' she yelled. 'I love you!'

She heard nothing. Neither had he. A profound sense of misery engulfed her. She was to die, never to see her son again, clasped in the arms of the man she loved, without settling the misunderstandings between them. To die with a lie on her conscience.

The mockery of the situation lanced through her in a sharp pain. She wouldn't be here if it weren't for Hassan. In discovering—too late—what was really important in her life, she was to be denied the chance to fight for it.

Driving rain sheeted down in a continuous wall of grey lead. Something massive smashed into the windscreen with such a force that they both grabbed each other in shock, gasping at the icy deluge which drenched them in seconds. Hassan desperately tried to cover her completely.

Flicking a narrowed eye at the windscreen, Tiffany saw that a tree had been driven against the truck, buckling the reinforced steel surround of the windscreen and shattering the glass. There was another impact and Hassan's body shuddered and became inert over her.

Her face muffled against his shoulder, she tried to move him, to no avail. The tumult rose to a crescendo. Another onslaught of grit and sand blasted the truck, sweeping it in a violent turbulence which threw them about inside.

Painfully bruised, Tiffany tried to protect Hassan, but he slowly, painfully, reached for her and covered her with his body again, a look of anguish on his face. A feeling of intense relief washed through her, making her whole body weak with joy and relief.

He was alive. She began to sob.

Flesh to flesh, bone to bone, they seemed united against the elements. Two bodies moulded into one, two hearts beating in unison, their lips touching and tasting each laboured breath, sharing a life experience that was theirs alone and bound them to one another more surely than anything else.

Her mouth moved on his and was immediately possessed in a smouldering kiss so fierce that she forgot everything around her—all sound, all fear, all danger. The kiss went on and on, her lips imprinted and branded by a glorious never-ending passion which reached way inside her mind.

'Oh, Tiffany,' he groaned.

She blinked. She'd heard! Hassan lifted himself back a little, the shock showing in his startled eyes.

'It's over,' he said hoarsely. There was a note of despair in his voice. 'It's over,' came the whispered words from his unhappy mouth.

Warily, he twisted around, scowling at his surroundings. Then he pushed himself right up on his arms to the seat beside her and wrenched at the door-handle.

'Be careful!' she cried, unable to stop herself.

He paused, as if she'd hit him, then swung his legs to the ground. After a moment, she followed, stiff and aching. It was an extraordinary scene. A pile of storm-blown debris lay heaped against the truck. The whole vehicle had been laid bare, stripped to naked metal.

'The truck is ruined!' she gasped.

'But we are alive.'

She turned slowly to look at him and he tipped his head back to massage his neck, then fixed her with an intense stare which made the breath catch in her throat.

His face was streaked with caked mud and red dust and she loved him more than she could ever say in words. When his expression became a grimace, she suddenly stared down at her own body. It was filthy. Her hand reached up and touched tangled, caked rats' tails which had once been her golden hair.

The wind dropped. The storm passed and it was as if a veil had lifted. She saw everything with enormous clarity. Everything.

She loved Hassan with a passion that surmounted all barriers.

'We need some water,' he muttered. 'There's some in the truck.'

He poured her a flask and it tasted like champagne. Her eyes sparkled appreciatively, but he didn't return her smiling look. He had tightened his mouth in disapproval.

'You might have been killed,' he rasped. 'Why? For God's sake, why risk your stupid neck by taking a camel into the desert? Am I that repugnant to you? Why the hell didn't you say so in the first place, instead of pretending and giving me the wrong impression?'

It hurt his pride, she thought sadly. He hated being fooled.

'I wanted to escape,' she said, a wistful look in her eyes. Now the storm was over, she found it hard to tell him what she felt. 'I didn't know there would be a sandstorm.'

'You must loathe and fear me very deeply. Come. I'll take you to clean up. Then you can make arrangements to fly to Oman.'

'To Josef?' she cried.

He turned his back on her. 'To Josef.'

There was misery in his body, in every agonised muscle.

'You're giving in?' she asked quietly. 'You've given up what you sought so single-mindedly?'

'I know when I'm beaten,' he grated. 'Follow me.'

She hesitated, then hurried after his dejected figure. Sand and mud had made their way into every part of her, it seemed. She caught up with him.

The ragged-edged sun's strength was weak. It must be late, but somehow the day seemed timeless. And the desert was blooming. Before her eyes, daisies and huge buttercups were spreading bright carpets across sand where once there had been only barren ground. Butterflies appeared from nowhere to take delight in the nodding blooms.

Hassan was taking no pleasure from them. He stopped near a circular whitewashed wall, and when Tiffany drew nearer she could see that a flight of steps led downwards into the ground. He descended and turned to make sure she followed.

'It's a ventilation shaft,' he said tonelessly. 'Only twenty feet down. Can you make it?'

'I'm afraid of nothing after that storm.' She smiled, reaching out her hand.

He ignored it and went on down. Once inside, she found it cool on her hot, caked skin. The steps wound down and finally arrived at a stone platform lit by warm gold light from above. Ahead lay a midnight-black pool, and to one side a pipe emptied into the pool like a miniature waterfall.

'What is this place?' she asked in wonder.

'A *felaj*. An underground aqueduct. Built by the Persians, two thousand years ago.'

'Where does the water come from?'

'Mountain springs. It's cold, but the sun will have warmed it a little.'

He mechanically slipped off his boots and tunic till he

wore only his thin cotton trousers, and dived in as if she didn't exist.

She was annoyed. He spent all his energies in making her lust after him and then switched off! But he'd relented. He was letting her go back to Jo and ending his cruel attempt to dominate her. She could be strong now.

Unless... She caught Hassan's dark, scowling eyes on her and drew back, suddenly afraid.

'Oh, for heaven's sake, Tiffany,' he raged at her, all control gone. 'I'm not going to drown you! Why the hell would I kill someone I love?'

She froze. 'That's cruel,' she whispered.

'Cruel?' he muttered, gripping the side of the pool and staring up at her with a haunted expression. 'That's rich! You make me mindless with desire, you drive me insane with jealousy, you repeatedly thrust knives into me by taunting me about your relationship with Nazim, and you say I'm cruel?'

She crouched down, beginning to see what he was saying, her eyes rapidly scanning his face for proof.

'I didn't like being treated like a sex object—'

'You were never that,' he said huskily. 'You were a celebration. It was like worship for me, touching you, knowing what we could do to each other.'

'Hassan!' she said slowly, in astonishment. He was serious. Deadly serious. 'I didn't mean what I said about Nazim. I regret my lie now. But I said it to stop you touching me.'

'I know,' he muttered. 'That's why I'm letting you go, however painful it is. I can't keep you like a caged bird. You and Josef must make your own—'

His mouth clamped shut and he disappeared under the water in a flurry of spray. Tiffany sat watching where he'd disappeared, her face intent. It was almost as if he was upset.

Her heart thudded and her face cleared, a sudden bright light seeming to illuminate her from within. Hassan *loved* her. Of that she was sure.

She stripped off her clothes. All of them. Somewhere in the darkness, he was swimming, desperately, violently, with a pent-up anger. All that vitality and fierceness, going to waste.

She worked the water into her hair and tried to clean the mud from her skin which felt as if it had been sandpapered. Still Hassan drove himself through the water, backwards and forwards, as if expiating a sin.

'Hassan,' she called. 'Hassan!'

His head bobbed up near her, the water pouring from his ebonised hair, pearlised droplets twinkling on his thick lashes.

'What?' he said ungraciously.

Her mouth curved. She'd seen the raw graze on his neck. There was a way to test her theory.

'You were hurt when the tree crashed into the truck.'

His hand lifted and touched the wound.

'I'll get the sand out,' she offered.

Before he could back away, she had placed her hands on his shoulders and let her fingers drift upwards. Deliberately she ensured that her body should flow against his and he drew in an agonised breath.

'Don't touch me,' he whispered.

Her mouth dropped to his wound and gently licked. A quiver ran through his body and she wrapped her legs around him.

'For God's sake,' he said thickly.

'I don't mind about Abdul,' she said gently, taking his

face in her hands. 'I don't mind that you and Faridah were lovers—'

'*What?*' he exploded.

'I'm sorry,' she said firmly. 'I talked to Faridah. She admitted it all. And I don't mind that you have a son. He'd naturally take first place in your heart. What we both once did is in the past, like Nazim, like everything that's gone between us.'

'Wait a minute,' he said sternly, taking her hands away. 'Faridah is claiming I have a son called Abdul? That he's her son—*our* son?'

'More or less,' she said awkwardly. 'Well, I came to that conclusion and she didn't correct me. You must understand why she told me. She loves you. That's why she hel—' Tiffany broke off, biting her lip.

'I see. She helped you to escape. She poisoned your mind against me.' Hassan's mouth became grim. 'Your trust wasn't very strong, was it? Otherwise why believe her, rather than the evidence of your own eyes, and your instincts?'

'I'd made a mistake before,' she said in a low tone. 'I learnt the painful way not to trust my instincts about men.'

'But it's the only way you can tell,' he said in gentle reproof.

'I almost wanted to believe her,' mused Tiffany. 'Because if I didn't, I'd have to accept that my love for you was as powerful as my love for Jo. I wasn't ready for that, or all of its implications. I didn't want to give up work, to be just your wife, loving you and not being loved in return.'

'Your…love? Did you say…?'

Tiffany held her breath, uncertain that she'd made the right decision. He loves me, he loves me not, he loves me, he loves me not, she chanted to herself, waiting for his reaction.

He didn't give much away. 'Give up work?' he frowned. 'I was expecting you to continue. You're not the kind of woman who enjoys sitting at home. I hadn't planned on your idling away our marriage. Didn't you think you could cope with me and your job?'

There was a faint amusement in his voice, but she had turned away and her face was stony, the terrible disappointment and embarrassment creeping through her. She tried to look aloof and carefree.

'Explain who Abdul al Sharif is,' she demanded. 'I didn't mistake the name. I know there's someone called that,' she persisted stubbornly.

'The only Abdul in our family is hardly a problem where you're concerned,' answered Hassan drily. 'He's my cousin and my closest friend. He runs the New York office for me, controlling those companies I built up there with his help.'

'But I thought…Faridah said…' Tiffany was so appalled by Faridah's duplicity that she found herself under water, and came up spluttering with Hassan's arms holding her securely. He pushed her to the side of the pool where they hauled themselves on to a ledge. His eyes dropped to her breasts as the water streamed from them, and then watched every last drop fall from their hardening points.

'You weren't in love with Faridah?' she asked hopefully.

Hassan was having some difficulty in mastering his self-control and concentrating on her anxious questions.

'Mmm? Of course not! I told you. She loved Nazim. A marriage was arranged between them but he left the country, claiming he wanted to finish his education in England. Once there, he refused to return, or to marry her. It caused a row because father said he had dishonoured her and her family. She came to live with us. We owed it to her. It is now my duty to care for her and protect her because she was wronged by my brother.'

Tiffany felt every bone in her body relax, every muscle, every tight tendon. She smiled blissfully.

'Hassan, I got in a muddle. I overheard you talking about handing over control of companies. I thought you were hastily getting rid of them to Abdul—your son—so that Josef couldn't inherit anything.'

'But why would I do that?' he asked in surprise.

'Because Jo had a claim on half of your business,' she said in a small, apologetic voice. 'He'd take away some of your power. So I imagined that you meant Josef harm.'

'Harm? A child?' Hassan looked very hurt. 'My brother really did sour you against men, didn't he?' he said quietly. 'Don't worry about the fact that I'm shedding the US companies. They're but a small section of the Sharif business. There's more than enough left for a dozen Josefs, most of them based in Riyam and Europe. Not too great a commuting distance.'

'Oh, Hassan! You make me sound grabbing! I didn't mean—!'

'Tiffany, I only wanted to cut down my transatlantic travel so I could spend all my time with you and Josef. I'd tied up the New York end rather well, arranging for Faridah to move there as managing director, under Abdul—they get on like a house on fire. I intended to tell her today. She'll do very well. She has a sharp mind. Too sharp,' he said wryly. 'In fact, your arrival and Faridah's reaction to you showed me that I was probably holding her back from marrying. I'd protected her for too long and she'd become possessive of me. She knows I don't love her. She's always known that. But she's never liked me to share my attention, especially with other women. She leaves in a week. She'll get her marching orders when I return. I don't think I want anything more to do with her unless it's absolutely necessary.'

'And you?' asked Tiffany, lifting her body erect.

Hassan was about to turn his head when she caught his hand and placed it on her heart.

'What do you feel?' she asked softly.

'You must be joking,' he croaked, his thumb jerking away from her nipple.

'The beating of my heart,' she smiled. 'Would it beat hard for a man I hated?'

His glance flicked up to hers.

'I love you,' she said simply, her eyes telling him so.

'After all I've done?' he whispered.

'You wanted to save Jo from a dreadful mother. Then you wanted me—'

'I fell in love,' he corrected, his hand curving around her drum-hard breast. 'Against my will, I fell in love. So crazily that I couldn't think straight, that I wanted you near me every second of the day, breathing the same air.'

She melted towards him. He kissed the line of her hair and slid her into the pool. He moved around her, kissing every inch of her skin where it met the water, working around her body until he had made a complete kissing circle and she was almost climbing up the wall from the erotic experience.

A delicate, wet finger trailed over her full breasts, bringing her nipples into angry, rose-tipped peaks. They submerged. Their bodies slid together, line for line, bone for bone. Her arms floated to his shoulders and then his mouth met hers as their loins jarred together in an unbearable demand.

In a flurry of spray they surfaced, still clinging together. Hassan's eyes were dark and lustrous with passion. Tiffany wound her hands in his thick wet hair and improvised as she'd never done before, wanting desperately to kiss every inch of his face. Then she took the short hairs in front of his ear between her teeth and gently tugged, then licked them flat again.

For the first time in her life, she felt free.

'I've loved you for so long,' she whispered, nibbling his earlobe.

'My darling,' he said, husky with emotion. 'You'll get cold. We must return.'

'You care about me, don't you?'

'Care! Darling, I nearly went mad wondering if I'd reach you before the sandstorm struck. You must have been terrified. Yet you struggled on, for Josef's sake. No mother could have done more to prove what she feels for her son. Come.'

He bundled up their clothes and led her, still naked, up the steps. In the fading warmth of the sun, its red light making their bodies glow, they dried their bodies before dressing each other, tenderly. Then she saw his face darken and become remote.

'What is it?' she asked urgently.

'Faridah,' he snapped. 'I'm thinking what I'll do—'

'No. Think how she must have felt, Hassan!' she cried passionately. 'First she learns that the man she loves has married an English girl. Then that very same woman turns up and appears to be luring away the second man she has fallen for. I don't bear Faridah any malice. I know what it's like to feel jealous and to know a one-sided love.'

'Well, she's going to America sooner than she thinks,' muttered Hassan. 'Would you like us to fly out to Oman, and see Jo? Would you feel safer there?'

'I trust you anywhere,' she smiled, her face radiant.

'Fool,' he laughed, his fingers shaping her waist. 'We'll go and tell your son what we feel about each other.'

'Our son.'

'Our son,' he repeated huskily.

'I'm still your hostage,' she breathed, reaching up and twining her hands around his neck.

'And I am yours,' he said, his lips claiming hers. 'A hostage to love.'